CW00704278

FLUID MECHANICS
FOR ENGINEERING STUDENTS

FLUID MECHANICS
FOR ENGINEERING STUDENTS

Fluid Mechanics is essentially an observational science, and clear visualization of fluid flows is desirable to achieve a full understanding of them. One method, applicable when there is a free surface, as in a model river, is to put aluminium dust particles on it and to photograph from above with a time exposure. The particles show the surface velocities as fine streaks, and reveal details of the flow pattern.

The photo above shows a small straight river, with a canal at right-angles taking about thirty per cent of the river flow. Notice on the river bank opposite the canal an area of low speed and eddies: and in the canal entrance a separation (= breakaway) of the flow, causing a large permanent eddy on one side. As well as aluminium dust, blobs of heavy water-colour paint have been put on the floor of the river to show the direction of the flow there—which guides the movement of sand and other bed material. Due to secondary currents (see page 171) the bottom current is curved far more than the surface: thus all the bottom sediment in the river (coming from the left) goes into the canal.

Downstream, near the canal, there are only very small bed-velocities, and this is where siltation easily occurs. A canal in this situation always has a higher concentration of silt than exists in the river.

(Photo by J. Gurr)

FLUID MECHANICS
FOR ENGINEERING STUDENTS

J. R. D. FRANCIS
B.Sc. (Engineering) London, F.I.C.E.

Professor of Hydraulics,
Imperial College of Science and Technology,
University of London

WITH A CHAPTER ON GAS FLOW
CONTRIBUTED BY

G. JACKSON, M.A. (Cantab.)
Professor of Mechanical Engineering, Brunel University

SI UNITS

EDWARD ARNOLD

© J. R. D. FRANCIS 1975

First published 1958
by Edward Arnold (Publishers) Ltd
25 Hill Street, London W1X 8LL
Reprinted 1960
Second edition 1962
Reprinted 1965
Third edition 1969
Reprinted 1971
Fourth edition 1975

Boards edition ISBN: 0 7131 3331 7
Paper edition ISBN: 0 7131 3332 5

All Rights Reserved. No part of this publication may be
reproduced, stored in a retrieval system, or transmitted
in any form or by any means, electronic, mechanical,
photocopying, recording or otherwise, without the prior
permission of Edward Arnold (Publishers) Ltd.

Printed in Great Britain by
William Clowes & Sons, Limited, London, Beccles and Colchester

PREFACE TO FOURTH EDITION

This book was originally written as an attempt to provide the least amount of instruction in the subject that can be accepted for a University degree in Engineering. No effort was made to write a complete text of all possible branches of the subject during a three-year course, but it is still believed that the necessary basis for at least the first two years' work is here. Third-year work often diverges in various ways according to the interests of the teacher and only some of these ways are reviewed in this text. As time has gone on, improvements and some additions have been made. For this edition, Chapter 9 was completely revised to include aspects of compressible flows which have become of importance since the first edition was published; and Chapter 14 was re-written in a greatly improved form to show more clearly the roles of energy and momentum changes in open channel flows. Some parts of this latter chapter, notably fig 14.2, are thought to be novel, and it is to be hoped that the ideas there will stimulate further improvements by teachers of the subject. In Chapter 12, an elementary consideration of mixing processes has been added, as an introduction to the dilution and pollution studies now receiving much attention as the engineers' responsibilities to the Environment increase. A number of new references are also provided.

In an attempt to make this book simple and easy to follow, many rigid proofs of mathematical formulae are omitted, and simplifications made to others. Also, detailed tables of experimental data have been avoided as far as possible; the undergraduate should begin to acquaint himself with these at a later stage, from more detailed textbooks. On the other hand, considerable attention has been paid to explaining in full the limitations of any theoretically derived equations; to the engineer, the practical limitations of a theory are of more interest than a perfect proof. It has been assumed, particularly in Chapter 9, that the student will be taking at the same time a course in elementary thermo-dynamics, and some proofs are omitted for this reason. It is to be hoped that the introduction in Britain and elsewhere of the Rational Metric system of units (Système International d'Unités) will supersede the foot-pound-second, the foot-slug-second and also the non-rationalized metre-kilogramme-second systems for measurement. All these systems were prolific in confusion for students, whose most common error is to confuse the word 'pound' (or 'kilogramme') in a dual meaning of a unit both of force and of mass.   While a revision to these units was made in the 3rd Edition, it is clear that progress towards using them in practical engineering work is still slow, in many parts of the world.   It would be quite wrong to leave our students unprepared for carrying out calculations in the old Imperial foot-pound-second system; so that in this edition there are still many references in the text to foot-pound-second units.   Also a number of problems in these units have been gathered into an Appendix, thus leaving all problems at the Chapter ends in metric S.I. units.   In the main text I often use the now well-known word 'cumec' for $1 \text{ m}^3/\text{s}$; this is not strictly metric S.I. but is so convenient as a pronounceable word that it should surely become international.

The author of any textbook depends largely upon his predecessors, and I have gained much from the works of Addison, Jameson, Lewitt, Hunter Rouse and Hunsaker and Rightmire.   In particular, the well-known volumes *Modern Developments in Fluid Mechanics*, edited by S. Goldstein, have been a constant source of information: this is undoubtedly the work to recommend to the graduate who is to practise in this field of engineering.   The present book also owes much to the teachings of Emeritus Professor C. M. White, for many of the ideas and simplifications herein have been suggested by him in the course of his lectures.   I also wish to thank many friends and colleagues who have read and commented on several of the chapters.   In particular, Professor G. Jackson has not only contributed Chapter 9, but has also suggested several valuable improvements.   The responsibility for any statements in the book, other than in Chapter 9, is however wholly mine.

Imperial College   J. R. D. FRANCIS
London S.W.7.

CONTENTS

THE PIONEERS

It is of considerable interest to know something about the men whose names are now regularly used in fluid mechanics. A very abbreviated list is given below. The original papers in which these pioneers have published their results are, in general, listed in the Royal Society Catalogue of Scientific Papers.

Archimedes	287–212 B.C.	Greek philosopher
H. Pitot	1695–1771	French inventor
D. Bernoulli	1700–1782	Swiss physicist
A. Chézy	1718–1798	French engineer
J. C. Borda	1733–1799	French mathematician
G. B Venturi	1746–1822	Italian engineer
P. S. Laplace	1749–1827	French mathematician
J. L. Poiseuille	1799–1869	French physicist
H. Darcy	1803–1858	French engineer
W. E. Weber	1804–1891	German physicist
W. Froude	1810–1879	British naval architect
J. B. Francis	1815–1892	American engineer
R. Manning	1816–1897	Irish engineer
H. Bazin	1829–1917	French engineer
L. A. Pelton	1829–1908	American engineer
E. Mach	1838–1916	Austrian philosopher
O. Reynolds	1842–1912	British physicist
C. G. P. de Laval	1845–1913	Swedish engineer
L. Prandtl	1875–1953	German engineer
N. Kaplan	1876–1934	Czech engineer
T. von Kármán	1881–1963	Hungarian engineer

1

THE PROPERTIES OF FLUIDS

1.1 Definition of a fluid

Most people realize that the term *fluid* includes such different materials as water and air; the essential property in common is that a volume of fluid cannot preserve its shape for any time at all, unless it is constrained by surrounding surfaces. It is clear that if the sides of a barrel of water were suddenly removed, the cylinder of fluid within would collapse at once and spread out to a thin layer over a large area. The motion only stops if the water reaches another set of boundaries. The same thing would happen, though much more slowly, if the material within the barrel was oil or pitch; in these cases the spreading might take seconds or even weeks or months, depending on the chemical composition of the oil or pitch. In this respect, then, oil and pitch are fluids as well as water and air. The speed of spreading, and of losing the original shape under a deforming force, is governed by the property of a fluid known as *viscosity*. Viscosity essentially governs the speed of a fluid motion but can *never stop it* entirely. Accordingly, the following comprehensive definition of a fluid may be based on this property:

A fluid is matter in a readily distortable form, so that the smallest unbalanced external force on it causes an infinite change of shape, if applied for a long enough time.

This definition clearly excludes solids, such as steel, concrete, wood or rubber, all of which distort only a certain amount when a shear force is applied. With a fluid, the same shear force gives no definite amount of distortion, the change of shape being continuous as long as the force is applied.

1.2 Viscosity

Consider a volume of moving fluid one view of which is the square ABCD shown in fig 1.1. The volume has unit length in a plane perpendicular to the paper. A shear stress τ (force per unit area) acts on top and bottom of ABCD in the directions shown, and as a result the top moves at a small speed δu relative to the bottom. In a short time δt, ABCD will distort to ABC'D', causing a change of

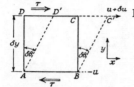

Fig 1.1 Deformation of a cube of moving fluid ABCD due to a velocity gradient producing a higher velocity at the top than at the bottom. The rate of deformation $d\theta/dt$ is caused by a shear stress τ on opposite sides. The cube has deformed to the shape ABC'D' in a time dt.

shape or *shear strain* which can be expressed by the magnitude of the angle $\delta\theta$. The distances CC' and DD' are both given by the product of speed and time,

that is,
$$\text{CC}' = \text{DD}' = \delta u . \delta t.$$

But if $\delta\theta$ is small, $\delta\theta = \dfrac{\text{CC}'}{\delta y}$, where δy is the small distance between the top and bottom of ABCD.

That is,
$$\delta\theta = \frac{\delta u . \delta t}{\delta y} = \textit{shear strain}.$$

This shear strain must now be connected to the shear stress τ that has caused it. Since θ continues to increase with time, it is not possible to consider τ as dependent on θ as is the case with solid materials (this assumption produces the well-known coefficient of shear elasticity). Instead, τ is considered to depend upon the *rate of change of* θ, $\delta\theta/\delta t$, the one being expressed as a multiple of the other thus,

$$\tau = \mu\frac{\delta\theta}{\delta t}$$

$$= \mu\frac{\delta u . \delta t}{\delta y . \delta t} = \mu\frac{\delta u}{\delta y}.$$

If the volume ABCD is now made infinitesimal τ is then the shear stress at one particular level, and

$$\tau = \mu\frac{du}{dy} \qquad . \qquad . \qquad . \qquad . \quad (1.1)$$

where du/dy is the gradient of velocity in the y direction, that is at right angles to the direction of the velocity itself.

Experimental data show that if a fluid is moving sufficiently slowly, within a tube of small cross-sectional area, then μ for that fluid depends neither on τ nor du/dy; it may decrease with the temperature of the fluid if a liquid, or increase if a gas. In fact, the shear stress is entirely balanced by intermolecular forces in the fluid, which try to prevent one layer moving over the next. Under these circumstances μ is called the *coefficient of molecular viscosity* and the fluids are called *Newtonian fluids* after Sir Isaac Newton who first observed their behaviour. Numerical values are given in an Appendix, p. 7.

If, however, a fluid is moving more quickly or is flowing in a tube of larger cross-sectional area, then μ is far less simply defined. It depends now on τ, du/dy and on many other variables, and is always greater than the molecular value, perhaps as much as 10^8 times as great. The mechanism connecting τ with du/dy is quite different from the previous case since irregular motions known as *turbulence* have appeared in the fluid, and these create occasional rotatory motions called *eddies*. Under these conditions μ is called the *eddy viscosity* and is no longer constant for a given fluid and temperature. A discussion is given in a later chapter on the function of eddies in the production of shear stresses.

Some materials appear on cursory inspection to be fluids, but prove after experiment to have variable values of μ, even when turbulence is absent. In these materials, non-Newtonian fluids, the intermolecular forces change with τ or du/dy and very complicated conditions of flow are set up. Mud, cream, and cheese are examples of these fluids, and are the concern of a separate branch of fluid mechanics, known as Rheology.

One further definition of viscosity is often used in fluid mechanics. It is often convenient to use the ratio of the coefficient of molecular viscosity to the density of the fluid μ/ρ. This ratio is called the *kinematic viscosity*.

Viscosity is a most important property of a fluid, for by its action shear forces are caused in a fluid. In fact, viscosity is the *only* cause of shear forces. Consequently, since τ depends on du/dy, then if there is no *velocity gradient* there can be *no shear force*. Velocity gradients are always caused when a fluid flows over a solid surface, for the layer of molecules next to the surface adhere to it, with the layers above slipping over the ones below. Thus a shear stress, sometimes called *fluid friction*, always exists when such a flow occurs, and this stress always opposes the fluid motion. If, however, the whole mass of the fluid is at rest relative to the boundaries, then there can be no velocity gradients, *and there are no shear forces at all*. This leads to a great simplification if it is desired to calculate the forces acting on the boundaries.

1.3 Compressibility

The property of viscosity has been shown to be concerned with the change of shape of a fluid volume, and is therefore rather analogous to the deformation of solids and the coefficient of shear elasticity. But another type of deformation is possible, and here fluids are precisely the same as solids : when a force is uniformly exerted all over all the boundaries of any material the volume V is decreased by an amount dV, and this decrease is proportional to the force p exerted per unit area of the boundaries, or

$$p = - K\frac{dV}{V}.$$

K is called the *coefficient of compressibility* of the fluid. For a gas, K depends upon the gas laws, but for a liquid it is nearly constant with temperature.

In fluid mechanics the compressibility only becomes important when the velocity is more than about $1/5$ of the velocity of sound waves in the fluid. Under these conditions the impact of fluid with any solid boundaries may cause the pressure to rise suddenly across a very narrow region due to the compression of the fluid (a shock wave), instead of varying smoothly from point to point.

1.4 Surface tension

The physical chemistry of every liquid is such that if one of its boundaries is a gas, the surface molecules of the liquid are always repelling each other. This gas-liquid interface is therefore in a state of tension, each molecule being kept in equilibrium by a tension on all sides. If, however, a solid surface intersects the interface, then molecules in contact with the solid still exert a tension on their companions, so that if there is a relative motion of the solid to the liquid, the interface is dragged along by this *surface tension* force. The force is proportional to the length of the intersection of the solid with the interface, and is usually small compared with the magnitude of the other forces found in engineering work, such as those due to viscosity, to pressure changes, or to the weight of the fluid. However, as will be described, small scale models of hydraulic engineering structures are often made and operated. In these models, surface tension forces on the fluid concerned, if there is a gas-liquid surface, may be relatively so much more important than those in the full size prototype that a simple scaling-up of total measured forces is misleading and errors will be introduced.

Surface tension is also of importance in some hydraulic measurements, when the height of a liquid-gas interface is required to be known accurately. The surface condition of the surrounding solid boundaries may be such as to deform the interface, as well as to cause the tension force (see fig 1.2). In some cases the deformation makes the interface nearly tangential to the solid surface. Consequently the surface tension force F is inclined to the major part of the interface, and will give a vertical component of force on the liquid, which will accordingly be raised or lowered somewhat. If the liquid is contained in a tube the vertical force will be exerted all round the periphery. This

Fig 1.2 Deformation of a gas-liquid interface by an intersecting solid surface. The tension force F is now inclined to the main part of the interface and a force is exerted tending to pull the solid surface into or out of the liquid.

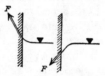

effect is sometimes called a *meniscus* or *capillarity* effect. As the deformation is critically dependent on the traces of impurities on the solid surface, the effect is very variable.

Although surface tension forces are always small (for example, a clean water-air interface gives a force of only 0·073 newton/m), they can entirely stop a fluid motion if they happen to be larger than the other forces acting on the liquid. In this respect, they must be contrasted to the effect of viscosity, which slows a motion but never stops it entirely. The surface tension of an interface may be reduced by chemical means (a soap or detergent reducing the water-air force by about 50 per cent), and this is sometimes done in model testing work in order to reduce the errors due to surface tension.

1.5 Vapour pressure, and solubility of gases

These two properties of liquids are grouped together, for their effects are to a large extent similar. Without transgressing into the realms of thermodynamics the phenomenon may be described as follows.

A body of liquid bounded partly by a gas-liquid interface continually sends off molecules of liquid in vapour form into the gas, until the pressure of the vapour is such that no more evaporation occurs. If the pressure above the liquid is reduced by any means, evaporation recommences until a new balance is reached. If the pressure is sufficiently lowered the liquid boils, when bubbles of vapour are formed in the fluid and rise to the surface, producing large volumes of vapour. Attempts to lower the pressure still further simply result in more vigorous boiling, and production of more vapour, which prevents the attempted reduction of pressure.

In hydraulic engineering work the vapour pressure of a liquid is of importance, for there may be places of low local pressure, particularly when the liquid is flowing over a solid surface. If, in one of these places, the pressure is reduced until the liquid boils, then bubbles of vapour are formed quite suddenly. When the liquid has moved on to a place of rather higher local pressure, the bubbles suddenly collapse. These very rapid collapsing motions cause high impact pressures if they occur against portions of the solid surface, and may eventually cause a local mechanical failure by fatigue of the solid surface. Severe pitting and damage of the surface may result. This effect is called *cavitation* and, as will be shown later, reduces the efficiency of machines, even if damage is not done.

Somewhat similar effects occur when the gases of the air are dissolved by a liquid, for air bubbles may be released in the same way as vapour bubbles. Air cavitation usually occurs at rather higher pressures than vapour cavitation and so usually occurs first.

1.6 The ideal fluid

The preceding paragraphs have reviewed the principal physical properties of fluids, and the Appendix to the chapter gives the numerical values of the several constants for air and water. It is, however, rare for a specific engineering problem to be solved taking into consideration all the properties concerned, for the mathematics soon become too complicated and a simplification is necessary. The simplification is usually done by assuming that the fluid is ideal. That is to say it complies with the definition of a fluid but its coefficient of viscosity is zero so that a velocity gradient cannot cause any shear stresses. Further, the ideal fluid is incompressible, has no surface tension and does not vaporize. Many problems of fluid motion can now be solved, although the results sometimes have an air of unreality about them, compared with the observed phenomena in real fluids such as air and water. For example, there can be no friction with an ideal fluid, which would not be slowed down near a solid boundary by viscous effects.

Experimental evidence must be used to convert the calculated result into the predicted result for the particular problem, and the value of the empirical coefficients thus used are an indication of the accuracy of the assumption of an ideal fluid. It is fortunate that water and air are surprisingly near an ideal fluid in many respects, so that the above approach to hydraulic problems is often sufficiently successful for engineering purposes.

1.7 Appendix: Numerical values for the properties of fluids

1. *Density* (denoted by ρ) is Mass per unit volume (ML^{-3}).

(i) In the metric (International system) system of units, the density of water is

$$\rho_{water} = 1000 \text{ kg/m}^3$$

and of dry air is $\rho_{air} = 1\cdot30 \text{ kg/m}^3$ at N.T.P.

(ii) In the f.p.s system of units (i.e. forces in poundals and pressures in poundals per square foot), the density of water is

$$\rho_{water} = 62\cdot4 \text{ lb ft}^{-3}$$

and of dry air is $\rho_{air} = 0\cdot0807 \text{ lb ft}^{-3}$ at N.T.P.

(iii) In the f.slug.s system of units (that is forces in pounds weight, denoted by lbf: pressures in lbf ft^{-2}), the density of water is

$$\rho_{water} = 62\cdot4/32\cdot2 \text{ slugs ft}^{-3} = 1\cdot94 \text{ slugs ft}^{-3}.$$

(iv) In the c.g.s system (forces in dynes) the density of water is

$$\rho_{water} = 1\cdot0 \text{ g cm}^{-3}$$

and of dry air is $\rho_{air} = 0\cdot00123 \text{ g cm}^{-3}$ at N.T.P.

(v) Do not confuse density with

(a) Specific gravity—the ratio of the density of a fluid to the density of water. It is numerically the same as ρ in c.g.s system.
(b) Specific weight—denoted by w. This is the weight *force* per unit volume so that in the f.p.s system w is expressed in poundals ft^{-3} For example, w for water is $62\cdot4 \times 32\cdot2$ poundals ft^{-3} in the f.p.s system, but is $62\cdot4$ lbf ft^{-3} in the f.s.s system.

Note. In this book w will not be used at all.

The Normal Temperature and Pressure (N.T.P.) are taken as 273 K (0 °C) and $101\cdot3$ kN/m^2 (76 cm of mercury under gravitational acceleration).

2. *Molecular Viscosity* (denoted by μ) is a Force per unit area per unit velocity gradient, and has dimensions

$$\frac{MLT^{-2}}{L^2} \div \frac{L}{TL} = ML^{-1}T^{-1}$$

The *Kinematic Viscosity* (denoted by v) is the molecular viscosity divided by the density and so has dimensions

$$ML^{-1}T^{-1} \div ML^{-3} = L^2T^{-1}$$

(i) In the metric (SI) system, water has viscosities

$$\mu = 1\cdot145 \times 10^{-3} \text{ Ns/m}^2$$

and $v = 1\cdot145 \times 10^{-6} \text{ m}^2\text{/s}$

(ii) In the f.p.s system, water has viscosities

$$\mu = 2\cdot39 \times 32\cdot2 \times 10^{-5} \text{ poundals s ft}^{-2}$$
$$= 2\cdot39 \times 32\cdot2 \times 10^{-5} \text{ lb s}^{-1} \text{ ft}^{-1}$$

and $v = 2\cdot39 \times 32\cdot2 \times 10^{-5}/62\cdot4 \text{ ft}^2 \text{ s}^{-1}$
$$= 1\cdot23 \times 10^{-5} \text{ ft}^2 \text{ s}^{-1}$$

(iii) In the f.slug.s system, water has

$$\mu = 2\cdot39 \times 10^{-5} \text{ lbf s ft}^{-2}$$
$$= 2\cdot39 \times 10^{-5} \text{ slug s}^{-1} \text{ ft}^{-1}$$
and $$\nu = 2\cdot39 \times 10^{-5}/1\cdot94 \text{ ft}^2 \text{ s}^{-1}$$
$$= 1\cdot23 \times 10^{-5} \text{ ft}^2 \text{ s}^{-1}$$

(iv) In the c.g.s system, water has

$$\mu = 1\cdot145 \times 10^{-2} \text{ gm s}^{-1} \text{ cm}^{-1} \text{ (called 'poises')}$$
and $$\nu = 1\cdot145 \times 10^{-2}/1 \text{ cm}^2 \text{ s}^{-1} \quad \text{(called 'stokes')}$$

(v) For air, the relevant values are

$$\mu = 1\cdot78 \times 10^{-5} \text{ Ns/m}^2 \text{ (metric SI system)}$$
$$= 0\cdot037 \times 10^{-5} \times 32\cdot2 \text{ lb ft}^{-1} \text{ s}^{-1} \quad \text{(f.p.s system)}$$
$$= 0\cdot037 \times 10^{-5} \text{ slug ft}^{-1} \text{ s}^{-1} \quad \text{(f.s.s system)}$$
$$= 1\cdot78 \times 10^{-4} \text{ Poise} \quad \text{(c.g.s system)}$$

and ν depends on the density at the pressure concerned.

All the above values are for 15 °C. In general the viscosities of liquids fall as the temperature increases, but those of gases increase somewhat.

Note on dimensions

Throughout this book, the metric (International system) system of units is used, with occasional references to the obsolescent foot-pound-second and foot-slug-second systems. The metric SI system is superseding all others, and it has the advantage of being dimensionally consistent and wholly decimal. It also has a striking advantage in that it discriminates between mass (measured in kilograms) and forces (measured in newtons).

The situation must be faced however that for years ahead the older systems may be used in many parts of the world. Engineers have become accustomed to use systems (both metric and foot-pound-second) which have a confusing lack of contrast between measurement of masses and forces ; one symbol (lb or kg for instance) is used, which stands for both force and mass. This variation is undoubtedly due to the influence of structural engineering where loads are generally caused by masses which are acted upon by gravity only. Thus a mass of (say) 1000 pounds (1000 lb) exerts gravity forces of 1000 × 32·2 poundals, but the engineer calls this force 1000 pounds weight (lbf). Now in fluid mechanics the masses concerned are frequently in motion and have accelerations, denoted by f, acting upon them which are greater or smaller than gravity. Consequently the above 1000 lb mass gives rise to forces of 1000f poundals which the engineer prefers to call 1000f/32·2 pounds weight (lbf).

If f.p.s units are employed for masses and accelerations in any calculation involving Newton's Second Law of Motion (Force is rate of change of momentum), then f.p.s units for Forces will obviously result. Thus all forces will be in poundals. The engineer can therefore either divide the final result by 32·2 to obtain the answer in pounds weight, or divide all masses (or densities) by 32·2 (obtaining slugs as the units of mass) before the calculation. It is, however, necessary always to watch that the division by 32·2 is not inadvertently repeated. The process is automatic to most engineers, though it is tantamount to mixing of f.p.s. and f.slug.s. units. If a metre-kilogram-second system of units is used, i.e. metric (*non* SI) system, then the relevant constant is 9·81.

In computations for which the data are metric, the student is advised to work throughout with metric constants. It is unnecessary and inadvisable to convert metric data to f.p.s. units, to compute as an f.p.s. problem, and to reconvert the answers to a metric form.

A useful aid is a booklet, PD 5686, *The Use of SI Units*, published by the British Standards Institution.

2

FORCES IN STATIC FLUIDS

2.1 When a body of fluid is at rest relative to its boundaries there are no velocity gradients and so no shear forces. A great simplification is therefore made when calculating the forces exerted by the fluid, for only the components normal to the boundaries need be taken into account. Under these conditions, known as *hydrostatic*, exact solutions can be obtained for the problems set out, and no experimental evidence is needed : a rare occurrence in fluid mechanics.

Gravity acting on a static fluid produces at each and every point in the fluid a compression which is not necessarily the same everywhere. If an object, or a boundary, happens to be in a fluid, then this compression is felt on it as a *pressure intensity*, p, expressed as a force per unit area.* If the boundary area a is large, a pressure force F will be felt on it so that

$$F = \int p \, \mathrm{d}a \quad . \quad . \quad . \quad . \quad (2.1)$$

the integral being taken over the whole area a. In this way the engineer can find the fluid force, providing it is known how p varies from place to place over the area. The force F must always act in a direction *normal* to the boundary area a, otherwise F would have a component, a shear force, acting parallel to the boundary. A shear force, however, cannot exist in a static fluid.

2.2 Variation of pressure intensity with direction at one point

Consider a right-angled triangular prism ABC of fluid within a larger mass of static fluid, BC being horizontal, fig 2.1. The prism

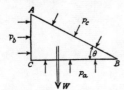

Fig 2.1 End view of a triangular prism of hydrostatic fluid showing pressure intensities on every side due to the surrounding fluid, and the weight force.

* Engineers often use ' pressure ' to mean both pressure intensity and pressure force. The context usually makes it clear which is meant.

is of unit length. Let the average pressure intensities on the three sides be p_a, p_b, p_c respectively on BC, AC, and AB. The forces on the sides are therefore p_a.CB, p_b.AC, p_c.AB per unit length of prism all acting normally to the sides. The mass of the prism is $\frac{1}{2}\rho$AC.BC per unit length, so that the downward weight force is $\frac{1}{2}\rho g$AC.BC.

Resolving the forces horizontally

$$p_b.\text{AC} - p_c.\text{AB} \sin \theta = 0$$

for the prism must be in equilibrium since it is in a static fluid. But from geometry,

$$\text{AC} = \text{AB} \sin \theta. \text{ So } p_b = p_c.$$

Now resolve the forces vertically.

$$p_a\text{BC} - p_c\text{AB} \cos \theta - \tfrac{1}{2}\rho g\text{AC}.\text{BC} = 0 \text{ for equilibrium.}$$

But from geometry,

$$\text{CB} = \text{AB} \cos \theta. \text{ So } p_a = p_c + \tfrac{1}{2}\rho g\text{AC}.$$

Now consider the prism to be made smaller until in the limit, as the prism becomes of infinitesimal size, AC $\rightarrow$ 0 so that the term $\frac{1}{2}\rho g$AC tends to zero.

Thus if A, B, C are coincident,

$$p_a = p_b = p_c \quad . \quad . \quad . \quad . \quad (2.2)$$

So the pressure intensities at a point are the same in all directions.

This result is of fundamental importance in hydraulic engineering, for hydrostatic pressure forces, even though they are caused by the downward attraction due to gravity, are exerted undiminished in all directions, even vertically upwards.

2.3 Variation of pressure intensity with height in a static fluid

It is nearly axiomatic with most people that great pressures exist at the bottom of high columns of fluid. The following proofs are given to place this common knowledge on a quantitative basis.

Consider a small vertical cylinder of fluid in a larger mass of static fluid (fig 2.2). Its cross-sectional area is a and its length δz. The bottom of the cylinder is at a height z above a purely arbitrary datum level. The fluid density is ρ so that the weight force W acting downwards is $W = \rho ag\delta z$. Because the fluid is static, this weight force must be balanced to preserve equilibrium: there can be no shear forces on the curved surface so there only remain the pressure intensity forces acting on the ends of the cylinder.

Let the pressure intensity on the bottom acting upwards be p, and that on the top acting downwards be $p + \delta p$.   (Notice that since z

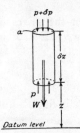

Fig 2.2   Perspective view of a vertical cylinder of hydro-static fluid, showing pressure and weight forces acting.

is taken as increasing upwards, so must all other variables, including p.   If in fact p *decreases* upwards, a minus sign will appear.)

Thus the balancing force $= pa - (p + \delta p)a = -a\delta p$

So $\rho a g \delta z = -a\,\delta p$

or $$\frac{\delta p}{\delta z} = -\rho g.$$

As δz approaches zero, the gradient of pressure becomes

$$\frac{\mathrm{d}p}{\mathrm{d}z} = -\rho g. \quad . \quad . \quad . \quad . \quad (2.3)$$

This is the *hydrostatic equation* for the pressure gradient at a point : it is only of direct use if it can be integrated to find p which will now be done for two particular cases.

2.4 Solutions of the hydrostatic equation

(*a*) For an incompressible fluid, whose density ρ is independent of pressure intensity and therefore constant, the hydrostatic equation is easily solved.   Water, and most other liquids, are sufficiently incompressible for the following analysis to be valid.

Writing $\mathrm{d}p = -\rho g\,\mathrm{d}z$

and integrating between the limits z_1 and z_2, p_1 and p_2,

$$p_1 - p_2 = -\rho g(z_1 - z_2),$$

or in words, the change of pressure intensity between two levels is proportional to the difference of height between the levels.   In the common case of a volume of liquid at rest with a free surface exposed to the atmosphere, where the pressure is p_a, the equation gives

$$p_a - p_1 = -\rho g(z_a - z_1)$$

where z_a is the height of the surface above datum level.

But $$z_a - z_1 = h,$$

where h is the depth below surface of the point where the pressure intensity p_1 has been developed,

thus $$p_a - p_1 = \rho g h$$

or $$p_1 = p_a + \rho g h \quad . \quad . \quad . \quad (2.4)$$

From this equation it can be seen that the pressure intensity at any point is partly due (i) to the atmospheric pressure on the free surface and (ii) to the density. (i) may thus be regarded as being transmitted without diminution throughout the fluid. The pressure intensity p_1 is reckoned from the same datum pressure as is p_a, that is, above a perfect vacuum : therefore p_1 is called the *absolute pressure*.

Engineers, however, often prefer to measure pressure intensity above a datum pressure at atmospheric pressure. They call $\rho g h$ the *gauge pressure*, and imply that if absolute pressure is required, p_a should be added. This is justified since it is often desired to find the difference of pressure intensity between two points. If the atmospheric pressure is the same at both points, the difference of gauge pressures is therefore the same as the difference of absolute pressures. The term gauge pressure also shows one use of the hydrostatic equation. When a pressure intensity has been measured, it is convenient to express it as h, the height or *head* of the fluid which, if static, produces this pressure. A great variety of pressure measuring instruments, called manometers, use the principle of balancing a static column of fluid (or several fluids) against the pressure, and then measuring h. Some of these are described in an Appendix, p. 23.

(*b*) For a compressible fluid, the law connecting ρ with p must be used. For instance, many gases obey the perfect gas law over a wide range of pressures and temperatures. That is $pV = RT$, where V is the volume of unit mass of gas at pressure p and absolute temperature T. Since ρ (mass per unit volume) is V^{-1} the gas law can be rewritten

$$\frac{p}{\rho} = RT \quad \text{or} \quad \rho = \frac{p}{RT}$$

and substituted into the hydrostatic equation to give

$$\frac{dp}{dz} = - p\frac{g}{RT}$$

or $$\frac{dp}{p} = - dz\frac{g}{RT}$$

If the temperature is constant at all heights, an integration can be made between the pressure limits p_1 and p_2, and height limits z_1 and z_2 to give

$$\log_e \frac{p_2}{p_1} = -\frac{g}{RT}(z_2 - z_1)$$

or $$\log_{10} \frac{p_2}{p_1} = -0.434\frac{g}{RT}h \qquad . \qquad . \qquad . \quad (2.5)$$

where $h = z_2 - z_1$ is the vertical height between the two places where the pressure intensities are p_1 and p_2 respectively. Notice that for air, R is 288 $m^2\,s^{-2}\,°C^{-1}$ in the metric system, but is 96×32.2 $ft^2\,s^{-2}\,°C^{-1}$ in both the foot-pound-second and foot-slug-second systems of units, since the unit of mass does not appear in its dimensions.

The logarithmic decrease of pressure with height in an isothermal gas is an approximation to the actual pressure distribution in the lower part of the atmosphere where in fact T varies considerably with z. On the average, there is a temperature gradient of about 6.5 °C per 1000 m, which can be inserted into the preceding integration to give a refined relationship, giving a more accurate expression for the change of pressure with height. However, a close approximation can always be made with the simpler relationship, eqn 2·5, using the mean temperature over the height range z_1 to z_2. The errors so introduced are usually smaller than those caused by neglecting the water vapour content of the air, which can also vary from layer to layer, causing different values of the gas constant R.

In any case, for engineering purposes, it is only necessary to assume that air is compressible if the height difference $z_2 - z_1 = h$ is large. For small values of h a sufficiently accurate estimate is usually made with the incompressible formula, $p = p_a + \rho g h$, eqn 2·4, assuming a mean value of the density ρ.

2.5 The forces due to hydrostatic pressure

If the variations of the pressure intensity p within a fluid are known, an integration $F = \int p\,da$ can be made to find the force F due to that pressure on a certain area a of the vessel walls containing the fluid. The integrations for finding F will be shown first when the pressure intensity remains constant everywhere over the area, and second when the pressure intensity varies linearly with depth. The first case is approximated when the change of p between top and bottom of the area concerned is small compared to the mean pressure intensity. The second case is required for the calculations of a multitude of engineering works where water lying to a depth is restrained by a solid wall or structure. The case of the pressure intensity varying logarithmically with depth (i.e. a compressible gas with variable ρ) is not dealt with, for engineering works are not large enough to make this variation significant. Any variation of pressure intensity with position can be treated by similar methods to those shown here, and the force found : for example, when the fluid is moving relative to a solid object, the pressure intensity may vary in a much more complicated fashion than the simple hydrostatic way. (See Chapter 7 for the reasons why the pressure should so vary.)

Having found the magnitude of the fluid force spread all over a surface, the engineer often wishes to balance it by a single force of the same magnitude acting at some point on the surface. This point is called the *centre of pressure* and is not to be confused with the centre of gravity (centroid) of the surface area, though in exceptional cases these centres coincide.

Case i (a)

Pressure intensity constant everywhere : surface area plane.

In fig 2.3, AB is the cross section of a plane area a subject to a constant pressure intensity p all over it to produce a total force F. On an

Fig 2.3 End view of a plane surface AB, on one side of which the pressure intensity is p greater than on the other. F is the single balancing force, acting at the centre of pressure.

elementary area δa the force will be $\delta F = p\delta a$, and since all these elementary forces act along parallel directions, normal to AB, they may be added arithmetically to give $F = pa$.

Also, since the elementary forces are uniform all over AB, then their resultant acts at the centre of gravity of AB, the centroid of the surface area concerned. It is at this point, therefore, that a balancing force must be applied to preserve equilibrium. So in this exceptional case, the centre of pressure and centre of gravity of the area are coincident.

Case i (b)

Pressure intensity constant everywhere : surface area *not* plane (fig 2.4).

AB is now the cross section of a non-plane area with elementary pressure force components $\delta F = p\delta a$ acting normally to every element of area δa. Thus δF is now no longer always in the same direction, and to find the resultant force on the surface, the elements must be added vectorially. It is convenient to find components of the total force in directions parallel to an arbitrary axis such as XX, and at right angles to XX. Thus if θ is the angle between one typical force element and XX, then the component force along XX is $p\delta a \cos \theta$,

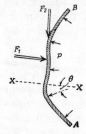

Fig 2.4   End view of a curved surface AB on one side of which the pressure intensity is p greater than on the other. F_1 and F_2 are component forces at right angles which just balance the pressure force. Note how the elementary pressure forces are always normal to the surface where they act.

and normal to it is $p\delta a \sin \theta$. Integrating, the total forces along and normal to the direction XX are $F_1 = \int p da \cos \theta$ and $F_2 = \int p da \sin \theta$ respectively, the integral being taken all over the area a. But $\int da \cos \theta$ is the area of the projection of the surface AB on to a plane at right angles to XX, and $\int da \sin \theta$ is the area projected onto a plane parallel to XX. So that $F_1 = p \times$ projected area normal to XX, and $F_2 = p \times$ projected area on XX. These force components can then be combined vectorially.

A rule can therefore be made to calculate the hydrostatic pressure force for this case : ' Decide upon three axes which are mutually at right angles ; project the curved surface in question onto planes at right angles to these axes ; multiply the projected areas by the constant pressure intensity to find the pressure force components along the axes ; and combine the components vectorially to find the total pressure force.' If there is an axis of symmetry to the curved surface

Fig 2.5   Side view of a curved cylindrical surface with an axis of symmetry OX. The projection of the area on to OX is symmetrical above and below OX so that there is no resultant pressure force normal to OX.

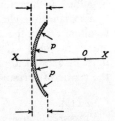

the projected areas on to this axis from each side of it are equal, so that the pressures forces normal to the axis on each half of the surface are equal and opposite (fig 2.5). There will therefore be no resultant pressure force in the direction normal to the axis of symmetry.

The centre of pressure of each component force F_1, F_2, F_3 is at the centre of gravity of each projected area so that each component is parallel to its axis and acts through the centre of gravity of its projected area. The centre of pressure of the total force will therefore be at the intersection of the lines of action of the component forces.

Case ii (a)

Pressure intensity increases with depth in fluid : surface plane.

Because so many engineering problems are concerned with liquids, which if static produce pressure intensities uniformly increasing with depth, this case of finding the resulting pressure forces is important. For example, the forces on lock gates, valves, walls and floors of engineering structures can all be estimated accurately.

Fig 2.6   Front and side elevations of a plane surface subject to a pressure intensity which increases with the depth h below a free surface of the fluid XX. Side elevation shows the pressure diagram and the balancing force F which acts at the centre of pressure.

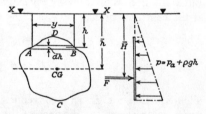

Consider a vertical plane surface such as ACBD in fig 2.6 which is subject to a hydrostatic pressure intensity on one side, and atmospheric pressure on the other. If the fluid is incompressible, then along any narrow horizontal strip AB, the resultant pressure intensity above atmosphere is $p = \rho g h$, where h is the depth below the free surface of the fluid XX. Thus the pressure force on AB which is δh wide and y long is

$$\delta F = \rho g h \, y \delta h$$

So that the total pressure force will be

$$F = \int_C^D \rho g h \, y \mathrm{d}h$$

$$= \rho g \int_C^D y h \mathrm{d}h$$

But $\int y h \mathrm{d}h$ will be recognized as the first moment of the area about the surface XX and is equivalent to $A\bar{h}$, where A is the total area ABCD and $\bar{h}$ is the depth below XX of the centre of gravity (centroid) of the area.

Therefore $F = \rho g A \bar{h} = A \rho g \bar{h}$.   .   . (2.6)

or in words, 'The pressure force is the product of the area of the surface, and the pressure intensity at the centre of gravity (centroid) of the surface '.

To find the centre of pressure of the area, the moment δM of the elementary force about XX is found.

Thus $$\delta M = \rho g h \, y \delta h \, h$$

and the total moment is $$M = \rho g \int_C^D y h^2 \, dh.$$

But this integral will be recognized as the second moment of area of the surface about XX and can be represented by Ak^2 where k is the radius of gyration of the surface about the axis XX.

So $$M = \rho g A k^2.$$

But we wish to replace M by the single force F as found above, acting at the centre of pressure CP, a distance $\bar{H}$ below XX.

That is, $$F\bar{H} = \rho g A k^2$$

Substituting $$F = A \rho g \bar{h}, \quad \bar{H} = \frac{k^2}{\bar{h}}$$

This equation for $\bar{H}$ is inconvenient to use because k for an area varies according to the distance of the area from the axis XX. However, by the theorem of parallel axes, we can express k^2 in terms of I_{CG}, the second moment of the area about an axis parallel to XX, but running through its centre of gravity (centroid).

That is $$Ak^2 = A\bar{h}^2 + I_{CG}$$

Substituting for k^2

$$\bar{H} = \bar{h} + \frac{I_{CG}}{A\bar{h}} \qquad . \qquad . \qquad . \qquad . \qquad (2.7)$$

This is an important result, for since the term $I_{CG}/A\bar{h}$ is always positive, then $\bar{H}$ must always be greater than $\bar{h}$: that is, the centre of pressure invariably lies below the centre of gravity. Further, since this term varies inversely with $\bar{h}$, the deeper a given surface is immersed, then the nearer $\bar{H}$ gets to $\bar{h}$: at great depths the centre of pressure is close to the centre of gravity and the difference may in some cases be ignored.

Some confusion is sometimes caused because though the magnitude of the force F depends on the magnitude of $\bar{h}$, the balancing force F does *not* act at this depth: it acts at $\bar{H}$ which is always below $\bar{h}$. A further confusion arises because a special application of the above formula gives an easily remembered answer. If the surface is a rectangle of depth *b*, *with the edge* a *lying in the surface* XX, fig 2.7,

then
$$I_{\mathrm{CG}} = \frac{ab^3}{12} \quad \text{and} \quad \hbar = \frac{b}{2}$$

so that
$$\hbar = \frac{b}{2} + \frac{ab^3}{12ab\,b/2} = \tfrac{2}{3}b$$

for the special case.

This result is sometimes used quite erroneously for other shapes or for rectangles which do not have one side in the surface of the fluid.

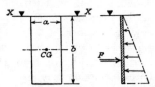

Fig 2.7   The special case of the force on a rectangular surface with one edge in the surface. The pressure diagram is a triangle and the balancing force acts at 2/3 of the depth of the rectangle below the surface.

The special case of a rectangle with one side in the surface is a common one, however, in engineering work, for the underwater parts of walls, gates and other structures are often equivalent to such a rectangle.

Case ii (b)

Pressure intensity increases with depth in the fluid: surface not plane.

This case occurs when assessing the forces on non-plane surfaces such as valves, gates, etc. It has a great similarity with Case i (*b*). The technique, Case i (*b*), of finding component forces in arbitrary directions is again used. The surface in question is projected in directions at right angles, and the forces due to the fluid on the imaginary plane surfaces of these projections are found, together with their centres of pressure, by the methods of Case ii (*a*). These component forces are then combined to find the total force and its line of action. It is nearly always convenient to take one of the arbitrary directions vertically downwards, for then the component force vertically downwards is merely the weight of fluid supported above the surface in question. For example, in fig 2.8, AB is a side view of a

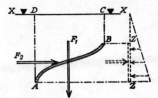

Fig 2.8   Side elevation of a non-plane surface AB subject to a pressure intensity increasing with depth. Vertical component of force F_1 is the weight force of the fluid above AB: horizontal force F_2 is that on the projected area ZZ.

non-plane surface in a fluid whose free surface is XX.   The downward component of force on AB, F_1, is merely the weight of the prism of fluid ABCD above it, for no other forces are applied to this part of the fluid to keep it static.   The horizontal component of force F_2 is the product of the projected area ZZ and the mean pressure on ZZ assessed as in Case ii (a).   The total force on AB will be the combination of the two components F_1 and F_2.

If the surface is curved in one direction only (for example a part of the surface of a cylinder) it is convenient to choose one axis in the direction along which there will be no projected area (the direction of the cylinder's axis).   There will only be two force components now to consider.

2.6   The foregoing method has been developed for a pressure intensity increasing with depth in a static fluid.   As previously mentioned fluids in motion may give rise to pressure intensities on solid shapes and these pressures vary otherwise than linearly with a certain distance ordinate.   The pressure distribution now follows no simple algebraical equation : it is found experimentally and obeys a very complicated law.

The total force $$F = \int p\,\mathrm{d}a$$

and the total moment $$M = \int p\,\mathrm{d}a\ x,$$

where a is the area concerned and x the distance from a reference plane, must now be found by one of the approximate, arithmetical (i.e. strip by strip) methods.   A total force and centre of pressure can thus be found for any pressure distribution, such as exists over an aeroplane's wing.

Example

A wind-tunnel test of a thin plane aeroplane wing 25 cm wide showed that the following pressures existed on the upper and lower surfaces, all measured with a water manometer, relative to the undisturbed pressure of the oncoming stream of air.   Positive signs show pressures above undisturbed pressure.   What is the total lift force on a 1 m length of the wing, and where should a single force of this magnitude act so as to balance the lift ?

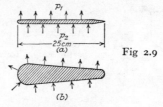

Fig 2.9

Distance from leading edge	cm	x	0	2·5	5	7·5	10
Pressure on upper surface	cm of water	h_1	−7·5	−3·5	−2·5	−2·0	−1·75
Pressure on lower surface		h_2	+2·5	+1·25	+0·75	+0·5	+0·25

Distance from leading edge	cm	x	12·5	15	17·5	20	22·5	25
Pressure on upper surface	cm of water	h_1	−1·25	−0·75	−0·5	−0·25	0	0
Pressure on lower surface		h_2	+0·25	+0·25	+0·25	0	0	0

Since the wing is thin and plane, all the pressure forces are parallel and so may be arithmetically added. This would be a poor approximation for a thick wing where pressure forces are not all parallel and which must be added vectorially, see fig 2.9.

Difference of pressure intensity $(p_1 - p_2)$ between top and bottom of wing at any value of x is the resultant vertical pressure intensity which causes a vertical pressure force $(p_1 - p_2)dx$, where dx is the element of area of a unit length of the wing on which this pressure acts.

The total lift is then $\int (p_1 - p_2)dx$. But $p = \rho g h$ where h is the height of the static fluid in the manometer.

The total force is therefore given by the area

$$\rho g \int (h_2 - h_1)dx = \frac{1000 \times 9\cdot81}{100 \times 100} \int (h_2 - h_1)dx \text{ newtons per metre length}$$

of wing if h is measured in cm and x in cm. Evaluate the integral graphically by the mid-ordinate rule as the area under the $(h_2 - h_1)$ curve (fig 2.10).

$$\text{Area} = 49\cdot4 \text{ (cm of water} \times \text{cm)}$$

$$\text{Total lift force} = 49\cdot4 \times \frac{1000 \times 9\cdot81}{10\ 000} \text{ N/m length of wing}$$

$$= 48\cdot6 \text{ N/m}$$

To find the point of application of the balancing force, it is necessary to find the moment of the elementary forces about a fixed point on the wing section. It is convenient to take the leading edge for this purpose. Then the moment of the pressure forces is

$$\int (p_2 - p_1)x dx$$

or, converting pressures to the corresponding head of water,

$$\frac{1000 \times 9\cdot 81}{100 \times 100 \times 100} \int (h_2 - h_1)x\mathrm{d}x.$$

The integral is the area under the $(h_2 - h_1)x$ curve, and this is found by the mid-ordinate rule to be 304 cm of water $\times$ cm^2.

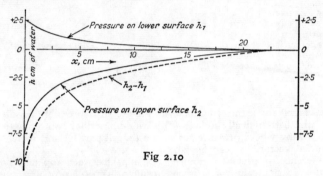

Fig 2.10

Thus the total moment of the pressure forces about the leading edge is

$$\frac{304}{100} \times \frac{1000 \times 9\cdot 81}{100 \times 100} \text{ Nm/m length of wing}$$

$$= 2\cdot 98 \text{ Nm/m}$$

But this moment also equals the balancing force, 48·6 N/m acting at a distance $\bar{x}$ from the leading edge.

That is, $2\cdot 98 = 48\cdot 6\bar{x}$
or $\bar{x} = 2\cdot 98/48\cdot 6 \text{ m} = 6\cdot 15 \text{ cm}$

The lift force on the wing is, therefore, 48·6 N per metre length, acting 6·15 cm from the leading edge. This point is called the Centre of Pressure of the wing.

2.7 Conclusion

This chapter has gone into some detail of an elementary part of the study of fluid mechanics. The finding of the fluid force on a surface against which is a static fluid is required so often in engineering work that the student must acquire complete facility with the methods used. Indeed, some engineers do no other calculations in fluid mechanics, for in many cases the hydrostatic pressure forces are overwhelmingly important, and the forces due to motion are insignificant.

It should not be thought, however, that these methods can be used for static fluids only. Even if the fluid is in motion the normal forces on a surface caused by the pressure distribution thereon can be found by essentially the same methods. This force is sometimes called the 'hydrostatic' force even if the fluid is not static. There will in general be other forces acting as well as this force : for example, there are likely to be shear forces acting parallel to the surface. The shear forces must be assessed by quite different methods, often involving experimental data, and may be of the same order of magnitude as the hydrostatic force. The two forces interact upon each other so that their combined effect is far more difficult to assess than is the single effect of the normal force in truly hydrostatic conditions.

Appendix : The measurement of pressure intensity

There are two essentially different ways of measuring the pressure intensity at a point in a fluid, whether static or moving. The fluid pressure may be applied to a movable diaphragm or piston which is balanced by a spring or by weights, the pressure intensity being then the applied force divided by the diaphragm area : or the fluid pressure may be balanced by a hydrostatic column of fluid of height h (either the same fluid as that in which the pressure has been generated, or another), when the pressure intensity p is then given by the hydrostatic equation for incompressible fluids, $p = \rho g h$.

A deadweight piston gauge (fig 2.11) is an example of the first type of measuring instrument. The pressure is transmitted from the point in question by a narrow tube A and applied to a piston P inside a closely

Fig 2.11

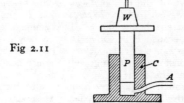

fitting cylinder C. Weights are then applied to P until the pressure force is balanced. Such gauges are mainly used to calibrate other types of gauge which are less bulky and easier to read, such as the *Bourdon gauge*. In this gauge the pressure is applied to the inside of a bent and flattened tube whose end is blocked. The tube tends to straighten due to the internal pressure and the straightening is limited by the elasticity of the tube. A pointer connected to the blocked end of the tube then shows the equilibrium position of the tube on a scale which is directly calibrated in pressure intensity. Bourdon gauges are convenient for engineering use because they can be made to suit a wide variety of pressures and are compact. They invariably require calibration at frequent intervals against some other sort of pressure gauge if they are to be relied upon.

The second kind of measuring instrument ('manometer') has more variation in its possible arrangement. The simplest device shown in fig 2.12 (a) is a vertical transparent tube (a *piezometer*) from the pipe or container P, inside of which is the fluid whose pressure p is to be measured. The fluid, water for example, rises to a height h, when the pressure p is said to be equal to a 'head' h of the fluid. This simple device cannot be used if the fluid inside P is a gas, which would escape : nor is it suitable if h is large (above about 2 m) as the tube is then unwieldy ; or if h is small (below about 7 cm), when the accuracy is low.

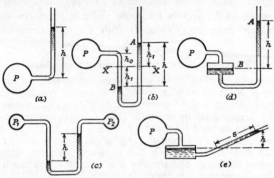

Fig 2.12

Recourse is then made to a U-tube manometer, fig 2.12 (b), where a bend in the transparent tube is filled with a heavier fluid (water or alcohol if air is in P ; mercury or acetylene tetrabromide if water is in P). The difference of level, h, of the two surfaces of the heavier fluid gives the gauge pressure *at the level of the lower surface B*, that is, $\rho_1 g h$, where ρ_1 is the density of the heavy fluid. The gauge pressure, p, at P is smaller than $\rho_1 g h$ because P is above B by a height $(h_1 + h_0)$ so that $p = \rho_1 g h - \rho g(h_1 + h_0)$. This equation is inconvenient to use because $(h_1 + h_0)$ is not a constant ; it changes with every position of the heavy fluid surface, so that the term $\rho g(h_1 + h_0)$ must be computed for each value of h. It is much more convenient to eliminate h_1, the amount by which each of the heavy fluid surfaces is separated from XX, the position of the surfaces when they are both at the same level.

Since now
$$h = 2h_1$$
$$p = \rho_1 g h - \rho g\left(\frac{h}{2} + h_0\right)$$
or
$$p = gh\left(\rho_1 - \frac{\rho}{2}\right) - \rho g h_0.$$

Both $(\rho_1 - \rho/2)$ and $\rho g h_0$ are now constants, and h is the only variable. Note that for a mercury-filled manometer used for finding the pressure of water $\rho_1 = 13 \cdot 56 \times 10^3$, $\rho = 1 \cdot 0 \times 10^3$ kg/m³, so that

$$p = 13 \cdot 06 \times 10^3 \times 9 \cdot 81 h - 9 \cdot 81 \times 10 h_0$$

in the SI system of units, where p is measured in N/m² and h in metres.

The above scheme of measurement is also used when a U-tube manometer has each side connected to pressure tappings in a piece of apparatus so that it measures the *difference* between the pressures at the tappings. It will be then found that the pressure difference is $p_1 - p_2 = gh(\rho_1 - \rho)$ $- \rho gh_0$, where h_0 is now the difference of height between the tapping points, the one at which the pressure is p_1 being assumed lower than the other.

Two modifications of the common U-tube manometer are shown in fig 2.12 (d) and (e). In (d) one limb of the manometer has been widened so that its cross-sectional area is much larger (100 times or more) than the other. For all practical purposes the movement of the surface of the heavy fluid in the widened side is now negligible, compared with the movement on the narrow side. The level B can therefore be regarded as constant so that only the height of the surface at A need be measured. Only one reading of the height of a meniscus is therefore required to find h in the narrow tube, and only this tube need be transparent.

The second modification, in fig 2.12 (e), is used when the pressure to be measured is small. By sloping the transparent tube of a widened limb manometer, there is a magnification of the distance that the meniscus moves along the tube, for a given pressure. If the slope is θ, then the distance s along the tube is $s = \dfrac{h}{\sin\theta}$. By making θ sufficiently small, s can be made large and it can therefore be measured more accurately than if the tube were vertical. It is not usual for the slope to be less than $\tan^{-1}\dfrac{1}{25}$, for then small changes of surface tension forces due to greasy patches in the bore of the tube may cause the meniscus to stick at some places, and so give inaccurate readings.

There are also other ways of measuring differences of pressure (differential pressures), particularly between pairs of tapping points in pipe systems. The simplest method is to arrange two piezometers alongside, each being connected to its tapping point, fig 2.13 (a). The

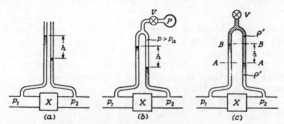

Fig 2.13 Methods of measuring a pressure difference caused by an apparatus X in a pipe.

difference of the heights of the fluid surfaces in them is the differential pressure. If this difference is large then each tapping point is led to one side of a U-tube manometer containing a heavy fluid as has been described. If the pressure difference is small enough to use the piezometer method, but both pressures are high compared to the atmospheric pressure, the tubes will be inordinately long : but if the tops of the tubes are connected together and to a small air pump, a false 'atmo-spheric' pressure may be applied to both fluid surfaces which are then equally depressed without affecting the difference, fig 2.13 (b). Thus much shorter tubes can be used. If the pressure difference is small, the tubes may be sloped to increase the distance traversed by the meniscus along the tube. Another method of magnifying the movement of the meniscus is to join the tops of a pair of piezometers and to fill the space above the surface of the fluid with another fluid of a slightly lower density, ρ'. As shown in fig 2.13 (c), the difference of pressure at the level AA is due to the difference between the pressures at the bases of columns of fluid of height h, and densities ρ and ρ' respectively. Thus $p_1 - p_2 = gh(\rho - \rho')$. Theoretically a great magnification of the difference of level h may be obtained by making $\rho - \rho'$ small enough : but a limit is soon reached because the meniscus between fluids of near densities becomes very sensitive to changes in the surface tension within the tube, due to traces of grease in the bore. The meniscus often then adheres to parts of the bore more than others and is deformed so that it is not horizontal and its level cannot be determined with accuracy.

The above descriptions are for a few basic types of manometer only. There are many other types each for its own range of duty and a very full account of them is given in H. Addison's *Hydraulic Measurements*. Certain precautions must be taken when measuring pressures with any sort of manometer. First, the connecting tubes from the tapping points must be full of the fluid whose pressure is being measured, and there

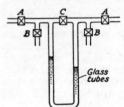

Glass
tubes

Fig 2.14 Valves A are to isolate manometer from tapping points. Valves B are for flushing air bubbles. C is the equalizer valve.

must be neither bubbles of water in the tubes of an air system nor air bubbles in a water system : the density ρ in the connecting tubes must be uniform. Secondly, it is desirable to be able to confirm, at any time, that if the pressures are equalized, then the readings of the surfaces of the manometer fluid are the same. A manometer system ought always to have valves in it to flush the connecting tubes, and to have an equalizing valve to ensure that both tubes can be brought to the same pressure as shown in fig 2.14.

PROBLEMS

1. A light aircraft engine is gravity-fed from a tank 1 m above the carburettor. If the machine is accelerated uniformly to 110 km/h on a catapult 36 m long, what is the maximum distance of the tank behind the carburettor for the engine not to be starved completely of fuel?
Ans. 0·756 m.

2. A steel sector (Tainter) gate on the crest of a weir 10 m wide is an arc of 7 m radius, arranged to lift by pivoting about its centre of curvature which is 4·2 m above and upstream of the crest. Find (a) the position, (b) the magnitude, and (c) the direction of the resultant force when the upstream water-level is 6·3 m above the crest and the gate is both closed and dry downstream.
Ans. (a) 2070 kN, (b) through centre, (c) $19\frac{1}{2}°$ downward.

3. A closed rectangular tank, 3·3 m high can be filled to a depth of 3·0 m with a volatile liquid (s.g 1·60). A safety valve in the roof is set to blow at 7 kN/m² gauge. (a) What is the maximum loading per horizontal metre run on each side? (b) Where should a tie bar be placed to take this load? (c) What is the maximum load when there is no liquid in the tank?
Ans. 93·7 kN/m : 1·16 m from bottom : 23·1 kN/m.

4. Vertical boards are being used to shore up completely waterlogged soil at the side of an excavation 6 m deep. Where should two horizontal beams be placed, one above the other, so that they are equally loaded? What is the load in each per metre run of boarding in the horizontal direction?
Ans. Equi-spaced about C.P but minimum bending if 2·84 m and 5·17 m from top : 88·5 kN/m.

5. A model of a 1·2 m pipe submerged in a river is tested in a stream and discloses the following pressures on the full-size pipe surface. Plot the pressures and find the horizontal and vertical components of the loading per metre run. Angles measured from the horizontal.

θ degrees	$p : \text{kN/m}^2$	θ	p	θ	p	θ	p
0	20·7	80	6·2	180	8·8	280	1·4
20	17·2	100	8·4	200	8·1	300	1·7
40	10·6	120	9·2	220	7·0	320	8·0
60	6·1	140	9·2	240	5·7	340	17·1
		160	9·1	260	3·7		

Ans. Horizontal 8810 : Vertical 6270 kN/m.

6. A spherical container is made up of two hemispheres, one resting on the other with the interface horizontal. The sphere is completely filled through a small hole in the top by a weight W of liquid. What is the minimum weight of the upper hemisphere in order to prevent it from lifting?
Ans. $W/4$.

3

FORCES ON IMMERSED OBJECTS

3.1 The preceding chapter has dealt with the forces on surfaces which are subject to the pressure of a fluid at rest. It is now intended to examine the consequences when the surfaces form part of the boundary of a body enclosing a finite volume surrounded by the fluid. Fig 3.1 shows the side view of a solid body totally immersed in a fluid

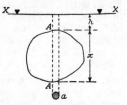

Fig 3.1   Side view of an object totally submerged in a fluid whose free surface is XX. An imaginary vertical cylinder (cross-sectional area a) is shown intersecting the object.

whose free surface is XX. Consider a vertical column of the body such as AA whose cross-sectional area in a horizontal plane is a and whose length is x. Then the downward hydrostatic force on the upper end of the column is ρgha, and the upward force on the lower end is $\rho g(h + x)a$, so that the resultant force on the column is ρgxa, in an upward direction. But xa is the volume of the column, V, so that the upward force F on the whole body, which is made up of many columns, is

$$F = \Sigma \rho g V = \rho g \mathbf{V} \quad . \quad \quad . \quad \quad . \quad \quad (3.1)$$

where $\mathbf{V}$ is the total immersed volume of the body. F is sometimes called the *buoyancy force*.

Since the upward hydrostatic force on the bottom area of the cylinder, and also the downward force on the top, both act through the centre of gravity of the cross-sectional area, therefore the resultant force ρgxa acts through the Centre of Gravity of the cylinder. The total force $\rho g \mathbf{V}$ therefore acts through the centre of gravity of the total immersed volume $\mathbf{V}$.

The relationship $F = \rho g \mathbf{V}$, attributed to Archimedes, is often expressed in words as 'The upward buoyancy force on a body is the weight force of the fluid displaced by the body', and it is used in all calculations where a body is wholly or partially surrounded by fluid. If the weight force of the body $\mathbf{M}g$ (where $\mathbf{M}$ is the mass of the body) exceeds the buoyancy force, then the body will sink, or alternatively an upward force ($Mg - \rho g V$) must be applied in some other way to preserve equilibrium. Correspondingly, if the weight force is smaller than the buoyancy force, then the body rises through the surface until the immersed volume has so decreased that $\rho g V = Mg$, where V is now not the total volume of the body, but merely the volume of the portion below the fluid surface. At this stage the body will float indefinitely if the conditions are preserved.

Archimedes' principle determines, then, whether a particular body will sink or swim; or alternatively, what volume of the body must be immersed in order to balance its weight and therefore allow it to float. But engineers are not only concerned with this principle as they also have to consider whether a particular body is stable in any one position. In other words, they are concerned to know whether the body will float right way up or whether it will capsize.

3.2 Stability of floating bodies

An object, acted upon by any set of forces (which may include buoyancy forces as above), is said to be in stable equilibrium if a change of its position caused by an externally applied force or couple gives rise to an opposing force or couple which just balances the applied force. Thus consider a rectangular box whose vertical cross section is ABCD in fig 3.2 (*a*), which is floating on the surface of a fluid XX. The buoyancy force F is, by Archimedes' principle, just equal to the weight force of the fluid displaced and acts through the centre of gravity of the immersed volume PQCD, that is at H. The only other force acting upon it is its weight force Mg acting vertically downwards and exactly balancing F. Mg acts through the centre of gravity G of the body, which must therefore be situated somewhere on the vertical line through H, i.e. on ZZ. The position of G on this line depends on the distribution of weight in the box, heavy ballast in the bottom lowering G, but weights on the deck AB raising G.

Now consider what happens if a couple of value Wgx is applied to the box; fig 3.2 (*b*), which causes it to tilt or roll through an angle θ. Assuming that the weights in the box are secured and do not move as the box rolls, G will not be affected and will remain somewhere on ZZ. The effect of the change of attitude is to change the shape of the immersed volume to P'Q'CD, a more trapezoidal shape than PQCD in fig 3.2 (*a*). The volume P'Q'CD is still the same as PQCD, for the downward forces on the box are unaltered and the balancing buoyancy force therefore stays constant. But the position through which the buoyancy force acts has changed, for the trapezium P'Q'CD has a centre of gravity nearer to the long edge CQ' than it had before, for example, it may be at H', say. The buoyancy force acts therefore on the *vertical* line H'M, M being the place where the buoyancy force cuts the original vertical centre line ZZ. [See fig 3.2 (*c*).]

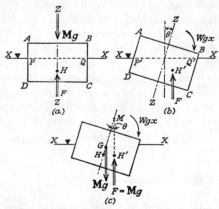

Fig 3.2   The forces on an object floating on the surface XX of a fluid.   (*a*) The object at rest with an axis of symmetry ZZ vertical.   The (vertical) buoyancy force F acts through H, the centre of gravity of PQCD.   (*b*) If the object is subjected to a torque, Wgx, it heels over to an angle θ.   In doing so, the immersed volume changes to a trapezium P'Q'CD with its centre of gravity at H', through which F now acts.   (*c*) If the centre of gravity G of the mass of the body lies below M, then there is a restoring couple $Mg.\overline{MG}\sin\theta$ which just balances the torque Wxg, and the object is stable.

Providing the centre of gravity G lies *below* M, the lines of action of the weight force and the buoyancy force are so separated that they cause a couple $Mg.\overline{MG}\sin\theta$ tending to bring the box upright. If this couple just equals the overturning couple Wgx the box will be in equilibrium at the angle θ. Thus the condition for the box to be in stable equilibrium is that G shall lie somewhere below M. There is no restriction in this respect about the position of G relative to H, the original position through which the buoyancy force acted. Thus in the upright position, fig 3.2 (*a*), it may appear that the box is in unstable equilibrium for G may be above H : it is only the circumstance that H moves sideways to H' that causes the overturning couple to be balanced by the so-called righting couple, $Mg.\overline{MG}\sin\theta$. The distance $\overline{MG}$ is called the *metacentric height* and the point M the *metacentre*. The distance between the vertical lines through G and M, $\overline{MG}\sin\theta$, is called the *lever arm* of the righting couple.

It is a matter of vital importance that certain floating bodies, ships, pontoons, barges and the like, shall not capsize, and it is therefore usual to carry out an experiment to see how far G lies below M. A couple is applied, usually by moving a weight of mass W across the deck by a distance x, and the deflection of the ship θ measured by a long pendulum hanging inside. Thus the overturning couple is Wgx and the righting couple caused by the deflection θ is $\mathbf{M}g \cdot \overline{MG} \sin \theta$.

So
$$Wgx = \mathbf{M}g \cdot \overline{MG} \sin \theta$$

$$\overline{MG} = \frac{W}{\mathbf{M}} \frac{x}{\sin \theta} \qquad \cdot \qquad \cdot \qquad \cdot \qquad (3.2)$$

M is found by noting the position of the waterline and calculating the displaced water. $\overline{MG}$ in practice usually lies between about 15 cm and 1·3 m; the upper limit will be discussed below.

The above experimental method of finding the metacentric height is of course only possible if the box or ship is already afloat and ballasted. It is, however, often necessary to determine in advance what $\overline{MG}$ will be for a proposed loading system. For example, when the girders of a bridge are being put into position from barges, the stability is of paramount importance as the girders are jacked up. It is clear that a unit volume of displaced water creates a larger righting couple if it is far from the pivoting axis of a box than if it is near the axis: a wide box, i.e. AB large, gives a larger couple and a larger $\overline{MG}$ than a narrow box of the same volume. $\overline{MG}$ thus depends on the way in which the waterline area is distributed, the waterline area being the area of the body intersected by the waterline XX. (In the case of a box this area is a rectangle: for a ship the area is rather of a cigar shape with the ship rolling about the long axis, fig 3.3.) In fact, it

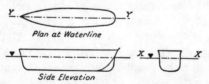

Plan at Waterline

Side Elevation

Fig 3.3 Plan and elevations of a ship to show the waterline area (on the plan) of which the moment of inertia I_{WLA} is required about the axis of roll YY, to obtain the height of the metacentre above the centre of buoyancy.

can be shown that for small angles of roll (θ small) and for the ship's sides being parallel in a vertical cross section as fig 3.2, the height $\overline{MH}$ is approximately $MH = I_{WLA}/\mathbf{V}$, where I_{WLA} is the second moment of the waterline area, or 'Moment of Inertia' about the axis of rolling, and **V** is, as before, the immersed volume. Notice that $\overline{MH}$ is not the metacentric height directly, but that $\overline{MH} = \overline{MG} + \overline{GH}$. $\overline{GH}$ must be found from other evidence such as the distribution of weights in the ship which fix the position of G relative to H.

All these terms can be calculated and $\overline{MG}$ found before ever a ship is constructed, though the determination of G is a long and tedious job for such a complicated structure. The predicted value of $\overline{MG}$ is usually checked by the experimental method after the ship is launched. To ensure that $\overline{MG}$ is suitable and is not so small as to endanger the ship, it is common practice to stipulate limitations to the loading of ships so that G does not rise so high that $\overline{MG}$ vanishes.

3.3 The period of rolling of floating bodies

Though the civil engineering problems associated with the stability of floating bodies are usually concerned with the static aspects described above, it is of interest in the field of fluid mechanics generally to examine what happens if an overturning couple is suddenly removed from a body which has been inclined to an angle θ. If the overturning couple is suddenly removed, fig 3.4, the only force acting on

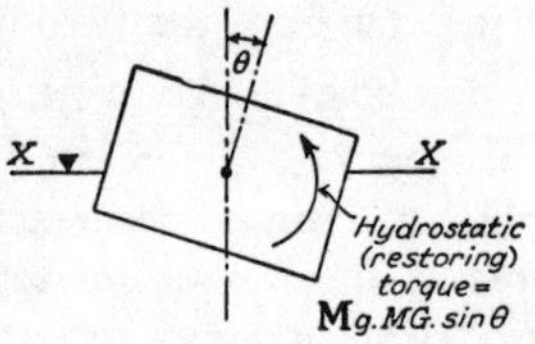

Fig 3.4   If the overturning torque Wxg is removed, the restoring torque causes the object to rotate about its axis of roll.

the body is the righting couple as above, $Mg . \overline{MG} \sin \theta$, so by Newton's Second Law of Motion a rate of change of angular momentum is caused, denoted by $I_s(d^2\theta/dt^2)$, where $d^2\theta/dt^2$ is the angular acceleration of the ship and I_s is the moment of inertia of the weights in the ship about the axis of roll.   Thus $Mg . \overline{MG} \sin \theta = - I_s(d^2\theta/dt^2)$, the minus sign indicating that the couple is acting in a direction such that it tends to decrease θ.

If θ is small enough, $\sin \theta \rightarrow \theta$

or $$- Mg . \overline{MG}\theta/I_s = \frac{d^2\theta}{dt^2} .$$

This is the well-known simple pendulum equation, or Simple Harmonic Motion, for which it can be proved that θ oscillates about the zero position with a period

$$t = 2\pi\sqrt{(I_s/Mg . \overline{MG})}.$$

Thus t is the period of rolling of the ship.   In the absence of fluid
friction, or damping, the oscillation will continue undiminished with
this period.   Fortunately, the relative motion between ship and water
causes fluid forces which oppose the motion in whatever direction it
occurs, so that rolling motions die out fairly quickly, unless of course
a new overturning couple is applied.

In the above expression it will be seen that a large metacentric
height $\overline{MG}$ causes a *small* period of rolling : such a ship will roll
rapidly from one side to the other and will not only be uncomfortable
to sail in but may damage its own structure.   A small $\overline{MG}$, though
giving a slower roll, is undesirable because a small error in loading
cargo, or a small amount of water on deck in a gale, may change G
so much that the ship will capsize.   It is usual to get $\overline{MG}$ in the range
0·15 to 1·2 m, and a ship with only a small amount of cargo on board
sometimes stows it on a deck much higher than the bottom of the ship
so as to have G in the required position to give a comfortably slow roll.

PROBLEM

A floating rectangular pontoon weighing 50 tonnes with C of G at
the waterline rolls 10° when an overturning torque of 59·8 kN m is
applied.   How high may a 5 tonne load be raised on a light scaffolding ?

Ans.   GM 0·7 m ;   7·7 m above W.L.

4

DEFINITIONS CONCERNING FLUIDS IN MOTION

4.1 The phenomena exhibited by fluids in motion are more complex than those which have already been described for static fluids. The motions of a fluid may vary from place to place, or from time to time, or both : they may appear simple at first but may later appear much more complicated as attention is concentrated on certain aspects of the flow. It is accordingly necessary to make certain definitions so that a flow is described accurately.

The first division of the types of flow is made by considering the ' steadiness ' or way in which the flow changes with *time*. A flow which, at one place, does not change its velocity with time is called *steady* : if the velocity changes with time it is called *non-steady*. Most fluid motions of interest to engineers are steady, for example, the flow through a pipeline when a short time has elapsed after the controlling valves have been opened. A great deal of experimental and theoretical work has been carried out on steady flow, which is usually far simpler to analyse than non-steady flow. However, considerable engineering problems are associated with non-steady flow : for instance, the conditions occurring in a long pipeline when a valve is suddenly shut may give rise to stresses which can wreck the pipe. Approximations and empirical knowledge are often needed for any analysis of such problems, though an imposing array of theory is sometimes available.

A further division of types of flow is concerned with ' uniformity ' or way in which the velocity changes with *position*. If the velocity does not change within a particular zone, then the flow is said to be *uniform* there : if the velocity changes from place to place, then it is *non-uniform*. Two distinct cases of non-uniformity can be distinguished. The velocity may vary over a cross section of a flow (for example, in a river where the water is slower at the sides and bottom than at the middle) ; or it may vary along the flow direction (for example, at the entrance to a river from a lake, where the water accelerates from a standstill to a relatively high velocity). Both sorts of non-uniformity often coexist, as in the latter case. However, it is observed that changes of the first sort of non-uniformity are connected with changes of the second sort. A flow which is non-uniform along the direction of motion may either suppress or enhance the non-uniformity across it.   In a converging pipeline, for instance, the flow is made more uniform as the cross-sectional area is decreased, the slower fluid near the walls of the pipe being speeded up more than the fluid in the centre.   In a diverging pipe the reverse is the case, and the non-uniformity across the flow is accentuated (fig 4.1).   Complete uniformity in the direction of a flow is common in engineering

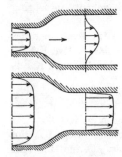

Fig 4.1   Non-uniformity of the cross section of the stream along the direction of flow affects the uniformity of the velocity distribution.   (*Above*) A diverging flow makes the velocity distribution less uniform.   (*Below*) A convergence tends to make a uniform velocity across the flow—a property used in the design of wind tunnels.

problems (for example, flow in a constant-bore pipe), but complete uniformity across the flow is rare.   Fluid friction is always present, making the velocity lower near solid surfaces, but the flow may be nearly uniform over limited areas of the cross section far removed from such surfaces.

A steady flow which is not uniform over its cross section can be described by a diagram of the change of velocity with position across it.   Such a diagram is called a *velocity distribution curve*.   A typical curve for the case of pipe flow is shown in fig 4.2.   The total quantity of fluid passing such a cross section in unit time is known as the

Fig 4.2   Non-uniform flow in a pipe.   The velocity distribution curve has a maximum at the centre.

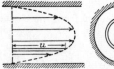

discharge Q.   In general, Q is found by an integration of the form $Q = \int u \, da$, where u is the velocity at right angles to the cross section, and da is an element of area over which the velocity is constant.   For the very common case of a flow through a circular pipe, the element of area is a ring of radius r and width dr.   Thus the discharge for such a pipe is

$$Q = \int_{0}^{R} 2\pi r \, dr \, u,$$

where R is the radius of the bore of the pipe.

The discharge through a pipe or along a river is often expressed by the engineer in terms of the mean velocity $\bar{u}$ across the section where $\bar{u} = Q/A$, A being the total cross-sectional area (πR^2 for the circular pipe). The mean velocity cannot be directly measured in a pipe, except by first measuring Q, although of course there are two places on the velocity distribution curve where $u = \bar{u}$. These places are not always at the same distance from the walls and it is not safe to assume that $\bar{u}$ can be measured by putting a velocity-measuring apparatus at one particular place.

As well as the discharge and mean velocity of a flow, it is sometimes necessary to know the total kinetic energy of the flow. The K.E of unit mass of fluid is $\frac{1}{2}u^2$, so that in a non-uniform flow the total K.E is

$$\rho \int \tfrac{1}{2}u^2 . u \, \mathrm{d}a$$

the integral being taken over the whole cross section, as was done for the discharge. It should be noticed that the above integral is not necessarily equal to the product of the mass flow, ρQ, and the K.E of the mean velocity, $\frac{1}{2}\bar{u}^2$: the true total K.E is always greater than $\frac{1}{2}\rho Q\bar{u}^2$, as the following example will show.

Example

At a certain cross section of a 1 m diameter water pipe the velocities were found to be as follows :

Velocity u m/s	4·99	4·95	4·88	4·73	4·29	3·65	2·75	0
Radius r m	0	0·1	0·2	0·3	0·4	0·45	0·475	0·5

What is the discharge, the mean velocity and the average kinetic energy per newton weight of fluid ?

(a) DISCHARGE $$Q = \int_0^R 2\pi r u \, \mathrm{d}r.$$

Calculate ru from the above table and plot against r (fig 4.3).

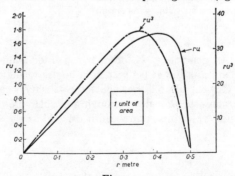

Fig 4.3

Area under curve is 10·7 units.

1 unit = 0·1 m × 0·5 m²/s = 0·05 m²/s

So $\qquad Q = 2\pi \times 0·05 \times 10·7$ m³/s (called cumecs)

$\qquad\qquad = 3·36$ cumecs

and $\qquad \bar{u} = 3·36/0·25\pi = 4·28$ m/s

(b) KINETIC ENERGY

Total K.E. of the fluid passing the cross section in 1 second.

$$\rho \int_0^R \tfrac{1}{2}u^2.u.2\pi r\mathrm{d}r$$

$$= \rho\pi \int_0^R ru^3\mathrm{d}r.$$

Calculate ru^3 from the above table and plot against r (fig 4.3).

Area under curve is 10·8 units.

1 unit = 0·1 m × 10 m⁴/s³ = 1 m⁵/s³

So, total K.E. of fluid = $\pi \times 1000 \times 1 \times 10·8$ N m/s

Weight flowing across the section in 1 second = $3·36 \times 1000 \times 9·81$ N/s
So average K.E per N of fluid

$$= \frac{\pi \times 1000 \times 1 \times 10·8}{3·36 \times 1000 \times 9·81}$$

$$= 1·03 \text{ N m/N } (= \text{joule J/N}) \ (= \text{metre})$$

This result should be compared to the K.E. per N of the fluid, assuming it is all travelling at the same mean speed $\bar{u}$, thus giving the same $Q = 3·36$ cumecs.

In this case $\qquad$ K.E. per N = $\bar{u}^2/2g$

$$= 0·935 \text{ N m/N } (=\text{m})$$

The true average K.E./N is always greater than the K.E./N based on the mean velocity, though for many purposes the ratio between them (in this case 1·11) is often ignored.

4.2 The next division of types of flow concerns the small irregular motions which are often superimposed upon the main motion. In the atmosphere, for example, the wind always blows in gusts with lulls between, and the direction of the wind constantly alters. In this respect the wind is air in non-steady motion, for the velocity is changing with time. But if average velocities are computed each over several successive periods and with each period fairly long compared with the time of a gust, it will be found that these averages will not change; the average wind is therefore steady though it has the non-steady motions of the gusts superimposed on it. This type of motion is called *turbulent*, and the relative magnitude of the superimposed non-steady motions can be used to express the degree of *turbulence* in the

Fig 4.4 Laminar and turbulent flow expressed as vectors. (*Above*) Steady laminar flow at a point is represented by a single vector of length *u*. (*Below*) Steady turbulent flow of the same magnitude is represented by a mean flow vector *ū*, with the addition of fluctuating velocities *u'*, *v'*, *w'*, which average out to zero over a sufficiently long period.

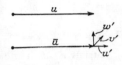

motion. The irregular motions do not affect all the fluid at the same instant, so that the general effect is of a continually changing map showing patches of fluid moving differently from the long-term average speed.   At the boundaries of the patches there must exist fairly abrupt changes of speed, i.e. there are large velocity gradients.   By the ordinary viscosity equation $\tau = \mu\dfrac{du}{dy}$ (eqn *1.1*) the presence of velocity gradients implies shear stresses and these may be large locally.   A force opposing a movement of matter (whether fluid or solid) requires energy to be expended in doing so, proportional to the product of force and velocity, and these stresses and irregular motions are no

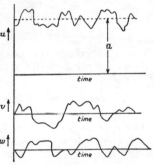

Fig 4.5 Another way of expressing steady turbulent flow.   The velocity at a point is plotted against time, all three components of motion *u*, *v* and *w* (in the *x*, *y* and *z* directions respectively) being shown. Components *v* and *w* average out to zero over a long period.   Component *u* averages out to *ū* over the same period.

exceptions. Mechanical energy (potential or kinetic) is continually being expended by turbulence and is converted into low-grade thermal energy. This constant degradation of energy is always present in turbulent flow, and is most noticeable at places where the irregular motions (sometimes called ' eddies ') are greatest.*

* The degradation of mechanical energy into thermal energy causes a small increase of temperature of the fluid.   In turn, the rise of temperature may cause chemical changes to take place, or the viscosity to change, or cause a local expansion and therefore reduction of density to occur.   The first

Occasionally, however, there is no turbulence present in a flow, so that the mean velocity and the actual instantaneous velocity are exactly the same. In this case the flow is called *laminar*. It has been found that laminar flow tends to occur if velocities are low, or viscosity high, or if the boundaries of the flow are close together. Such conditions are rare in engineering problems, where a low viscosity fluid, air or water, is usually moving at a sufficiently high speed to give turbulent flow. The mathematical analysis of laminar flow problems is in general well known, for the equations concerned can be solved with no additional experimental information, but the corresponding analyses for turbulent flow give equations which cannot be directly solved with the mathematics at our command. Experimental data are required to obtain even approximate solutions to turbulent flow problems.

It is sometimes desirable to have a complete diagram of the direction of motion at a number of points in a fluid motion. This can be done by drawing *streamlines* on a plan or elevation of a flow. These lines are drawn so that they are tangential to the direction of flow at any point on them. Streamlines are therefore often curved and an infinite number of them can be drawn in any particular part of a flow. For clarity a few only are shown on any one diagram. No two streamlines can ever cross, for if they did, the particle of fluid at the intersection would have two directions of motion, one tangential to each streamline; this cannot occur. A succeeding chapter will describe how streamlines can be plotted. A streamline has no width and so has no cross-sectional area. If it is desired to consider a finite portion of a flow, a *streamtube* is often postulated. This is a prism of fluid bounded by streamlines along its length. No flow can occur across the walls of a streamtube.

When fluid flows over a solid surface or shape, it is sometimes found that a streamline which is touching the surface at one place is no longer

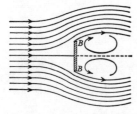

Fig 4.6 Streamline pattern around a badly streamlined shape (a flat plate) in an extensive stream. Notice the breakaway points BB, and the large, permanent eddies behind the shape.

change is only of importance if chemically active fluids are being used : the second and third changes are usually assumed not to affect the conditions of flow although in certain meteorological problems the buoyancy forces due to the changed density may be comparable to other forces acting in the atmosphere.

touching somewhere else. The flow is now said to *breakaway* or *separate* from the surface. A mass of fluid called the *wake* which does not take part in the main flow remains between the separated streamline and the surface. This mass may rotate slowly, forming an eddy as shown in fig. 4.6. Such an eddy, which remains permanently in one position, should not be confused with the irregular motions in turbulent flow, which can also make rotary, though non-permanent, eddies. Some shapes, notably aircraft wings and well-designed ship hulls, have no breakaway on them at all in their normal operating condition, so that their shape is that of a streamline. Their shapes are therefore called *streamlined*—a word which has been badly misused in modern times.

5

PLOTTING STREAMLINES—A PROBLEM IN SURVEYING

5.1 A fluid flow can be characterized by its streamlines. These are imaginary lines, usually curved, which can be drawn in the fluid so that tangents drawn to them are in the direction of flow at the tangential points. Streamlines cannot cross, for if they did so, then the fluid at the intersection would have two velocities, one along the tangent to each streamline. This is clearly impossible.

In the same way that a country is not known until a map has been made of it, so the knowledge of a fluid stream is not complete until the paths of all the streamlines are known. For a particular configuration of the solid boundaries, and of the sources and outlets of the flow, a map can be drawn up showing a selection of the infinite number

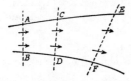

Fig 5.1 Portion of a fluid flow with only two streamlines ACE, BDF shown. No fluid can pass across either streamline, so that if a volume Q passes across AB in unit time, then Q also passes across CD and EF. Since EF > AB, velocity at AB > velocity at EF.

of streamlines existing in any stream. Because the flow is always along a streamline, no fluid can pass across it, so that the quantity passing per unit time across a line between two streamlines is the same as the quantity passing any other lines between the two same streamlines (see fig 5.1). The velocity of flow, therefore, varies inversely with the spacing of the streamlines, if the flow is two-dimensional, i.e. depth of stream is constant in a direction at right angles to the plane of the streamline pattern, and the patterns at all levels are the same.* A streamline can always be replaced by a solid boundary, which also has no flow across it, so that the spacing between such a boundary and a nearby streamline gives the velocity there. Use of

* In this brief summary of streamline plotting, two-dimensional flow is assumed throughout. In the far more complicated case of three-dimensional flow, i.e. when the depth of the stream varies, and the pattern changes from one level to another, the convergencies and divergencies of streamlines in all three directions must be considered.

Bernoulli's equation (Chapter 7, p. 76) then gives the fluid pressure intensity acting against the boundary surface.

5.2 The experimental method of streamline plotting

If the direction of flow is known at a number of successive points, then the streamlines can be drawn as tangents to these directions. This technique, though tedious, can be used in a fluid stream, with suitable vanes, similar to wind vanes, or flags to show the directions. A more direct method, often employed, uses particles suspended in, or floating on, the fluid. The paths of the particles may be directly plotted, and if the flow is steady they follow the streamlines into which they have been launched. Streamlines have been plotted in this way even in large-scale fluid flows such as rivers, sometimes from photographs of floats taken at short intervals.

Another method, particularly applicable to laboratory studies, is to release into the stream a small jet of smoke (if the fluid is a gas) or dye (if a liquid) of the same density as the flowing fluid. The particles liberated successively at the same place trace out the streamline passing through the jet : the trail, now made visible, can be photographed. Although this method is not successful with a very turbulent flow (since the dye, or smoke, mixes rapidly with the main stream and no longer remains visible), yet it can often be used to explore certain places in a stream even if there are turbulent patches present. Some examples showing experimental methods of finding streamlines are shown in Plates 5 and 6, facing pp. 148 and 149.

All the above methods, and variations of them, are used in engineering fluid mechanics where often the shape of the boundaries of the flow is so complicated that the theoretical methods of finding streamlines, described below, are tedious and therefore expensive. Furthermore, as these theoretical methods often break down, giving a quite unreal map of the streamline in certain areas of a flow, the experimental methods are always needed as a check. In general, the experimental methods give a less precise map than the theoretical methods, but this lack of precision must be accepted in areas where the latter give a misleading answer anyway.

5.3 Theoretical properties of streamlines

Although experimental methods of finding streamlines are the only final evidence of a flow pattern, it is frequently desirable or necessary to predict a flow pattern at the design stage of an engineering job.

By using the essential property of streamlines, that they do not cross, it is possible to produce a method of plotting the lines on the drawing-board in advance of experiment. The limitations to the method are reviewed in section **5.11**.

Consider any two streamlines, AB and CD, not necessarily parallel, of a fluid in motion (fig 5.2). The fluid is of constant depth and

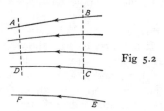

Fig 5.2

there are other streamlines between AB and CD. Since there is no flow across streamlines, the same quantity of fluid per unit time passes AD as passes BC.

That is
$$\int_{A}^{D} u \, dn = \int_{B}^{C} u \, dn = \text{Constant} = \psi,$$

where u is the velocity at any point on the lines AD or BC and dn is a small length at right angles to the streamline at that point. The quantity is expressed as a volume per unit time, or, in other words, streamline CD is always a 'discharge' of ψ distant from AB even if the length it is distant from AB changes. Consequently CD can be labelled by its discharge from AB, and it can be called streamline $\psi\left(=\int_{A}^{D} u \, dn\right)$ relative to AB. Another streamline such as EF, further from AB than CD, will clearly have a larger value of ψ than CD. ψ is called the *stream function* of a streamline and is only a method of labelling streamlines, to give them a quantitative meaning, depending on their position within the stream.

5.4 A quite different method of marking a flow which eventually proves useful is by the plotting of 'potential' lines on it. Along any one streamline values of a quantity $\phi = \int u \, ds$, called the *potential*, can be marked off, where s is the distance measured along the streamline. The potential, though having this precise meaning, is a fictitious quantity and it cannot be measured directly with instruments. Referring to fig 5.2, if A is taken as the zero point for potential on AB, then

$$\phi \text{ at } B = \int_{A}^{B} u \, ds.$$

(Note the family likenesses and differences with ψ : n is measured across streamlines, s along them.) Points on other streamlines can also be marked off with their values of ϕ, and those with the same value on different streamlines linked to give contours of the same ϕ, called *equipotential lines*. Since the potential is by definition a property that increases only along the direction of a streamline, and never has a component across it, the equipotential lines are *always* normal to streamlines.

There is also another important link between the streamlines and equipotential lines. It has already been shown in section **5.1** that if the velocity u increases along a streamline, then adjacent streamlines come closer and converge : and if u decreases they diverge. But if u increases, then a given potential $\phi(= \int u \, ds)$ is developed in a *smaller* distance s than it did for a smaller u. If streamlines converge, then the equipotential lines become closer together also.

The two properties, stream function ψ and potential ϕ taken together, are used to draw streamline maps or patterns by a method of successive approximations.

5.5 Numbering convention

It is conventional to label a streamline by the value of its stream function ψ, that is by the quantity of the flow passing between the streamline and an arbitrary, reference streamline. It is also conventional to regard the value as increasing positively to the *left* of the reference line, while looking *downstream* (see fig 5.5). The unit of stream function used for such numbering is entirely optional, but it is often convenient to use cumecs (m³/s), passing in a stream of 1 m depth.

5.6 Drawing streamlines by a method of successive approximations

Consider a streamline map drawn perfectly correctly for the

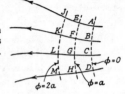

Fig 5.3 A perfectly correct streamline pattern with equipotential lines also drawn in. If ABFE is chosen to be a 'square', then so is FBCG, GCDH.

boundaries of the flow concerned (fig 5.3). The streamlines are drawn at equal intervals of ψ. At one arbitrarily chosen point draw a line normal to the streamline there and continue the line (curving it as necessary) to cross all other streamlines at 90°, e.g. ABCD. This line will be an equipotential line in the flow and can be given a value of ϕ = zero, say. Any number of other equipotential lines can also be drawn, each of which will have a value of ϕ, but consider only EFGH which has been drawn so that its value of ϕ is $\int_A^B u \, dn$.

That is
$$\phi = \int_A^E u \, ds = \int_A^B u \, dn.$$

If the streamlines have been drawn fairly closely together, then u is nearly uniform at all places in the area ABFE, and in the limit, when there are an infinite number of streamlines drawn, u will be quite uniform. Thus to a first approximation, u is independent of both s and n if the streamline interval is fairly small, and

$$\int_A^E ds = \int_A^B dn$$

or
$$EA = AB.$$

So EABF is a shape bounded by curves which intersect at 90° and which has two sides EA and AB of the same length. The shape is conveniently called a ' square '. Similarly, FBCG and GCDH are ' squares ', though not the same size as EABF : FB = GC = EA only if AB = BC = CD, the condition of uniform velocity. If the streamlines and equipotential lines are close enough, then shapes such as ABFE, GCDH will be true squares.

Again, another equipotential line JKLM may be drawn at the same interval of ϕ, e.g.
$$\int_E^J u \, ds = \int_E^F u \, dn$$
so that,
$$JE = EF.$$

Thus another set of ' squares ' are produced, again not all of the same size, getting larger as the streamlines diverge. However, there is one common property : if the interval of ϕ between equipotential lines is kept the same, and was chosen to give ' squares ' at one part of the map, then ' squares ' are produced in *every* part of the map if the streamline pattern is already correct. Even if the streamlines are drawn well apart the ' squares ' will still be approximately formed.

This important property can be used by the engineer to draw streamline patterns for flows around complicated shapes. The boundaries of the flow are drawn to scale, and a ' guessed ' set of streamlines put in, using the boundaries as streamlines, for there is no flow across them. At one part of this ' guessed ' pattern, preferably at a place where the velocity is uniform, commence drawing smooth curved lines at 90° to the guessed streamlines, spacing these lines so that at one point they produce ' squares '. It will soon be found that if ' squares ' are drawn in the space between two streamlines then the continuation of the lines at 90° will *not* result in ' squares ' between other pairs of streamlines. Clearly this is due to errors in the original guessed streamlines. Revisions can therefore be made to the streamlines at the places where the ' squares ' are most in error, but this process will be found to make the original ' 90° ' lines now no longer correct, so that revisions are again necessary to the ' 90° ' lines. In this way, successive adjustments to the streamlines and to the lines at 90° to them make a closer and closer approximation to the correct streamline and equipotential line pattern. In places where there are rapid changes of streamline spacing, additional streamlines and equipotential lines can be drawn between the original set of both. If the pattern is correct, then the smaller ' squares ' so formed are even better approximations to true squares than the big ones.

As a final check on the accuracy of the squares, diagonals can be drawn across them. These should be smooth curves over the whole pattern. The amount of correction necessary will depend, of course, on the experience, judgement and intuition of the draughtsman in producing the first, guessed, pattern, but comparatively unskilled people can eventually produce correct patterns. Large scale diagrams are advisable : soft pencils and plenty of indiarubber are essential. The method has no limitations on it so far as boundaries are concerned but the more complicated configurations demand more adjustments. Patience and accuracy will invariably succeed.* An example is shown in fig 5.4 (see insert between pp. 52 and 53).

5.7   Simple streamline patterns

Although the trial-and-error method above always produces a correct streamline pattern for any given boundaries, a more accurate way is to combine two or more simple patterns together, until one of the streamlines coincides with the shape of the boundaries concerned. Some of the simple patterns are shown in fig 5.5. These are :

(*a*) Uniform straight line flow. Both the streamlines and equipotential lines are uniformly spaced forming a rectangular grid.

* A slightly different method of drawing streamlines by an approximate method is given by S. Leliavsky in *The Engineer*, vol. 185, pp. 464–5 and 488–90. Some valuable hints which simplify the drawing of the first guessed pattern are given by H. A. Foster in *Trans. Amer. Soc. Civ. Eng*, vol. 110, pp. 1237–51.

(b) A point source of fluid. The flow is radially outward so that the streamlines diverge. The spacing of the circular equipotential lines will therefore increase outward from the centre. The streamline of value $\psi = 0$ is a radius, quite arbitrarily chosen, and the remaining radial streamlines are successively numbered as shown in accordance with the numbering convention.

(c) A point 'sink' or outlet of fluid. The pattern is radial, precisely the same as the source, but with the direction changed. The numbering is thus reversed, according to the numbering convention.

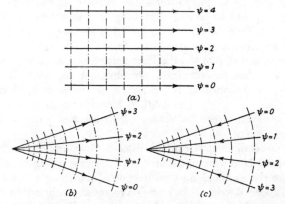

(a)

(b)   (c)

Fig 5.5 Three simple streamline patterns, all drawn with the streamlines at the same interval of stream function. Potential lines are dotted. Note the numbering convention.

5.8 Combination of streamline patterns by a graphical method

Consider two superimposed simple patterns, A and B, each with its streamlines drawn at the same interval of ψ. At a certain point x, y, two streamlines intersect, one of pattern A whose stream function is p, called $_A\psi_p$: the other from B whose stream function is q, called $_B\psi_q$. Since 'discharge' (flow per unit time) is a scalar quantity, the total discharge at x, y, due to both patterns, is simply $p + q$: so that the stream function of the combined pattern at that point is the algebraic sum $p + q$. The streamline of the combined pattern through this point is called $_{A+B}\psi_{p+q}$.

All other intersections of streamlines can thus be labelled with the sum of the stream functions, and smooth curves drawn between points of the same value. These curves are the streamlines of the combined pattern. In this graphical manner any number of simple patterns, centred or oriented differently, can be successively combined to form patterns of considerable complexity. Sometimes the combination will give one streamline that is a closed curve : in this case the streamlines outside the curve are those which would result from the fluid flowing around a solid object of the shape of the curve (see fig 5.6, facing p. 52).

5.9 Combination of streamline patterns by an algebraical method

Graphical methods to produce complicated combinations of more than two or three simple patterns tend to be tedious and slight errors of plotting gradually accumulate to give inadmissible errors. An alternative method, always to be preferred if more than three simple patterns are involved, is to add algebraically the equations of ψ for the patterns and to plot the resultant pattern. Any number of simple patterns can thus be combined, and although the resultant equation for ψ may be complicated, it can always be evaluated at given points x_1, y_1; x_2, y_2 . . ., etc. With ψ known at a number of places, lines of constant ψ can be drawn which are the streamlines of the combined pattern.

Thus the combined streamline pattern for a uniform straight line flow of speed U and a point source of Q cusecs is obtained as follows : First, take the x-axis along the direction of the straight-line flow, and the y-axis normal to it. The equation to *any* streamline of the uniform flow is $_A\psi = Uy$ since the flow between the streamline concerned and the x-axis is independent of x. Secondly, it is convenient to take the point source on the co-ordinate origin and to number the streamlines due to the source from the x-axis as a reference streamline. Due to the numbering convention, the value of ψ at P (fig 5.7) will be positive.

Fig 5.7 System of axes for combining a uniform straight-line flow parallel to the x-axis, with a point source at O.

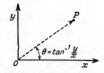

Thus the equation to any streamline of the source such as OP is
$$_B\psi = \theta Q/2\pi.$$
Alternatively, if a point x, y, is considered, whose radius to O makes an angle of $\tan^{-1}y/x$ with the x-axis, the stream function of a source streamline passing through that point is
$$_B\psi = \frac{Q}{2\pi} \tan^{-1} \frac{y}{x}.$$

Thirdly, the two equations for $_A\psi$ and $_B\psi$ are added to give the stream function of streamlines at the point x, y, due to the combined pattern, so that

$$_{A+B}\psi = Uy + \frac{Q}{2\pi}\tan^{-1}\frac{y}{x}.$$

This is the equation to the streamlines of the combined pattern. The plotting of this equation can be done in two ways. The first, as already mentioned, is to find values of $_{A+B}\psi$ at a number of points, x_1, y_1; x_2, y_2, etc., and to interpolate the streamlines : the second way is to decide on a value of $_{A+B}\psi$ for which a streamline is desired, and then find pairs of values of x and y which satisfy the equation. A number of co-ordinates are thus found for one streamline. The process must be repeated for each streamline drawn on the diagram. The second method of plotting is more tedious than the first but does not involve interpolation. The streamlines drawn to the above equation will be found to be precisely the same as those drawn in fig 5.6 by the graphical method.

5.10 An important combination of streamlines

The case of the streamlines given by the combination of a point source and a point sink leads to a most important pattern. The combining may be done by the graphical method, but the algebraical method will be demonstrated as it is more convenient later.

Consider a source S, with a flow Q coming from it situated a distance SK from a sink K with the same flow going into it (fig 5.8). Let the reference direction for a polar co-ordinate system be SK. Then at a point P the stream function ψ due to S is $_A\psi = \frac{\theta_1}{2\pi}Q$, and that due to K is $_B\psi = \frac{\theta_2'}{2\pi}Q$. (Note the influence of the numbering convention on the directions in which θ_1 and θ_2' are measured.) The combined stream function at P is therefore

$$_{A+B}\psi = \frac{Q}{2\pi}(\theta_1 + \theta_2')$$

but

$$\theta_2' = -\theta_2.$$

So

$$_{A+B}\psi = \frac{Q}{2\pi}(\theta_1 - \theta_2).$$

Since Q is a constant, every value of $_{A+B}\psi$ has its value of the angle $(\theta_1 - \theta_2)$. Consequently, every point having the same $_{A+B}\psi$, that is every point on that streamline, has the same value of $\theta_1 - \theta_2$ subtended at it by the length SK. By simple geometry, all these points

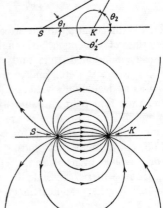

Fig 5.8 (*Above*) Definition sketch for the algebraical combination of a source at S and a sink at K. (*Below*) The combined streamline pattern for a source at S and a sink at K.

must be on a circle, so that the streamlines must all be circles passing through S and K (see fig 5.8).

It is now convenient to work in terms of the radial distances r_1 and r_2 of P from S and K respectively. For example,

$$\frac{SK}{\sin (\theta_2 - \theta_1)} = \frac{r_2}{\sin \theta_1}.$$

So the stream function equation can be rewritten

$$_{A+B}\psi = \frac{Q}{2\pi}(\theta_1 - \theta_2)\frac{SK \sin \theta_1}{r_2 \sin (\theta_2 - \theta_1)}.$$

The importance of the source and sink combination lies in the streamline pattern which results if SK tends to zero, that is, as the sink and source become coincident. To avoid an indeterminacy it is assumed that Q is increased so that the product of Q and SK remains constant. In this case

$$\theta_1 \rightarrow \theta_2 \rightarrow \theta ; \quad \sin (\theta_2 - \theta_1) \rightarrow \theta_2 - \theta_1 \rightarrow -(\theta_1 - \theta_2) ;$$

and

$$r_1 \rightarrow r_2 \rightarrow r.$$

So that

$$_{A+B}\psi = -\frac{Q}{2\pi}\frac{SK}{r} \sin \theta$$

or since

$$Q . SK = \text{Constant} = C$$

$$_{A+B}\psi = -\frac{C}{2\pi}\frac{\sin \theta}{r},$$

r now being the radial distance of the point P from the source-sink position.

This pattern is again a series of circles (see fig 5.9) all passing through the common point where both source and sink are assumed to be. The pattern is called a *doublet*. It has no existence in a real fluid for it is

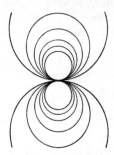

Fig 5.9 Streamline pattern for a doublet.

impossible for a source and sink to coexist at the same point. It is studied for the sole reason that when it is combined again with a straight uniform flow a pattern of great significance is produced. For example, add a doublet pattern to the pattern $_C\psi = Uy$, where U is a constant and y is a distance normal to the line SK of the source-sink pattern. The combined pattern is now

$$_{A+B+C}\psi = Uy - \frac{C}{2\pi}\frac{\sin\theta}{r}.$$

Converting polar to rectangular co-ordinates, taking the origin at the source-sink position, then

$$\sin\theta = \frac{y}{r} \quad\text{and}\quad r = \sqrt{(x^2 + y^2)}$$

so that

$$_{A+B+C}\psi = Uy - \frac{C}{2\pi}\frac{y}{x^2 + y^2}.$$

For convenience only, write $\dfrac{C}{2\pi} = Ua^2$, where a is another suitable constant.

Then

$$_{A+B+C}\psi = Uy\left(1 - \frac{a^2}{x^2 + y^2}\right).$$

At values of x and y which are large compared with a it will be seen that $_{ABC}\psi \rightarrow Uy$: that is, the uniform straight-line flow is unaffected by the doublet flow at large distances from the doublet point, as might be expected. For points where $x^2 + y^2 = a^2$, $_{ABC}\psi = 0$, so that a streamline passes through these points. Further, since $x^2 + y^2 = a^2$ is the equation to a circle, the streamline is a circle with the source-sink point as centre (see fig 5.10, facing p. 53).

It has already been explained that any streamline can be replaced with a solid surface without changing any of the other streamlines. The circle $_{A+B+C}\psi = 0$ can so be replaced, and the remaining pattern outside the circle then becomes the flow pattern around a cylinder in a straight uniform flow. This pattern is a most important one in fluid mechanics where frequently cylindrical structures are exposed to fluid flows.

Still more complicated patterns may be built up by distributing doublets of varying strengths along a line, and combining them with a straight-line flow. There is often a closed streamline in the combined pattern and a well chosen set of doublets can give shapes similar to aerofoils. The flow around, and pressure against, aerofoils can be predicted by this sort of calculation.

5.11　Limitations of the theoretical streamline patterns

The methods (just described) for drawing streamlines give patterns which are confirmed by experiment only if certain additional conditions are observed. These conditions refer to the ways in which forces and rotations are applied to the fluid. Some ways produce streamline patterns having equipotential lines not at right angles to streamlines ; or, if lines are drawn at right angles to the streamlines, then they are not equipotential lines. Thus the theoretical methods, which depend on the property that *streamlines are normal to potential lines*, sometimes

Fig 5.11 A straight-line flow near a solid surface XY. Due to fluid friction the velocity near the surface is less than that further away. Lines drawn at an equal potential are not normal to the streamlines.

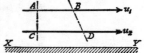

fail, and produce a quite misleading pattern. Streamlines still exist, but they do not obey the laws of construction which have been given above.

Consider a fluid flow, part of which is shown in fig 5.11, where the streamlines AB, CD, have been constrained to be straight and parallel, such as occurs when a fluid flows in a straight pipe. Suppose an external shear force is applied to the fluid in such a way that the velocity along AB, u_1, is greater than that along CD, u_2 : this situation arises if the flow is near a solid boundary XY so that the fluid friction with XY slows the nearer fluid more than the further. Attempt now to

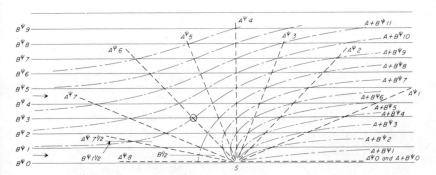

Fig 5.6 Graphical combination of 2 streamline patterns. A source S of 16 cumecs (pattern $_A\psi$) is combined with a uniform stream of 1 m/s flowing 1 m deep ($_B\psi$). Note that the streamline intervals for both $_A\psi$ and $_B\psi$ are the same, namely 1 cumec, and that only half the pattern is shown. The pattern is symmetrical about the axis $_B\psi_0$. The numbering conforms to the convention. The encircled point lies on both $_A\psi_6$ and also on $_B\psi_3$ so that the combined streamline passing through there has the value $_{A+B}\psi_{3+6} = _{A+B}\psi_9$.

Additional streamlines $_A\psi_{7\frac{1}{2}}$ and $_B\psi_{\frac{1}{2}}$, $_B\psi_{1\frac{1}{2}}$ are drawn to improve the accuracy of the points of inflexion on the upstream edge of the combined pattern.

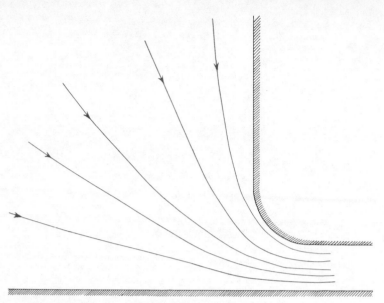

(a) The boundaries and a set of guessed streamlines are drawn.

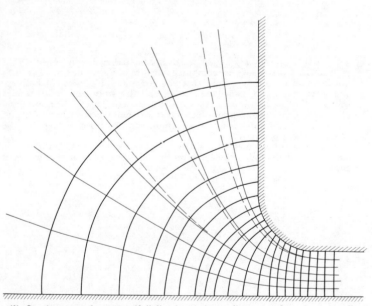

(b) On the guessed pattern (full lines) are drawn lines at 90° to the streamlines, starting at the constant velocity part of the map, where the spacing of the 90° lines is such as to produce ' squares '. In many places the streamlines are clearly in error because the 90° lines make elongated rectangles instead of ' squares '. The dotted lines are revisions to the streamlines to improve the ' squares '. But these revisions put the original 90° lines now in error.

Fig 5.4 The approximate trial-and-error method of drawing stream-

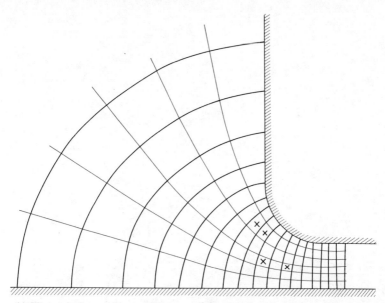

(c) The revised streamlines of (b) are now transferred, and a new set of 90° lines drawn. There are now errors only in the regions marked X.

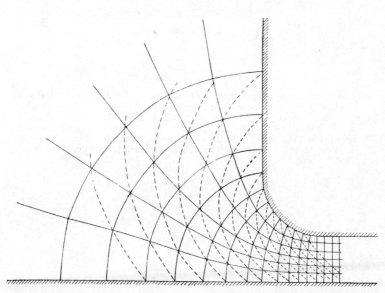

(d) Small revisions are now made to the streamlines of (c), and yet another set of 90° lines inserted. The errors have now nearly disappeared, leaving a network of 'squares' only. A useful check is to draw the diagonals, dotted, which must be smooth curves.

lines applied to the flow into the well-rounded entry to a pipe.

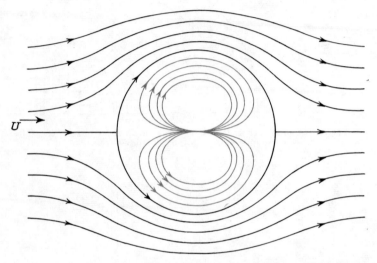

Fig 5.10 Streamline pattern for a doublet combined with a uniform stream. The single circular streamline can be replaced by a solid surface, in which case the remaining streamlines are those of a uniform flow deflected around a circular cylinder. Observe how the flow at some distance from the cylinder is less affected than the flow near the cylinder. The blue streamlines are those of the doublet flow, which, though deformed, do not lose their identity.

draw equipotential lines at an interval of ϕ. Along AB this increment of potential requires a distance ϕ/u_1, and along CD, ϕ/u_2.

Since $\qquad u_1 > u_2$, $\quad \phi/u_1 < \phi/u_2$ and AB $<$ CD.

But the line equipotential BD is no longer normal to the streamlines, even if AC was normal to them. Alternatively, if lines are drawn normal to the streamlines, then they are not always equipotential lines. The rules for drawing streamline patterns have broken down.

Another possible type of flow is shown in fig 5·12, where AB and

Fig 5.12 A rotary flow about a centre Z. If the velocity increases outward proportionately to the radius, equipotential lines are not normal to the streamlines. They are only normal if the velocity is inversely proportional to the radius.

CD are streamlines of a fluid which are bent to circular arcs about a centre Z. The fluid is further constrained to move so that it has a constant angular velocity ω everywhere. The velocities along AB and CD are therefore ωr_1 and ωr_2 respectively. Such a situation occurs when a paddlewheel rotates without slipping in a fluid, and makes all the fluid move in the same flywheel manner. As before, an increment of potential ϕ is measured out along each streamline, and occupies along AB a distance $\phi/\omega r_1$ and CD $\phi/\omega r_2$. Since $r_1 < r_2$, the distance $\phi/\omega r_1 =$ A'B' is greater than $\phi/\omega r_2 =$ C'D' so that the equipotential lines A'C' and B'D' for the potential interval ϕ are not everywhere normal to the streamlines. The rules have again broken down.

The theoretical methods of drawing are applicable, however, if there are no shear stresses on the fluid (either an ideal fluid, or a real fluid some distance from a solid surface), or if a type of rotation is present which allows equipotential lines to be normal to the streamlines. For example, consider fig 5.12 again, but now the rotation is such that $u_1 r_1 = u_2 r_2 = K$, i.e. the velocity *decreases* outward. The increment of ϕ is now achieved in distances $\phi r_1/K$ and $\phi r_2/K$ respectively along AB and CD. These distances increase proportionately with the radius, so that the equipotential lines are radii, normal to the streamlines. The theoretical methods of plotting are thus applicable to such a flow, which is called a *potential* or *free vortex*, in contrast to a *forced* or *flywheel vortex* for which the theoretical methods do not apply. Alternatively, if the plotting methods are used on a set of boundaries which involve curved flow, then a free vortex will be predicted, even if a forced vortex is actually present.

It must not, however, be thought that all forces applied to a fluid cause the plotting methods to be vitiated. If the restraining forces are applied uniformly all over the fluid instead of being applied only at a boundary, then the theoretical methods give a pattern which is correct. Take the instance of a fluid moving through a bed of sand or other small particles, the resistance of each grain contributing to the total resistance to the fluid. The fluid at no one streamline is retarded more than any other, contrary to frictional forces at boundaries which affect nearer fluid more than that further away. Experiment, moreover, shows that a pressure p is necessary to drive the fluid through the bed, and that $p \propto \int u \, ds$ (u = velocity, s = distance along streamlines). The physical quantity p thus has precisely the same properties as the potential ϕ, so that the equipotential lines as plotted are also lines of equal pressure in the sand bed. Streamline plotting methods are thus of considerable importance and value in finding the pressures and flows inside sand and gravel beds, which often pose important problems to the engineer.

A striking example of the limitations of the theoretical streamline plotting method is given by the case of the flow round a circular cylinder. The theoretical pattern was described and shown in fig 5.10 and it will be seen that the pattern is symmetrical, with the leading half-cylinder having a pattern near it which is exactly the same as that near the trailing (rear) half. If the pattern is found experimentally it will be found that the theoretical pattern is fairly well reproduced at low speeds of the fluid, or with small cylinders or with great kinematic viscosities ν of the fluid. (In fact, the combination is such that $Ud/\nu < 1 \cdot 0$ for this condition.) At higher speeds, however, the streamlines appear to be those given by the theoretical pattern only near the leading edge : around the trailing half-cylinder the pattern is widely different, there being a large zone of highly turbulent fluid called the *wake*. The discrepancy can be attributed to the shear forces exerted on the fluid by the friction with the cylinder's surface. At low speeds they cause little modification to the theoretical pattern : at higher speeds they lead to considerable changes, thus causing the actual flow pattern to be greatly different from that predicted by theory.

The discrepancies from ideal fluid flow round cylinders are further shown on Plate 6 (page 149).

Summing up

Methods of plotting streamlines using the theoretical properties of ideal fluids can be usefully employed if there is no boundary friction and if the rotations are of the free vortex type. Such a restriction must appear onerous to engineers accustomed to real fluids. However, it has been found that conditions sufficiently approximating to those restrictions are found near the leading edge of solid objects in a fluid stream, for instance, aeroplane wings and ship hulls. Further back, nearer the trailing edge of such bodies, the frictional forces may modify the flow sufficiently to cause serious changes from the theoretical pattern. Streamline patterns calculated or plotted from the theoretical considerations described may therefore be used, with caution, for many real fluid flows, and a great deal of useful information about velocity changes may be obtained from them.

Appendix

Stream and potential functions have been extensively studied, and there are available other more elaborate proofs of their properties. In particular, it can be shown that ψ is a number which obeys the laws

$$\partial\psi/\partial y = u \quad \text{and} \quad \partial\psi/\partial x = -v$$

with respect to rectangular co-ordinates x and y. Here u and v are velocity components at a point in the x and y directions respectively. It is assumed that there are no velocity components in the z direction, i.e. that the flow is 2-dimensional.

Now, as described in section **5.11,** the effect of boundary friction or of forced vortex motion is to cause elements of fluid to rotate about their own centres. This rotation, or *vorticity*, can be written

$$R = \frac{\partial v}{\partial x} - \frac{\partial u}{\partial y}$$

Substitution between the above equations gives Poisson's equation

$$\frac{\partial^2\psi}{\partial x^2} + \frac{\partial^2\psi}{\partial y^2} = R$$

This equation can be used to determine streamlines in a flow near boundaries. Each boundary is assigned a value of ψ and elsewhere each point has its value ψ_1 which must be related to the values at neighbouring points so that Poisson's equation is correct everywhere. When ψ is known at a large number of points, lines of equal values of ψ can be drawn which are, of course, streamlines. R is not necessarily a constant, but may vary with x or y.

By a similar set of proofs it can be shown that the potential ϕ is defined as

$$\partial\phi/\partial x = u \quad \text{and} \quad \partial\phi/\partial y = v$$

Also, by assessing the discharges of fluid entering and leaving a given ' control ' volume (see section **6.1**) the nett increase or decrease of fluid within the volume (if the flow is steady) can be shown to be

$$V = \frac{\partial u}{\partial x} + \frac{\partial v}{\partial y}$$

Again, substitution between these properties gives a Poisson equation, this time in ϕ,

$$\frac{\partial^2\phi}{\partial x^2} + \frac{\partial^2\phi}{\partial y^2} = V$$

and this may be used to find values of ϕ throughout a flow.

In the special case of an incompressible flow which is continuous everywhere (so that the same volumetric discharge leaves a given control volume as enters it), and which is irrotational everywhere, then

$$R = 0 \quad \text{and} \quad V = 0$$

so that
$$\frac{\partial^2 \psi}{\partial x^2} + \frac{\partial^2 \psi}{\partial y^2} = 0 \quad \text{and} \quad \frac{\partial^2 \phi}{\partial x^2} + \frac{\partial^2 \phi}{\partial y^2} = 0$$

These are the celebrated Laplace equations. Their form is such that it can be shown that lines of equal ψ must be at right angles to lines of equal ϕ : this is the basis of the graphical ' squares ' method of drawing streamlines (section 5.6). The equations can be used to determine ψ and ϕ arithmetically at every one of a number of points in a flow, from which lines of equal ψ and ϕ can be interpolated. Notice, however, that such use of Laplace equations is tantamount to assuming an incompressible inviscid fluid in 2-dimensional flow with no boundary friction, and with no rotations other than free vortex motions. A flow pattern of streamline so obtained, graphically or by computation, may therefore be quite different in some respects from a pattern found experimentally in a real fluid.

An excellent book on the more advanced aspects of potential flow is *Applied Hydrodynamics* by H. R. Vallentine (Butterworth, London).

PROBLEMS

1. Draw the streamline and potential patterns for

(a) A uniform flow of 18 m/sec parallel to the x-axis.
(b) A source of strength 3·6 cumecs (m³/s) at the origin.
(c) A source of strength 3·6 cusecs in a uniform flow of 18 ft/sec.
(d) A doublet of strength $\frac{9}{4}\pi$ at the origin.

In each case specify the scale of the diagram, and the interval between streamlines and potential lines.

2. The stream function ψ for the flow round a circular cylinder of radius a in a stream of velocity U is

$$\psi = U\left(- y + \frac{a^2 y}{x^2 + y^2} \right) \text{ in rectangular co-ordinates}$$

or
$$\psi = - U\left(r - \frac{a^2}{r} \right) \sin \theta \text{ in polar co-ordinates.}$$

Compute and plot the streamlines $\psi = 0$, $\psi = 2a$, $\psi = 3a$.

3. The ground levels on the two sides of a vertical retaining wall are 210 m and 200 m above datum respectively, and the 2 m thick wall has its base at 197 m above datum. The sandy soil rests on an impervious clay bed at level 190 m. Sketch the flow pattern by the approximate ' squares ' method, if the soil is everywhere waterlogged but there is no free water standing above either ground level. Use the sketch to estimate if there is a risk of the ground lifting on the lower side.

Hint. Will the weight of the soil be everywhere greater than the hydrostatic force tending to lift it ?

4. Sketch the streamlines at the surface of a canal through which a boat is progressing steadily in a straight line (*a*) as seen from a road bridge, (*b*) as seen from the boat. In each case give two patterns, one for an ideal, frictionless fluid, the other for the real fluid in which the boat leaves a wake far astern.

5. A horizontal bed of sand is 8 m deep, below which is clay. The cross section of a dam resting in the sand is a right-angled triangle, with the base 4 m above the clay, the leakage path under the dam thus being unsealed. The base is 20 m wide, and the reservoir is 12 m deep. Plot by an approximate method the streamlines of the flow through the sand, and estimate the leakage per metre length of the dam if the permeability of the sand is 10^{-3} m/s per m head per m.

6. Determine the stream function for a free vortex whose tangential velocity V at radius r is

$$V = - \frac{10}{r} \text{ cm sec}^{-1}.$$

If a free stream defined by $u = 20$ cm sec^{-1} is superimposed on the vortex, determine the stream function for the combined flow pattern. On a diagram locate a stagnation point and plot the streamline $\psi = 5$.

Ans. $\psi = 10 \log r$; $\psi = 20y + 10 \log r$; (0, -0.5) ; $\log r = 0.5 - 2y$—so choose values of r and solve for y.

7. The stream function $\psi = \dfrac{\omega R^2}{2} \left[\dfrac{\theta}{2} - \left(\dfrac{r}{R}\right)^2 + \dfrac{1}{3}\left(\dfrac{r}{R}\right)^3 \right]$ represents in polar coordinates the absolute motion of ideal fluid through the impeller of a pump where the impeller has a radius R and constant angular velocity ω. Determine the radial and tangential velocity components, v_r and v_θ respectively. Show that $\psi_r = \dfrac{\omega R^2}{4} \left[\theta + \dfrac{2}{3}\left(\dfrac{r}{R}\right)^3 \right]$ is the flow pattern relative to the rotating impeller, and plot a few points on one of the streamlines of ψ_r in the range $0.2 \leqslant r/R \leqslant 1.0$.

6

FORCES DUE TO FLUIDS IN MOTION

6.1 With a fluid in motion several classes of hydrodynamic forces may be acting at each point to cause the observed pattern and distribution of pressure, of velocity and of other properties. These classes are each characterized by the properties of a fluid already described in Chapter 1. Thus, in general, the force system on a portion of a fluid is complicated, each force requiring separate data to enable it to be estimated in size and direction. General problems of motion involving all the possible forces, and confining the fluid between complicated boundaries therefore need complex algebra for their solution; indeed, our knowledge of mathematics is usually quite inadequate for general solutions of this kind. However, in many problems of importance to the engineer, the force system is less complicated, and in some it is found that the effect of only one force predominates; these simpler problems can often be solved in a general way. Among these simpler problems are those where a force caused by a pressure difference just balances the reaction of an acceleration, which in turn produces the observed velocities; and those where a shear force caused by viscosity (conveniently but somewhat misleadingly called ' friction ') just balances a pressure force, and so causes the observed velocities. Much of this book is concerned with these two simplified families of problems, but it should not be forgotten that, in addition, more complicated families exist (e.g. friction, pressure and accelerations) and these often are the important ones in engineering practice. Solutions of these complicated families can often be only made by direct experiment, since calculation has failed, and the methods of presenting such information are reviewed in Chapter 11. In addition to hydrodynamic forces, there are of course always hydrostatic forces, due to the weight forces on the fluid. The latter must always be added to the former to obtain, in a specific case, the total force acting at a point. The methods of Chapter 2 are available for estimating ' hydrostatic ' forces in moving fluids.

Estimating the hydrodynamic forces when there are accelerations present *always* involves using Newton's Second Law of Motion. For a fixed mass m, all of which is moving at the same speed u, the law can be written

$$\overrightarrow{Force} = \frac{d}{dt}(m\overrightarrow{u}),$$

the arrows meaning that the force in a particular direction is linked
with a movement in that same direction.   The law is also quite
applicable to a mass of fluid, so that the hydrodynamic force exerted
on it can be found if its rate of change of momentum can be assessed.
    Consider in fig 6.1 the mass of fluid lying within a streamtube

Fig 6.1 Portion of a streamtube
ABCD in steady flow.   The typical
element of mass δm undergoes a
change of velocity as it travels from
one end to the other.   The dotted
lines A′B′ and C′D′ show the
movement of the mass of fluid
originally in ABCD in a time δt.

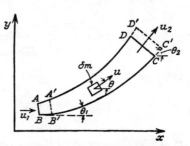

ABCD at the beginning of a time δt.   The ends of the streamtube
are perpendicular to the sides there.   The fluid is in steady motion,
with the streamtube of sufficiently small cross section for the velocities
u_1 and u_2 to be constant across each end respectively.   At the end of
the short time δt, this mass of fluid will have moved forward somewhat,
to the new position A′B′C′D′, and if u_1 is not the same as u_2 it will
have changed its momentum.
    The momentum in the x-direction (called x-momentum) possessed
by an element δm of the mass is the product

$$\delta m \, u \cos \theta,$$

where $u \cos \theta$ is the component of velocity in the x-direction.   Thus
the total x-momentum possessed by the whole mass in the streamtube
at the beginning of the time δt is

$$\sum_{\text{ABCD}} \delta m \, u \cos \theta$$

and that at the end of this time is

$$\sum_{\text{A′B′C′D′}} \delta m \, u \cos \theta.$$

The change in the x-momentum of the mass is therefore

$$\left(\sum_{\text{A′B′C′D′}} \delta m \, u \cos \theta \right)_{\text{after } \delta t} - \left(\sum_{\text{ABCD}} \delta m \, u \cos \theta \right)_{\text{before } \delta t}$$

which may be expanded to

$$\left(\sum_{ABCD} \delta m \, u \cos\theta + \sum_{CDD'C'} \delta m \, u \cos\theta - \sum_{BAA'B'} \delta m \, u \cos\theta\right)_{\text{after } \delta t}$$

$$-\left(\sum_{ABCD} \delta m \, u \cos\theta\right)_{\text{before } \delta t}$$

Since the flow is steady $\sum_{ABCD} \delta m \, u \cos\theta$ is the same before as after

the period δt. The change of x-momentum is then

$$\left(\sum_{CDD'C'} \delta m \, u \cos\theta - \sum_{BAA'B'} \delta m \, u \cos\theta\right)_{\text{after}}$$

If δt is sufficiently short the velocity component $u \cos\theta$ is very nearly the same for every element of mass δm in the volume CDD'C', or the same (at a different value) for every element in ABB'A' because the streamlines do not diverge or converge much in the short distance AA', DD', etc., although they may converge considerably between

A and C or B and D. Summations $\sum_{CDD'C'} \delta m$ and $\sum_{BAA'B'} \delta m$ are there-

fore the masses of fluid which have crossed the boundaries CD and AB respectively in the time δt; so that the summations $\sum_{CDD'C'} \delta m \, u \cos\theta$

and $\sum_{ABB'A'} \delta m \, u \cos\theta$ are the momentum of the fluid respectively leaving

and entering the volume ABCD in the time δt.

It is therefore shown that the change of x-momentum in time δt of the mass of fluid considered is the difference of the momentum leaving and entering the ends of the streamtube in that time.

Now the mass of fluid entering ABCD through AB in time δt is $\rho_1 a_1 u_1 \delta t$ where a_1 is the cross-sectional area of the streamtube at AB. The x-momentum of this fluid is therefore $\rho_1 a_1 u_1 \delta t (u_1 \cos\theta_1)$. Similarly the x-momentum of the fluid leaving ABCD through CD in the same time is

$$\rho_2 a_2 u_2 \delta t (u_2 \cos\theta_2)$$

So that the change of x-momentum of the mass ABCD (that is the difference of x-momentum entering and leaving) is

$$\rho_2 a_2 u_2 \delta t (u_2 \cos\theta_2) - \rho_1 a_1 u_1 \delta t (u_1 \cos\theta_1).$$

Applying now Newton's Second Law, the force in the x-direction, F_x, must be equivalent to the *rate* of change of x-momentum, that is,

$$F_x = \frac{1}{\delta t}\left\{ \rho_2 a_2 u_2 \delta t(u_2 \cos \theta_2) - \rho_1 a_1 u_1 \delta t(u_1 \cos \theta_1) \right\}$$

$$= \rho_2 a_2 u_2{}^2 \cos \theta_2 - \rho_1 a_1 u_1{}^2 \cos \theta_1 .$$

F_x is the total force in the x-direction exerted on the fluid in the stream-tube ABCD. It may be made up of the x-components of pressure forces acting normally on the periphery and ends of the streamtube, or of the x-components of tangential forces acting along the periphery. A precisely similar analysis can also be made for the y-momentum and therefore the force F_y in the y-direction, which is composed of the y components of the pressure (normal) and tangential forces on the streamtube. That is

$$F_y = \rho_2 a_2 u_2{}^2 \sin \theta_2 - \rho_1 a_1 u_1{}^2 \sin \theta_1 .$$

Since F_x and F_y are the forces exerted on the fluid to produce the observed accelerations, their reactions, $-F_x$ and $-F_y$, are the forces exerted by the fluid on its boundaries as a result of the im-posed accelerations. It is usually these reactions which it is desired to calculate.

The two force equations, one for F_x, the other for F_y, can also be used for a bunch of adjacent streamtubes, not all of which contain fluid travelling at the same speed. It is convenient to regard this bunch as enclosed within a volume (sometimes called a *control volume*) to the boundaries of which the forces, normal and tangential, are applied. The cross-sectional area of the streamtube areas, previously a_1 and a_2, are now only elements da_1, da_2 of the total end areas of the control volume, so that the force equations are

$$F_x = \int_{a_2} \rho_2 u_2{}^2 \cos \theta_2 da_2 - \int_{a_1} \rho_1 u_1{}^2 \cos \theta_1 da_1 \qquad . \quad (6.1)$$

and
$$F_y = \int_{a_2} \rho_2 u_2{}^2 \sin \theta_2 da_2 - \int_{a_1} \rho_1 u_1{}^2 \sin \theta_1 da_1 \qquad . \quad (6.2)$$

where a_1 and a_2 are the cross-sectional areas of the ends of the control volume. These two equations are the basis for all determinations of the forces exerted by a fluid on its boundaries. Independent data are always required from experiment or from more advanced theory to give the velocities at the ends of the control volume. Then, in general, the above integrations must be made of the flow of momentum across the end surfaces. In the examples to follow it will be seen that a good choice of control volume may make the integrations easier than a poor choice, but that the resultant forces are not dependent on this choice.

6.2 In a great number of engineering applications considerable simplifications may be made to the force equations *6.1* and *6.2*. If the fluid is incompressible, $\rho_1 = \rho_2 = \rho$; if the x-direction is deliberately chosen to be at right angles to one end of the control volume, and the flow is parallel there, then $\cos \theta_1 = 1$ and $\sin \theta_1 = 0$; if the incoming and outgoing velocities u_1 and u_2 are both constant over their respective areas a_1 and a_2, then the integrations for the x-momentum are simplified to $\rho u_1^2 a_1$ and $\rho u_2^2 \cos \theta_2 a_2$. The integrations for the y-momentum are zero and $\rho u_2^2 \sin \theta_2 a_2$. Further, since the flow (or discharge) of fluid into the control volume is

$$Q = a_1 u_1 = a_2 u_2 ,$$

the force equations may be further simplified to

$$F_x = \rho Q(u_2 \cos \theta_2 - u_1)$$
$$F_y = \rho Q(u_2 \sin \theta_2 - 0).$$

A final simplification may also sometimes be made. If the changes of direction of the fluid are small and if the x-direction has been chosen as above, $\cos \theta_2 = 1$ nearly, but $\sin \theta_2$ is still finite. In this case

$$F_x = \rho Q(u_2 - u_1) \quad . \qquad . \qquad . \qquad . \quad (6.3)$$

and
$$F_y = \rho Q(u_2 \sin \theta) \quad . \qquad . \qquad . \qquad . \quad (6.4)$$

In this simplification, F_x is the product of the mass flow ρQ and the velocity change $(u_2 - u_1)$. It is, of course, essential in any particular application of the simplified expressions to ascertain if the simplifying assumptions are indeed valid. In some cases it is very evident that they are so ; in other cases it is safer to use the more elaborate equations *6.1* and *6.2* for F_x and F_y . Even in the simplified case, experimental evidence is still required to determine the velocities from which the forces can be computed.

6.3 The force of a fluid jet on a normal surface

A jet of fluid emerging from the end of a pipe will exert a force on a solid surface which it later strikes. This force can be found by the momentum theorem as above. Consider a jet of fluid, of density ρ and cross-section area a with a uniform speed u all over it, striking a large flat surface normal to its axis (fig 6.2). The x-direction is taken along the axis of the jet, and the control volume is taken along the surface and across the jet as shown. The discharge of the jet is $Q = au$, and the rate at which x-momentum arrives in the control volume is $\rho Q u = \rho a u^2$.

Fig 6.2   A jet of fluid striking a plane surface.   The surface is normal to the jet
axis and the fluid eventually leaves
parallel to the surface.   It does not
reflect.   The 'control' volume is shown
dotted.

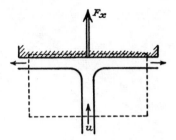

To determine the rate at which x-momentum leaves the control
volume after the impact of the jet on the surface, recourse must be
made to experiment.   It is observed that if the plate is large enough
compared with a, the fluid travels away parallel to the surface and
at right angles to its original direction; the fluid does not reflect off
the surface like light from a mirror.   There is therefore no component
of the final velocity in the original direction of flow, so that no
x-momentum leaves the control volume at all.   Thus the total rate
of change of x-momentum in the system is just $\rho a u^2$, and this must
be the force F_x in the x-direction which the jet exerts on the surface.
Since the jet is divided equally by the impact, the y-momentum to
the right is the same as that to the left and there is no resultant
y-momentum; but since there was no y-momentum arriving in the
control volume, there is no change of y-momentum at all and consequently no force F_y at right angles to the incident jet.

It should be noticed that if ρ, a and u are all expressed in the
foot-pound-second units respectively, then the force $\rho a u^2$ will also
be in f.p.s units, that is in *poundals*.   As engineers habitually use
pounds weight as the unit of force, it is usual to express the force as
$\rho a u^2 / 32 \cdot 2$ lbf weight, because a force expressed in poundals is numerically $32 \cdot 2$ times the value expressed in lbf weight.   It is therefore
quite wrong to express the force as $\rho a u^2 / g$.   The SI system avoids
this difficulty since a force such as $\rho a u^2$ is directly measured in units
of newtons, ρ having been measured in kg/m^3.

6.4   The force of a fluid jet on an inclined surface

If, in the previous case, the surface upon which the jet impinges
is inclined at an angle θ as shown in fig 6.3, the fluid is again diverted
along the surface, but now it is not symmetrical in both directions.
More fluid flows up the surface than flows down.   Some x-momentum
is therefore retained by the fluid in the original jet direction after it
has struck the surface.   Additional experimental evidence would

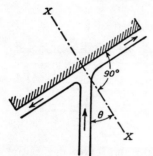

Fig 6.3   A jet of fluid striking a plane surface which is inclined to the jet axis.

therefore be required to give the speeds and quantities of the fluid flowing up and down the surface, if the method of the previous paragraph is used.

An alternative method, which will require an additional assumption, is to consider the *component* of the oncoming rate of momentum at right angles to the plate, on the line XX, that is $\rho a u^2 \cos \theta$. After the fluid has been diverted, none of this momentum remains as all the fluid is now moving at right angles to XX. A force $F = \rho a u^2 \cos \theta$ must therefore be exerted along the line XX.

Consider now the component of the oncoming momentum parallel to the surface, i.e. at right angles to XX, namely, $\rho a u^2 \sin \theta$. If this component is to suffer a change, then a force would be necessary parallel to the surface. Such a force must therefore act as a shear force on the fluid moving along the plate. But if it is assumed that the fluid is an ideal one and the surface is smooth, no shear forces are possible, so that the component $\rho a u^2 \sin \theta$ is not changed at all. There will therefore be no force exerted in a direction at right angles to XX.

The only force caused by the impact of a jet of *ideal* fluid is therefore the one normal to the surface concerned, in the direction XX, of magnitude $\rho a u^2 \cos \theta$. This force may of course be resolved into components in the original direction of the jet, $\rho a u^2 \cos^2 \theta$, and at right angles to it $\rho a u^2 \cos \theta \sin \theta$. If the fluid is noticeably non-ideal, or if the surface is roughened, then there may be a significant change of the momentum in the direction parallel to the surface and this must be added vectorially to the force normal to the surface. Still more experimental evidence is required to assess such a tangential force.

6.5 Flow round a pipe bend

The forces due to the flow of a fluid round a bend in a pipe is another case where consideration of the change of momentum is necessary.

Consider a pipe of uniform cross-sectional area a, laid horizontally with a 90° bend as shown, and with fluid of density ρ passing through at a velocity u, fig 6.4. If the gauge pressure intensity of the fluid, p,

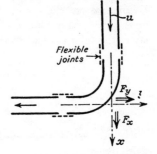

Fig 6.4   Fluid being deflected through 90° in a bend of a pipeline. The forces due to the changes of momentum are resolved into the x and y directions.

is constant throughout, then by Case i (b) of Chapter 2, the purely hydrostatic force on the bend in the x-direction is $F_{x_1} = pa$ acting outwards. Similarly the hydrostatic force in the y-direction is $F_{y_1} = pa$ also acting outwards, as shown.

Now consider the hydrodynamic forces acting on the bend due to the changes in the velocity of the fluid. The fluid entering the bend brings with it a momentum flow of $\rho Q u$ in the x-direction, where Q is the quantity of fluid arriving per second. After the bend, none of this x-momentum remains, because the fluid no longer has a velocity in that direction. A force $\rho Q u$ must therefore have been exerted by the bend on the fluid to cause the deceleration. The reaction of this force, F_{x_2}, is the force of the fluid on the bend, where $F_{x_2} = \rho Q u$, acting in the direction of the x-arrow shown.

Similarly, the fluid originally has no y-momentum, but leaves the bend with a flow of $\rho Q u$ in that direction. A force is needed for this acceleration and the reaction is the force of the fluid on the bend, F_{y_2}, where $F_{y_2} = \rho Q u$ acting in the direction of the y-arrow. The total force on the bend is thus composed of the four forces above, in the x-direction $F_{x_1} + F_{x_2} = pa + \rho Q u$; and in the y-direction $F_{y_1} + F_{y_2} = pa + \rho Q u$. Using the parallelogram of forces, the total force on the bend is $(pa + \rho Q u)\sqrt{2}$ acting in a direction at 45° to both x and y. To prevent movement of the bend by this force, a restraining force must be applied. On many pipes, the joints are designed to be strong enough to supply this force. On large pipes, such as are used for conveying water at high velocity and pressure to hydro-electric installations, it is uneconomical to make the joints so strong; a large concrete anchorage is therefore provided to secure the bend in place.

6.6 The force due to a flow along a surface

If an ideal fluid flows along a solid surface, no forces are exerted, for there cannot be any shear forces in an ideal fluid.   In fact, however, because no real fluid is ideal, the fluid close to the surface is retarded by the shear forces due to viscosity.   Outside the retarded or *boundary* layer, the fluid is unaffected by the surface (fig 6.5).   It is a common

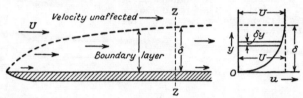

Fig 6.5   (*Left*) The friction of a fluid on a surface causes a reduction of speed in the adjacent layer, called a *boundary layer*.   The shear force has reduced the velocities at the cross section ZZ to the values shown by the plot of *u* against *y* on the right.

engineering requirement to find this shear force which has retarded the fluid, and which has produced a given boundary layer.

Imagine an extensive flat solid surface AB over which a fluid flows (fig 6.6).   A is the leading edge of the surface and a boundary layer has been formed which in general becomes thicker towards B.   It is assumed that the pressure is uniform all over AB, so that there are no pressure forces acting on the fluid.   The only force acting is the shear force *F*.   At a certain point Z the boundary layer thickness has become δ because of the action of *F*.   Outside the layer the velocity is constant at a value *U*; within it the velocity *u* changes with *y*, the distance from the surface, and $u < U$ everywhere.   The way in which *u* varies with *y* must be found experimentally, or by more advanced theory, which is more fully discussed in Chapter 12.

The shear force *F*, between A and Z, can *only* be found by applying the momentum theorem given at the beginning of this chapter.   It is convenient to choose the control volume shown in fig 6.6, bounded

Fig 6.6   The boundary layer on a surface AB is the retarded fluid in the depth δ at the cross section ZQ. A ' control ' volume APQZ has been drawn through which the momentum changes are assessed.   The boundary layer is limited by a line AQ, but AP is drawn to such a length that the total flow across it is the same as that across ZQ.

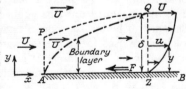

by the surface AZ, the lines PA and QZ at right angles to the surface, and by the curved line PQ. It is also convenient to make QZ equal to δ, the boundary layer thickness; and to make PA, which is wholly within fluid that has not yet been affected by the friction of the plate, of such a length that the total volume of fluid passing across it in unit time is the same as that passing across QZ. If these choices are made, then there will be neither flow nor momentum transferred across the line PQ nor, of course, across the solid impermeable surface AZ. Momentum is only transferred across PA and QZ so that the increase of x-momentum in a unit width of surface is

$$\int_Z^Q \rho u^2 \cos\theta\,\mathrm{d}y - \int_A^P \rho U^2 \mathrm{d}y$$

if the x-direction is taken along AZ. The increase of x-momentum must equal, by Newton's Second Law, the force exerted in the direction of motion by the surface on the fluid. Actually of course F acts to oppose the direction of motion and is therefore negative; there is really a *reduction* of x-momentum in the direction of motion. That is

$$-F = \int_Z^Q \rho u^2 \cos\theta\,\mathrm{d}y - \int_A^P \rho U^2\,\mathrm{d}y$$

or

$$F = \int_A^P \rho U^2\,\mathrm{d}y - \int_0^\delta \rho u^2 \cos\theta\,\mathrm{d}y.$$

Since U is a constant all over AP, $\int_A^P U^2\,\mathrm{d}y = U^2.\mathrm{AP}.$

Also since AP was chosen to make the discharge across it equal to that across QZ,

$$\int_A^P U\,\mathrm{d}y = \int_Z^Q u\,\mathrm{d}y = \int_{y=0}^{y=\delta} u\,\mathrm{d}y$$

or

$$U.\mathrm{AP} = \int_0^\delta u\,\mathrm{d}y,$$

so that

$$U^2.\mathrm{AP} = U\int_0^\delta u\,\mathrm{d}y$$

and therefore

$$F = U\int_0^\delta \rho u\,\mathrm{d}y - \int_0^\delta \rho u^2 \cos\theta\,\mathrm{d}y.$$

It is found in practice that θ, the inclination of the flow to the x-direction at the outlet section QZ, is always small, so that to a first order approximation $\cos\theta = 1$ and therefore

$$F = \rho\int_0^\delta u(U - u)\mathrm{d}y \qquad . \qquad . \qquad . \quad (6.5)$$

An alternative derivation of the above integral can be made because the restrictions of the simplified momentum theorem are approximately complied with, as follows. Consider only a unit width of the surface in a direction at right angles to the plane of the diagram (fig 6.5), that is, across the flow. A small increment of height δy in the diagram is the projection of an area δy high and unit length long across the flow. Through this slot, the mass of fluid passing in unit time is $\rho u dy$. Now every unit mass of fluid which passes through this slot originally had a velocity U, so that its x-momentum change has been $(U - u)$, and therefore the x-momentum change per second of the fluid passing through the slot is $\rho u dy(U - u)$. All the fluid within the boundary layer has been retarded to some extent, so that the total change of momentum throughout the whole layer is

$$\int_{y=0}^{y=\delta} \rho u(U - u) dy$$

and this equals the force F per unit width of the surface, which has caused the retardation, i.e. the drag force of the fluid on the surface between A and Z.

The integral cannot be evaluated without knowing how u varies with y, a matter of experiment or advanced theory. But under conditions of uniform pressure, i.e. pressure at A = pressure at B, an approximation which gives a fairly accurate estimate is $\dfrac{u}{U} = \left(\dfrac{y}{\delta}\right)^{1/5}$.

Writing $dy = \delta . d\left(\dfrac{y}{\delta}\right)$, substitution into the force integral (6.5) gives

$$F = \rho U^2 \delta \int_{y/\delta=0}^{y/\delta=1} \frac{u}{U}\left(1 - \frac{u}{U}\right) d\left(\frac{y}{\delta}\right) = \frac{5}{42}\rho U^2 \delta \qquad . \quad (6.6)$$

The boundary layer thickness δ depends on the roughness of the underlying surface, on the fluid properties and on the distance AZ. Experiment, or more advanced theory, is again needed to determine it in any particular case. In some conditions, when the pressure is not constant along AB, as occurs on the surfaces of an aeroplane's wing, more complicated velocity distributions may apply than the simple one of the foregoing example, so that quite different equations are obtained for F. Such pressure differences also cause forces on the surface normal to the direction of motion, in the same way as a hydrostatic pressure exerts a force on a surface. This ' hydrostatic ' pressure force on an aircraft wing produces the lift on it (see Chapter 2 for an example), but the drag is caused partly by the tangential force of the boundary layer (the ' skin drag '), and partly by the components in the direction of motion of the pressure differences (the 'form drag ').

6.7 Drag force of a solid object in a stream

When there is relative motion between a solid object and a surrounding fluid, one exerts a drag force on the other. This force is often required for engineering purposes and its measurement can be made in two distinct ways. First, the object can be mounted on a support which connects to some sort of weighing machine ; when the flow takes place past the object, the drag is directly measured. It may be impracticable to use this method if the object is large (e.g. aeroplanes) or if the drag of the support is large compared with that of the object. The second method is universally applicable and consists of an experiment to measure the fluid velocity behind (in the wake of) the object. The reaction of the drag force of the fluid on the object is a retarding force on the fluid, which is decelerated immediately downstream of the object.

In fig 6.7 an object O which is two-dimensional, like a cylinder, is subjected to an oncoming velocity U. Behind O, on a cross section XX of the wake, the fluid velocity is decreased somewhat to a velocity u (which varies with y, the distance in a direction across the flow). At some distance δ_1 from the centre line the fluid will be unaffected by the drag of the object, so that the only part of the fluid suffering a loss of momentum is that between $y = \pm \delta_1$. The approximations for the simplified momentum theorem equations are valid for this case, but a rigorous solution using a control volume can also be made.

For the object O, which has the same cross section in all planes parallel to that of fig 6.7, the mass flow through a slot in the wake δy wide is $\rho u \delta y$, and the momentum change suffered per unit time

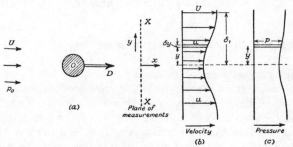

(a)   Plane of measurements

(b) Velocity   (c) Pressure

Fig 6.7   The drag force D on an object O in a fluid flow is accompanied by a reduction of velocity in the wake of the object. (a) Position of plane of measurements. (b) Graph of fluid velocity u in the plane of measurements. The velocity is unchanged at the original value U at a distance δ_1 from the line of symmetry. (c) Graph of pressure in the plane of measurement.

by this fluid is $\rho u(U - u)\delta y$. The total momentum change per unit time by all the fluid in the wake is therefore

$$\int_{y=-\delta_1}^{y=+\delta_1} \rho u(U - u)\mathrm{d}y,$$

which is the same expression as was derived for the boundary layer. This change of momentum is, by Newton's Second Law, equal to the sum of all the forces acting on the fluid between the upstream cross section (where the velocity was U) and the section XX. These forces are the drag force D, and also any force caused by the pressure along XX not being the same as the upstream pressure p_0. Experiment shows that the latter forces are often present, the pressure in the wake being different from p_0, a common distribution curve being shown in fig 6.7 (c). Outside the wake, but still in the same plane of measurement XX, the velocity u and pressure p are the same as those upstream, that is, U and p_0. The total force on the fluid is therefore

$$D + \int_{y=-\delta_1}^{y=+\delta_1} (p - p_0)\mathrm{d}y,$$

which has caused the observed momentum change. That is,

$$\int_{-\delta_1}^{+\delta_1} \rho u(U - u)\mathrm{d}y = \int_{-\delta_1}^{+\delta_1} (p - p_0)\mathrm{d}y + D. \qquad . \quad (6.7)$$

In order to find D, therefore, two separate measurements must be made, one of the velocity distribution, the other of the pressure distribution in the wake. Only if $p = p_0$ all through the wake, then the expression simplifies to

$$D = \int_{-\delta_1}^{+\delta_1} \rho u(U - u)\mathrm{d}y.$$

6.8 Drag and lift forces on aerofoils

The lift on the wings of an aircraft is caused solely by reason of the changes of air velocity due to the cross-sectional shape of the wings. A typical cross section is shown in fig 6.8 (these shapes are called *aerofoils*). An aerofoil is merely a body which if moving horizontally diverts the fluid approaching it so that there is a change of momentum in a vertical direction; this change causes a vertical force to be exerted on the body. Take, for example, the aerofoil section shown in fig 6.8, which may be regarded as stationary with fluid approaching it at a velocity U. (This is precisely the same case as the aerofoil moving at velocity U into still fluid.) The shape,

Fig 6.8 An aerofoil is an apparatus for producing a change of momentum in the oncoming fluid. The flow direction is changed by the angle θ, which is not necessarily the same for all streamlines.

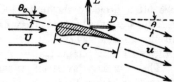

which is necessarily asymmetrical with respect to the direction of the velocity U, is such that the fluid leaves the aerofoil at velocity u, having been diverted through an angle θ. Originally the fluid has no momentum in the lift or y-direction (at right angles to that of U), but finally has a momentum of $\int \rho u^2 \sin \theta \, dy$ in that direction. This change of momentum requires a force L to accomplish it and this is the lift on the aerofoil, which appears as an excess of pressure on the lower surface over the pressure on the upper surface.

Theoretically, then, the lift on an aerofoil can be found by an experiment measuring u and θ, and evaluating the integral $L = \int \rho u^2 \sin \theta \, dy$. Actually it is difficult to determine θ sufficiently accurately, because the flow behind an aerofoil is always turbulent, and sometimes very turbulent; the direction of flow undergoes great and sudden changes, so making it difficult to measure the mean value. The experimental determination of the lift is therefore usually done directly by fixing the aerofoil to some sort of weighing machine, or by finding the pressure intensity at a number of places around the aerofoil and integrating the elementary pressure forces so found (see Chapter 2).

It is usually found that u is not greatly different in magnitude from U for a well-designed aerofoil, so that if θ' is the *mean* angle over which the fluid is deflected, L is proportional to $U^2 \sin \theta'$. It is also evident that θ' will be fixed by θ_0, the angle that the aerofoil itself makes with the direction of U (this angle is called the *angle of incidence*). An aircraft of a given weight must therefore fly at a larger θ_0 at low speeds than at high speeds, so that the product $U^2 \sin \theta'$ remains constant. At the lowest speed of all, when the aircraft is landing, θ_0 may have to be so large that a radical change of the flow pattern takes place round the aerofoil, and breakaway takes place (see Chapter 4). The air is not then deflected on the average by such a large angle θ', so the lift suddenly decreases and the aircraft *stalls*. Flaps (see fig 6.9)

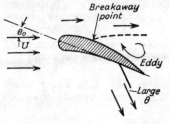

Fig 6.9 A flap on an aerofoil at a large angle of incidence diverts the air through a large angle and preserves the lift, even though breakaway on the top surface causes the air there not to be fully diverted by the aerofoil.

are often fitted to the underside of the aerofoil so as to increase θ' locally, despite the breakaway caused by the large θ_0 of the aerofoil itself. In this way the lift may be preserved at low speed, and control of the aircraft retained.

The boundary layers on an aerofoil are the main cause of the drag force D, which may be found, as described earlier in this chapter, by assessing the changes of horizontal or x-momentum arriving and leaving the system, that is

$$D = \int \rho U^2 dy - \int \rho u^2 \cos \theta dy,$$

the integrals each being taken over such a height that they both refer to the same quantity of fluid (see the preceding paragraphs on the boundary layer). Since most aerofoils are used at a small angle of incidence, θ is always small, so that $\cos \theta$ is always nearly $1 \cdot 0$. The drag, D, does not therefore change much with θ, until breakaway commences, when D increases greatly as the pattern of flow alters and the aerofoil stalls.

The design and testing of aerofoils forms a highly specialized part of fluid mechanics practice. It is clearly advantageous to make aerofoils to give a high value of L/D, but other considerations often have to be taken into account and compromises are usually made.

PROBLEMS
Some of these problems also involve principles not discussed until Chapter 8.

1. Derive, from first principles, a general expression for the forces exerted by a fluid jet wholly intercepted by a single moving plate whose plane is perpendicular to the axis of the jet. A sharp-edged hole, 15 cm diameter and coefficient of contraction 0·62, is situated 3 m below the water surface in the side of a large tank. What force is required to move a large patch slowly up to the hole, and what force will suffice to hold it there? Explain the differences.

Ans. 656 N : .520 N.

2. Wind-tunnel tests on a solid of revolution held axially in an airstream show that the velocity in its wake decreases uniformly from the undisturbed velocity u at double the solid radius to zero at the axis, the pressure in the wake being constant throughout and the same as that in the undisturbed stream. What will be the drag if a 1·2 m diameter solid is travelling at 100 m/s through still air at 500 mm mercury pressure and 0 °C?

Ans. 6470 N.

If the pressure in the wake decreases uniformly towards the axis, being $\frac{1}{8}\rho u^2$ below the undisturbed pressure there, what is now the drag?

Ans. 8130 N.

3. A discharge of 0·05 m³/s comes from above into a tank which is moving from left to right at 5 m/s. The jet has a velocity of 15 m/s

and is inclined at 30° to the horizontal in the same direction as the tank movement. What are the forces exerted on the tank ?

Ans. 375 N : 400 N.

4. State the momentum theorem for the steady flow of a fluid.

A thin flat plate of 2 m chord and aspect ratio large enough for end effects to be negligible is held at zero incidence in a uniform stream of incompressible fluid.   At the trailing edge the boundary layer thickness is measured and found to be 1·67 cm when the drag coefficient is 0·0032. If the velocity in the boundary layer at the trailing edge is assumed to be proportional to the $(1/n)$th power of the distance from the surface, what must be the value of n ?   Assume n is greater than unity.

Ans. 7·14.

7

PRESSURE INTENSITY AND VELOCITY
CHANGES IN MOVING FLUIDS

7.1 It is shown in Chapter 6 that a force is exerted when there is a change in the flow of momentum of a moving fluid. This force, calculated by means of equations *6.1*, *6.2* or *6.3*, *6.4*, is the total of several component forces all acting in the region where the momentum change takes place. As well as this total force, the engineer often requires more detailed knowledge of the variation of both pressure intensity and velocity within the region. A relationship between velocity and pressure intensity is thus required, and it can be obtained if certain restrictions are imposed.

Consider a part of a steady but non-uniform flow where a small tube of ideal (non-viscous) fluid is enclosed by streamlines and has plane ends—a streamtube. The velocity of flow is, however, sensibly uniform over any one cross section of the small tube, though further along the tube, and in adjacent tubes, the velocity may be quite different. In a length δs of the streamtube, the cross-sectional area changes from a to $a + \delta a$; the velocity changes from u to $u + \delta u$; the pressure intensity changes from p to $p + \delta p$; and the height of the centroid of the end planes changes from z above an arbitrary datum level to $z + \delta z$ (see fig 7.1). Notice how all the variables are assumed to increase in the direction of motion. There can be no flow into or out of the streamtube except through the ends, so that the changes in cross-sectional area are connected with changes in u. At the same time there are changes in p, and these will be found by Newton's Second Law, equating the total force on the streamtube to the changes of momentum in it.

The total force in the direction of motion has three components. Firstly, the varying pressure intensities on the sides of the tube cause a force F_1 acting in the direction of motion. If it is assumed that δs is small, then F_1 is the product of the *mean* pressure intensity on the sides and the projected area in the desired direction, δa (see Case i (*b*) of Chapter 2).

That is
$$F_1 = \delta a\left(p + \frac{\delta p}{2}\right) = p\delta a,$$

ignoring the second order term.

74

Secondly, the pressure intensities p and $p + \delta p$ exert forces on the plane ends of the streamtube in opposite directions, so that the force

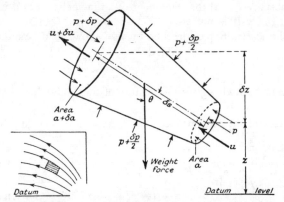

Fig 7.1   Small portion of a streamtube with flow from right to left.   Pressure intensities, velocity and areas are marked, and the positive direction of increase of all variables is the direction of motion.   The inset figure shows a general view of the streamlines surrounding the element of streamtube in the larger diagram.

in the *direction of motion* is F_2 where

$$F_2 = -(p + \delta p)(a + \delta a) + pa$$
$$= -p\delta a - a\delta p.$$

Thirdly, the element of streamtube has a weight force F_3 in the direction of motion, because its mass is $\rho\left(a + \dfrac{\delta a}{2}\right)\delta s$; the total weight force acts vertically downwards so that the component required, F_3, is

$$F_3 = -\rho\left(a + \frac{\delta a}{2}\right)\delta s \, g \cos \theta,$$

where θ is the angle between the element's axis and the vertical.

But

$$\cos \theta = \frac{\delta z}{\delta s}$$

so that

$$F_3 = -\rho\left(a + \frac{\delta a}{2}\right)\delta s \, g\frac{\delta z}{\delta s}$$
$$= -\rho a g \delta z,$$

ignoring the second order term.   The assumptions that have already been made preclude the possibility that any other forces act on the element of streamtube.   In particular, there can be no shear forces acting on the outer envelope of the tube, for the fluid has been assumed ideal and therefore non-viscous.   In practice this assumption is often not too much in error, for the influence of viscosity in a steady flow is usually confined to the immediate vicinity of solid walls and the wake behind obstacles. All the remainder of a flow behaves as if it is ideal even if actually it is not so.

Now the acceleration of the fluid in steady flow, du/dt, can be written

$$\frac{du}{dt} = \frac{du}{ds} \cdot \frac{ds}{dt} = u \; du/ds,$$

so that the rate of change of momentum of the fluid is $Mu\dfrac{du}{ds}$ where M is the mass in the streamtube. Since $M = \rho\left(a + \dfrac{\delta a}{2}\right)\delta s$, Newton's Second Law gives

$$\rho\left(a + \frac{\delta a}{2}\right)\delta s . u\frac{du}{ds} = F_1 + F_2 + F_3$$
$$= p\delta a + (-\,p\delta a - a\delta p) + (-\,\rho ag\delta z).$$

Replacing the finite increments by infinitesimals and ignoring second order terms

$$\rho au du = -\,a dp - \rho ag dz$$

For convenience, divide throughout by ρag

$$\frac{u}{g}du + \frac{dp}{\rho g} + dz = 0.$$

Integrating all terms on both sides this becomes

$$\frac{u^2}{2g} + \int\frac{dp}{\rho g} + z = \text{Constant} \qquad . \qquad . \qquad . \quad (7.1)$$

For many engineering purposes a liquid may always, and a gas may sometimes, be considered to be incompressible; that is, ρ does not vary with p. In this case, a further simplification can be made, as the second term can now be integrated so that the equation reads

$$\frac{u^2}{2g} + \frac{p}{\rho g} + z = \text{Constant} = H \qquad . \qquad . \quad (7.2)$$

This equation is sometimes called *Bernoulli's equation* after its first enunciator, and applies only to incompressible fluids in steady flow. The earlier relation (7.1) is used if the flow is compressible, putting a relation between p and ρ, such as the Gas Laws, into the second term; this will be demonstrated in Chapter 9. Notice that p and ρ must be measured in the same system of units as all the other terms; for example, in the SI system p is in newtons/m^2 and ρ in kg/m^3; in the f.p.s. system p is in poundals ft^{-2} and ρ in lb ft^{-3}, while in the foot-slug-second system p is in lbf weight ft^{-2} (the engineer's usual unit) and ρ in slugs ft^{-3}.

It will be seen that each term of the Bernoulli equation has the dimensions of a length, so that it can be regarded as a quantity of energy in a volume of fluid of unit weight, i.e. joules per newton in the metric system; but since a joule is a newton metre, each term has the measurement in metres. The term $u^2/2g$ represents the kinetic energy; $p/\rho g$ the energy due to the pressure existing in the fluid; and z the potential (height) energy due to gravity.* H is often called the *Total Energy* or *Total Head* of the fluid in the particular streamtube concerned.

Since it will be seen that the distance s along the streamline does not appear above, H does not vary with s, and Bernoulli's equation can be thus stated—that along any one streamtube of ideal incompressible fluid the Total Energy remains constant if the only forces are pressure and weight forces. If an additional force is applied to the streamtube and does work on the fluid within, then energy will be added to, or taken from, the fluid, depending on whether the force is in the direction of motion or against it. The former type of force can be applied by mechanical means, such as pumps, and the latter by friction forces or again by a mechanical method, such as a turbine. Under these circumstances, H is not constant all along the streamtube. It should also be understood that strictly the value of H applies only to one streamtube. Under special circumstances H may indeed be the same for several adjacent streamtubes but in general it is not, when the total energy changes from place to place across the direction of motion.

7.2 Limitations of Bernoulli's equation

If it is desired to apply Bernoulli's equation to find velocity changes from pressure changes, or vice versa, it is necessary to limit the applications to cases of steady flow of ideal incompressible fluid wherein there is no change of total energy along any streamtube. If these limitations are observed, then between two places A (upstream) and B (downstream), both on one streamtube,

$$\text{Total energy at A} = \text{Total energy at B}$$

or
$$\frac{u_A{}^2}{2g} + \frac{p_A}{\rho g} + z_A = \frac{u_B{}^2}{2g} + \frac{p_B}{\rho g} + z_B$$

or
$$\frac{u_A{}^2 - u_B{}^2}{2g} + \frac{p_A - p_B}{\rho g} + z_A - z_B = 0 \ . \qquad . \quad (7.3)$$

* The phrase pressure energy, though frequently used for the term $p/\rho g$ by engineers, is not strictly pressure energy in a thermodynamic sense; for example, Keenan's *Thermodynamics* calls this term ' flow work '.

In this way it will be seen that a change of pressure p is accompanied by changes of velocity or height or both.

In engineering practice, the limitation which proves to be the most onerous is that which specifies ideal fluids and so prohibits shear forces, for real fluids are all viscous to some extent and produce shear forces in the direction of motion. These forces, ignored in the foregoing analysis, cause energy to be used in overcoming them, this energy being degraded into a form of energy which is not included in the Bernoulli equation. This is low-grade thermal energy, which cannot be reconverted at a later stage into any of the three forms of energy included in H (see footnote on p. 38). The total head H is therefore diminished as energy is degraded, and if E is the loss of energy between two points A and B, then Bernoulli's equation must be modified to

$$\frac{u_A{}^2}{2g} + \frac{p_A}{\rho g} + z_A = \frac{u_B{}^2}{2g} + \frac{p_B}{\rho g} + z_B + E . \qquad . \quad (7.4)$$

In general, E must be found experimentally or by more advanced theoretical reasoning.

If the fluid concerned is a gas, then some of the thermal energy is taken into account when it changes the properties of the fluid by the Gas Laws. It is usually assumed that no heat is allowed to escape through the boundaries of the flow, and an energy balance equation is derived for compressible fluids (in Chapter 9) which corresponds to the Bernoulli equation for incompressible flow.

Shear forces occur in both laminar and turbulent flows. In the former, wherever a velocity gradient du/dy is formed, a shear stress $\tau = \mu \dfrac{du}{dy}$ appears with it. In the latter, shear forces and their associated degradation of energy occur by reason of the irregular motions in the flow. There are, at any one instant, places where the instantaneous velocity is different from the mean velocity. On a river in flood, for example, it is easy to see from a bridge overhead that there are patches of water which move for a short time relative to the surrounding water. Eventually the motions of these patches die out and are replaced by those of a quite different arrangement of patches. There is a tendency too for these patches to have rotary motion within them, so that, in general, turbulent motion is said to have *eddies* in it. Eddies have comparatively large velocity gradients du/dY at their boundaries (Y is a direction at right angles to the velocity u at a certain point). These gradients, by the definition of viscosity in Chapter 1, produce local shear forces $\tau = \mu \dfrac{du}{dY}$ in the fluid and cause a consequent degradation of energy into heat, which is usually much greater than the degradation occurring if laminar flow was occurring at the same velocity. Sometimes the degradation of energy E is sufficiently small that it can be neglected, even though the flow is turbulent, in which case the simple Bernoulli equation (7.2) may be used. One of these occasions is when the cross-sectional area of the flow is decreasing; for reasons that will be discussed in Chapter 12 on the Boundary Layer, it is common experience to find that if the streamlines representing a flow are converging in the direction of the motion, then the turbulence is decreased, so that the energy degradation is small. Consequently, in a convergence, Bernoulli's equation predicts pressure and velocity changes accurately enough for most engineering purposes. If, however, a flow is diverging in the direction of motion, then the turbulence is increased, energy degradation is large, and Bernoulli's equation gives quite misleading results.

7.3 Power requirements

Consider a flow where all the fluid undergoes a change ΔH of its total head H as it passes from one cross section to another further downstream. Such a change would be negative (decreasing H) when going downstream if there is a degradation of energy into heat; or it would be positive (increasing H) going downstream if energy is being injected to the fluid by a suitable machine, such as a pump. The change ΔH is an energy change per unit weight of fluid, so that if the discharge of the flow is Q (volume per unit time), then the mass flow is ρQ, and the weight of fluid passing a given point in unit time is $g\rho Q$. Since each unit of weight of the fluid changes its energy by ΔH, then the rate at which energy is being degraded or given to the fluid is $g\rho Q\Delta H$ per unit time. Such a rate of change of energy is the *power* degraded or supplied. In the SI system, with power measured in watts, a water stream of density 1000 kg/m³ in the Earth's gravitational acceleration $g = 9.81$ m/s² gives

$$\text{Power} = 9.81 \times 10^3 \; Q\Delta H \text{ watts} \qquad (7.5)$$

In the obsolescent foot-slug-second system (water density 1.94 slug/ft³ and 550 ft lbf/s = 1 horsepower)

$$P = 0.113 \; Q\Delta H$$

Power will be required by a flow in a number of circumstances. If the potential energy z of the fluid is increased (that is, the flow is uphill) while the pressure and velocity remain constant, then power must be supplied to the fluid to achieve this increase of energy. In addition, there will be a degradation of energy to heat, caused by the friction at the solid boundaries of the flow. Power will therefore also be required to balance this drain of energy from the fluid. Another way in which power is taken from a fluid is with a suitable machine (called a turbine), when the above power equation can again be used, now putting ΔH as the change of H across the turbine.

PROBLEMS

1. Find the hydraulic forces acting on a 90° reducing bend joining two pipes (30 cm and 15 cm bores) when the pressure is 150 kN/m² in the 30 cm pipe and when
   (a) there is no flow, and
   (b) when the flow is 0·3 m³/s of water.
   Note In (b) Bernoulli must be used for pressure intensities.
        Ans. (a) 2700 N : 10 800 N. (b) 11 870 N : 7170 N.

2. A horizontal water-pipe reduces from 50 cm diameter to 30 cm diameter. The pressure at the downstream end of the reducer is 160 kN/m² and the flow is 0·3 m³/s. What is the pressure at the upstream end, if the energy degraded in the reducer is 1·0 J/N.
                                        Ans. 162 kN/m².

3. A stream of fluid of density 800 kg/m³ has energy taken from it between the points A and B at the rate of 75 kW. At A, the velocity is 1·5 m/s and the cross-sectional area is 1 m² ; at B, 1 m higher, the area is 0·4 m². What is the absolute pressure at B when the pressure at A is (i) atmospheric, (ii) 150 kN/m² gauge ? What pressure at A gives cavitation pressure at B ?
   Ans. (i) 24·4 kN/m² absolute ;   (ii) 174·4 kN/m² absolute ;
                                        75·6 kN/m² absolute.

4. Water is to be pumped, at the rate of 0·03 cumec, from a river through a 10 cm diameter pipe which discharges to atmosphere at a height of 7 m above the river. The combined efficiency of the pump and the pipe is 25 per cent. What power will be required to drive the pump ?
   Note Remember velocity energy.
                                        Ans. 9·1 kW.

5. If a circular cylinder moves sideways through an ideal fluid, show from the equation to the streamline pattern (Chapter 5) that the relative velocity at the surface of the cylinder is $2U \sin \theta$, where U is the relative velocity of the cylinder axis with respect to the still fluid. Determine the pressure distribution around the surface, and the force tending to separate the two halves of the cylinder if cut on the diameter in the plane of the motion.

$$\text{Ans.} \quad \frac{p - p_0}{\frac{1}{2}\rho U^2} = 1 - 4\sin^2 \theta \; ; \quad F = p_0 d - \frac{5d}{6}\rho U^2.$$

6. A source, 0·5 m³/s, is placed 20 cm directly upstream of a sink, 0·25 m³/s, in a uniform stream of 2 m/s and 30 cm deep. Plot the

streamlines and determine how far the stagnation point is distant upstream from the source. Find the velocity and the difference in pressure from the undisturbed stream pressure at two points on the streamline passing through the stagnation point, one point being 45 degrees forward of the source and the other level with it.

7. Show that in a hydrostatic fluid of constant density $(p/\rho g) + z$ is a constant everywhere. How is this modified when the fluid is moving ?

8

APPLICATIONS OF BERNOULLI'S EQUATION

8.1 Flow in a converging pipe

Consider a flow in a pipe which decreases from a cross-sectional area a_1 to a_2 in a distance not much greater than about $3\sqrt{a_1}$ (fig 8.1). (This restriction is necessary to avoid consideration of long, gently tapering pipes wherein the shear or friction forces become of importance, rendering inaccurate the estimate of the pressure changes which will be derived.) The pressure of the fluid at these cross sections can be found by connecting suitable manometers to *tapping*

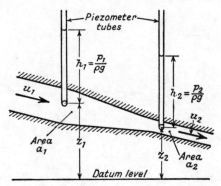

Fig 8.1   Flow in a converging pipe. The piezometer tubes show the pressure at two places.

holes in the pipe walls. The fluid velocity, which is assumed uniform and parallel over each cross section, increases from u_1 to u_2 where $u_1 a_1 = u_2 a_2 = Q$, the discharge of fluid through the pipe. It is assumed that the pressure distribution at either section varies with depth in the same way as occurs in a static fluid, so that $(p/\rho g) + z$ is constant all over any one cross section. Since the velocity is uniform also, then the total head $H = \dfrac{p}{\rho g} + z + \dfrac{u^2}{2g}$ is the same for every streamline passing each section; furthermore, since a convergence of the flow decreases the turbulence, and reduces the energy degradation to a negligible amount, the total head H is constant along every streamline, so that Bernoulli's equation may be directly applied between the two sections. That is

$$\frac{u_1^2}{2g} + \frac{p_1}{\rho g} + z_1 = \frac{u_2^2}{2g} + \frac{p_2}{\rho g} + z_2$$

or

$$\frac{u_2^2 - u_1^2}{2g} = \left(\frac{p_1 - p_2}{\rho g}\right) + (z_1 - z_2).$$

But

$$u_1 = u_2 \frac{a_2}{a_1},$$

so that

$$\frac{u_2^2}{2g}\left(1 - \left(\frac{a_2}{a_1}\right)^2\right) = \left(\frac{p_1 - p_2}{\rho g}\right) + (z_1 - z_2)$$

or

$$u_2 = \left\{1 - \left(\frac{a_2}{a_1}\right)^2\right\}^{-\frac{1}{2}} \sqrt{\left(2g\left\{\frac{(p_1 - p_2)}{\rho g} + (z_1 - z_2)\right\}\right)}$$

and

$$Q = a_2 u_2 = a_2\left\{1 - \left(\frac{a_2}{a_1}\right)^2\right\}^{-\frac{1}{2}} \sqrt{\left(2g\left\{\frac{(p_1 - p_2)}{\rho g} + (z_1 - z_2)\right\}\right)}$$

(Note that p must be measured in the consistent units of the system of measurement used, i.e. N/m^2 in metric; pdl/ft^2 in f.p.s.)

Actually, of course, there is a small energy degradation due to turbulence even when the convergence is well designed. Further, it has been assumed that uniform flow exists at both cross sections; although this is nearly true at the downstream section, it is not so at the upstream one, where there is usually a boundary layer, with the fluid close to the walls travelling more slowly than that at the centre. The total energy at the upstream section is therefore not the same for all streamlines: it is lower for ones near the wall than for ones at the centre. However, it is convenient to retain $\frac{u_1^2}{2g}$ in the Bernoulli equation, where u_1 is now the *mean* velocity of flow $\bar{u}$, even though the mean velocity energy is a few per cent higher than $\bar{u}^2/2g$ (see example in Chapter 4). The error so incurred, together with the error due to the ignored energy degradation, is compensated by introducing a numerical coefficient C_d, called the *coefficient of discharge*, so that if Q is the actual discharge

$$Q = C_d a_2\left\{1 - \left(\frac{a_2}{a_1}\right)^2\right\}^{-\frac{1}{2}} \sqrt{\left(2g\left\{\frac{(p_1 - p_2)}{g\rho} + (z_1 - z_2)\right\}\right)}. \quad (8.1)$$

Experiments conducted with well-shaped convergences in pipes, having long straight sections upstream, and air or water as fluids, show that C_d is about 0·98; in other words, the measured discharge through a convergence is about 98 per cent of that predicted by the

Bernoulli equation which has been developed for non-viscous, ideal, fluids. This constant and high proportion is fortunate, for it allows the engineer to use contractions as meters in pipelines to measure the quantity of fluid passing. It is only necessary to know the pressure difference between two cross sections of the convergence ; this is done by drilling small holes (tapping points) in the wall of the pipe and connecting them to a suitable differential manometer. A knowledge of the reading of the manometer, $(p_1 - p_2)/\rho g$, together with the constants $(z_1 - z_2)$, a_1 and a_2, enables the discharge Q to be computed.

Contractions in pipelines from one diameter pipe to another, fig 8.2 (a), are, however, rare because it is always desirable to keep

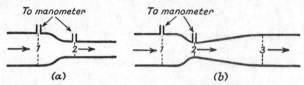

Fig 8.2 (a) A contraction in a pipe used as a flow-measuring apparatus. (b) The pipe downstream of a contraction is expanded again to form a *Venturi meter*.

the mean speed of the fluid fairly low to avoid undue degradation of energy to heat by the eddies in the flow (see Chapter 13). If a convergence is to be used for measuring the discharge, then it is desirable to return the fluid to its original, lower speed as quickly as possible downstream of the convergence. Such an arrangement, fig 8.2 (b), is called a *Venturi meter*, of which the smallest cross section is called the *throat*.

In the diverging cone downstream of the throat there are conditions very suitable for the production of eddies, and there is consequently an energy degradation. In this diverging outlet cone, the Bernoulli equation can only be applied if the degraded energy E is included, that is

$$\frac{u_1^2}{2g} + \frac{p_1}{g\rho} + z_1 = \frac{u_3^2}{2g} + \frac{p_3}{g\rho} + z_3 + E.$$

Since $\qquad u_1 = u_3, \qquad \dfrac{p_1 - p_3}{g\rho} = E + (z_3 - z_1).$

Thus there will always be a drop in pressure between the ends of the meter, and the amount of degraded energy represented by this drop in a large Venturi meter may be of economic importance. Care is therefore taken to make E a minimum. Good design of the divergence can make E about 10 per cent of $u_2^2/2g$ and this is done with a cone of semi-vertex angle of about 6°. A longer cone of smaller angle gives higher values of E; this is because the degradation of energy by the ordinary fluid friction forces in the longer cone now becomes larger than the saving of energy due to the more gentle divergence.

A Venturi meter may be made for any size pipe, though those in

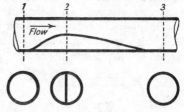

Fig 8.3 Venturi meter made by welding a plate into the bore of a pipe so that the throat section is D-shaped.

large water mains are expensive pieces of equipment. It is not necessary for either the pipe or the throat of the meter to be circular, as only the areas a_1 and a_2 are important. One way of making Venturi meters in large pipes is to insert a longitudinal diaphragm as in fig 8·3, thus giving a somewhat D-shaped throat section.

8.2 Orifices

In the preceding section it appears that the final diverging portion (sometimes called a *diffuser*) is not an essential part of a Venturi meter; it is only used to minimize the energy degradation in the meter as a whole. It certainly increases the capital cost of the meter.

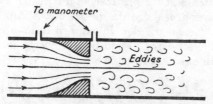

Fig 8.4 A possible flow-measuring apparatus of the pipe contraction type—sometimes called a *streamlined orifice*. Note the eddies downstream which cause a large degradation of energy. Approximate streamlines shown.

In places where it is not necessary to minimize E a perfectly satisfactory meter is a convergence without any diffuser, as shown in fig 8.4. Such an arrangement is called a *streamlined orifice*, for which precisely the same flow equation is used as for the Venturi meter, that is

$$Q = C_d a_2 \left(1 - \left(\frac{a_2}{a_1}\right)^2\right)^{-\frac{1}{2}} \sqrt{\left(2g\left\{\frac{(p_1 - p_2)}{\rho g} + (z_1 - z_2)\right\}\right)}.$$

Orifices can be designed to fit between the flanges at the ends of two lengths of pipe.

But even streamlined orifices are sometimes unnecessarily expensive to install and use. A simpler type of orifice is the so-called *sharp-edged orifice*, which is simply a hole drilled in a flat plate, the hole being bevelled to a sharp edge (fig 8·5). The bevelled side of the plate faces downstream. In the figure, streamlines of the flow are shown which approach and pass through the orifice. It will be seen that the jet of high speed fluid continues to contract for some distance downstream of the plane of the orifice, becoming parallel sided at a distance

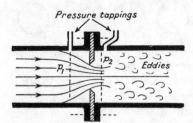

Fig 8.5 A cheaper form of measuring apparatus—the sharp-edged orifice. Note how the flow continues to contract downstream from the plane of the orifice to the minimum cross-sectional area, known as the *vena contracta*.

of about the diameter of the orifice. Here the pressure is uniform all over the cross section, so that the pressure at the walls is that of the whole of the fluid stream; in the curved, contracting section the pressure at the flow boundaries may not be the pressure throughout the stream (see Chapter 11). Consequently, the Venturi meter formula may be used for such a contraction, taking section 1 as upstream and section 2 at the place where the jet first becomes parallel again. Downstream of section 2 the jet breaks down into a highly turbulent area wherein the flow is returned to its original area, and in doing so suffers a large degradation of energy into heat.

The Bernoulli equation then gives

$$Q = C_d a_2 \left(1 - \left(\frac{a_2}{a_1} \right)^2 \right)^{-\frac{1}{2}} \sqrt{2g \left(\frac{p_1 - p_2}{\rho g} \right)},$$

assuming the axis of the pipe is horizontal and $z_1 = z_2$. This formula requires a measurement of the jet area a_2, which is inconvenient and difficult for the engineer, who however can measure the size of the orifice itself to a high degree of accuracy. He therefore substitutes a_0, the orifice area, for a_2, preserving the accuracy of the formula by multiplying throughout by another coefficient C_c so that

$$Q = C_d C_c a_0 \left(1 - \left(\frac{a_0}{a_1} \right)^2 \right)^{-\frac{1}{2}} \sqrt{2g \left(\frac{p_1 - p_2}{\rho g} \right)}.$$

To a first order of approximation $C_c = \dfrac{a_2}{a_0}$, if the effect of the term $(a_0/a_1)^2$ is ignored in the denominator, so that C_c is often called the *coefficient of contraction*, for it now expresses the amount by which the jet is smaller than the orifice from which it emerges.

For a sharp-edged orifice with a 45° bevel on it, and with smooth, well-finished surfaces everywhere, C_c is usually about 0·63. Thus the product $C_d . C_c$ is about 0·62, and is usually called the *coefficient of discharge* of the orifice. The coefficient C_d, which was the *coefficient of discharge* of the Venturi meter, is now called the *coefficient of velocity*, as it indicates the ratio between the actual velocity u_2 and that predicted by Bernoulli's equation.

8.3 Orifices in large tanks or reservoirs

The Bernoulli equation for flow through a contraction is much simplified if the upstream area of flow a_1 is very large compared with a_2. An example is when an orifice, streamlined or sharp-edged, is in the bottom or side of a large tank (fig 8.6). Cross section 1 is

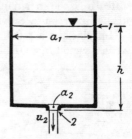

Fig 8.6 A rounded orifice in the bottom of a large tank. Cross-sectional area a_1 is very large compared with a_2. The water level in the tank is shown by the triangle mark.

now the whole cross section of the tank, and it is convenient to consider it as at the free water surface, a height z_1 above datum. Here the pressure is atmospheric and the gauge pressure p_1 is zero. The pressure of the out-flowing jet is also atmospheric at the place where it becomes parallel sided, if from a sharp-edged orifice, or at the orifice outlet if streamlined. Hence, the Bernoulli equation is now

$$\frac{u_1{}^2}{2g} + z_1 = \frac{u_2{}^2}{2g} + z_2 .$$

But since $a_1 \gg a_2$, $u_1 \ll u_2$, so that $u_1{}^2/2g$ can be neglected.

Thus
$$u_2 = \sqrt{2g(z_1 - z_2)}$$

and
$$Q = a_2\sqrt{2g(z_1 - z_2)}.$$

As before, a coefficient of discharge is applied to care for the neglected degradation of energy to heat, so that $Q = C_d a_2 \sqrt{2g(z_1 - z_2)}$. If the orifice is sharp-edged, a coefficient C_c is applied, as before, if a_2 is taken as the area of the orifice instead of the area of the jet.

The equation may be still further simplified by writing $z_1 - z_2 = h$, where h is the vertical distance between the free water surface and the outlet or parallel portion of the jet, so that

$$Q = C_d a_2 \sqrt{(2gh)} \quad . \qquad . \qquad . \quad (8.2)$$

8.4 Pressure distribution and lift on aerofoils

In Chapter 2 the method was shown of finding the lift force on an aerofoil by integration of the pressure distribution on it. If a model or full sized aerofoil is tested in a wind tunnel, this pressure distribution can be found experimentally by connecting tapping points all around it to suitable manometers. But in the design stage of an aerofoil, it may be necessary to predict the pressure distribution and so the lift before any such model has been tested. Provided the velocity all around the aerofoil is known, and this can be done by calculating the streamline pattern by the methods outlined in Chapter 5, then the pressure can be found as follows.

Imagine the aerofoil being stationary and air being forced past it, as in a wind tunnel (fig 8.7). Well upstream of the aerofoil the speed

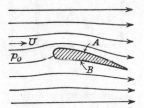

Fig 8.7 Aerofoil under test in a wind tunnel. Approximate streamline pattern shown. Note that the streamlines tend to be closer together above the upper surface than in the undisturbed stream, and vice versa below the lower surface.

and pressure are uniformly U and p_0 (a great deal of effort is expended in wind tunnel design in order to ensure this uniformity). The streamlines, originally uniformly spaced upstream, are distorted by the aerofoil, usually being brought closer together on the upper surface and further apart on the lower. The spacings become nearly uniform again well downstream of the trailing edge. Thus the air is accelerated above and decelerated below the aerofoil. Velocities, such as those at A and B, u_A and u_B respectively, can be measured from the spacing of the streamlines there. Now consider Bernoulli's equation for streamlines between the upstream position and A or B. There are, in well designed aerofoils, only slight shear forces due to friction of the flow over the upper or lower surfaces. Consequently the total energy along these streamlines is constant and the pressure p_A or p_B can be found by

$$\frac{U^2}{2g} + \frac{p_0}{g\rho} = \frac{u_A{}^2}{2g} + \frac{p_A}{g\rho} = \frac{u_B{}^2}{2g} + \frac{p_B}{g\rho},$$

ignoring the changes of z which are usually small compared with the changes of the other terms. In this way, the excess or deficiency of pressure $(p_A - p_0)/g\rho$ and $(p_B - p_0)/g\rho$ can be computed for every point on the aerofoil surface. Comparison of the pressure distribution thus found with the experimental values found from wind tunnel tests usually shows fair or good agreement near the leading edge, with increasing errors towards the trailing edge as the shear forces become more important. If the main flow breaks away from the aerofoil, leaving an eddy adjacent to the surface, then large errors may be expected, for the theoretical streamline pattern will not show breakaway at all. As will be explained later, breakaway only occurs on the upper side, that is, the side of the aerofoil where the velocity is greater than that of the oncoming stream and where the pressure is therefore lower than that upstream.

An alternative method of using a theoretical streamline pattern around an aerofoil is to find the thickness of the boundary layers around the aerofoil by much more advanced theory and experiment. The streamlines just outside the boundary layer suffer no degradation of energy at all, and Bernoulli's equation can therefore be applied precisely to find the pressure at points on them. It is then assumed that these pressures are those produced at the surface of the aerofoil. Again, some error is inevitable near the trailing edge where the boundary layers are thick. A combination of a streamline plotting technique and of Bernoulli's equation can thus give a first approximation to the lift force on an aerofoil.

8.5 The stagnation point pressure

An important application of Bernoulli's equation is in finding the pressure intensity which is generated at the upstream point of a solid body subjected to a fluid flow. The shear forces, and therefore degradation of energy, are quite negligible, so that Bernoulli's equation holds good for all parts of the flow near the forward end of the body. In fig 8.8. the streamlines are shown of a uniform flow, laminar or turbulent, approaching a symmetrical solid body. The streamlines are deflected, being crowded together near the shoulders of the body at AA. In particular, the fluid velocity near the point B is decreased,

PLATE I Three flow measuring instruments.

(*Top*) A sharp-edged orifice at the flanged joint of a pipeline. Tapping points must be provided on each side of the joint.

(*Middle*) A sectioned Venturi meter. Notice that the pressure at both the upstream pipe position and at the throat is taken at several tapping points around the periphery which are connected to common annular passages, and thence to the manometer.

Photo by G. Kent Ltd.

(*Bottom*) A broad crested weir photographed through the glass side of a laboratory channel. Notice how the flow over the weir crest becomes parallel at a depth of 2/3 the height of the upstream water surface above the crest. See Chapter 14.

PLATE I

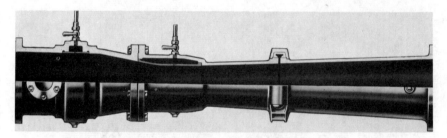

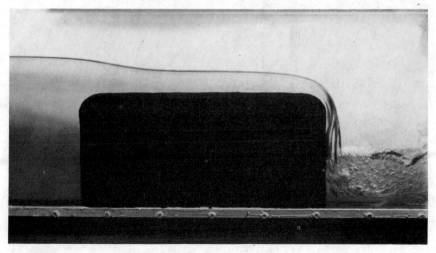

PLATE 2

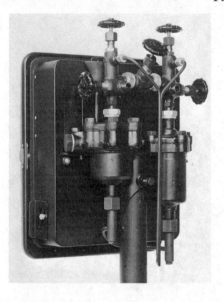

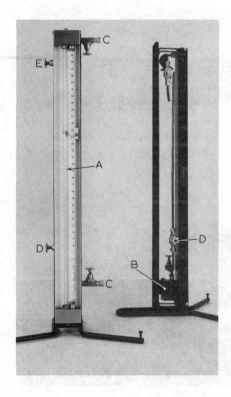

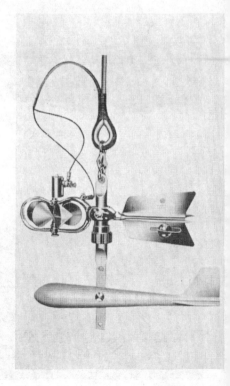

Facing page 91

PLATE 2   Two views of a recording manometer system.

(*Top left*) Back view showing two steel containers which are the enlarged ends of a mercury U-tube.   A float on the mercury surface operates the recording mechanism in the front of the box.   The valves are for shutting off the manometer from the pressure system, for purging the connecting pipes of air, and for connecting the two sides of the manometer together to check the zero pressure reading.

(*Top right*) Front view showing visual pointer (which is calibrated for the flow through an orifice connected to the manometer), recorder pen and chart, and above, an integrator to give the volume of fluid which has passed the orifice.

Photo by G. Kent Ltd.

(*Bottom left*) A modern mercury-filled manometer, with an enlarged limb, which concentrates the meniscus movements into one glass tube only.   Front and side views.   A—glass reading tube ; B—enlarged limb ;   CC—connexions to pressure tappings ;   D—interconnecting valve for flushing ;   E—air vent valve.

Photo by G. Kent Ltd.

(*Bottom right*) A current meter used to find water speeds in rivers.   It is suspended on a wire cable kept nearly vertical by the streamlined weight below.   The rotor is revolved by the fluid forces on the conical buckets and an electrical pulse is sent once per revolution to the operator above.

Photo by Hilger & Watts Ltd.

for it will be seen that the streamlines become wider apart there. In fact, close examination of the pattern shows that an interval between the streamline of symmetry at B and another streamline close to it suffers a great proportionate widening near B. The velocity near B is therefore much lower than the velocity U in the undisturbed flow upstream at C. At B itself the streamline of symmetry meets the solid surface, which is also a streamline, because there can be no flow across it (see Chapter 5); the streamline divides in a T shape so that the fluid at the junction point B should have three different directions, along and at $\pm 90°$ from the original direction. This is quite impossible unless the magnitude of the velocity is zero. The fluid is stagnant at B, which is therefore called a *stagnation point*.

Applying Bernoulli's equation to the streamline at B, the relation between p_0, the undisturbed stream pressure, and p_B is given by

$$\frac{U^2}{2g} + \frac{p_0}{g\rho} = \frac{u_B{}^2}{2g} + \frac{p_B}{g\rho},$$

but since $u_B = 0$, $p_B - p_0 = \rho \dfrac{U^2}{2}$.   .   .   .   (8.3)

or, in words, 'the pressure at a stagnation point is higher than the pressure in the undisturbed stream by the product of the fluid density and the undisturbed kinetic energy per unit weight of fluid.'

The property of a solid body in having a stagnation point on or near its leading edge gives a convenient way of finding the undisturbed velocity of a stream, by disturbing the flow with a solid body. A

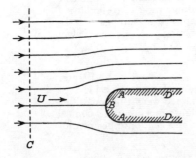

Fig 8.8 Streamlines of flow around a symmetrical round-nosed object in a stream. Note that the streamlines some distance away are hardly affected but that those near B have wider intervals than those at C.

hole is drilled in the body at the stagnation point and is connected by tubing to a manometer, which therefore measures p_B. The undisturbed pressure p_0 can be measured in two ways: if the flow is in a pipe, then another tapping point in the wall of the pipe somewhat upstream of the solid body can be connected to the other limb of the manometer, which therefore now shows $p_0 - p_B$; or another tapping can be placed on the solid body in a position such as D (fig 8.8), where experiment has shown the pressure to be such that $p_D = p_0$. Both arrangements are used extensively in experimental work, the solid body being made as a small cylinder put on a stem which permits a traverse across the stream (see fig 8.9). Arrangement (a) is sometimes called a *total pressure* or *Pitot* tube, named after the inventor, for the

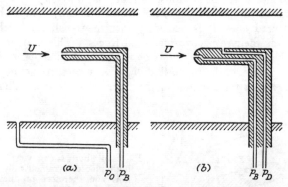

Fig. 8.9 Two methods of finding the velocity at a point in a pipe, using the stagnation pressure on a blunt nosed object. (a) is a *total head* tube, with a wall tapping point ; (b) is a *Pitot-static* tube.

stagnation pressure alone, $\rho U^2/2 + p_0$, is the total pressure of the fluid at that particular level. Arrangement (b) is called a *Pitot-static* tube, implying that the *static* pressure p_0 is measured by the same instrument as measures the *dynamic* pressure $\rho U^2/2$.

The stagnation pressure is also used in another important way. As has already been explained, the forces on a solid body (such as the lift and drag) can be found by a direct weighing technique, or by the method of finding the rate of change of momentum of the fluid caused by the drag. But a mere statement of the force is without meaning unless it is accompanied by statements of the velocity and density of the fluid, and of the size of the body. It is therefore a convenience to be able to quote instead a *Coefficient of Drag*, C_{drag} (or C_{lift}, as the case may be) defined as

$$C_{\text{drag}} = \frac{\text{measured drag}}{\text{hypothetical drag force}} \quad \text{or} \quad C_{\text{lift}} = \frac{\text{measured lift}}{\text{hypothetical lift}}$$

The hypothetical forces are defined as the product of an area appropriate to the body concerned and the excess pressure at the stagnation point, $(p_B - p_0)$. Thus, if D = drag force, L = lift force, A = area, U = undisturbed flow velocity, then

$$C_{\text{drag}} = \frac{D}{A_1 \rho U^2/2}; \quad C_{\text{lift}} = \frac{L}{A_2 \rho U^2/2}$$

(Notice that all terms must be in consistent units; thus in the f.p.s system, L and D are in poundals, and $\frac{1}{2}\rho U^2$, the excess (stagnation) pressure, is in poundals ft^{-2}, so that ρ is in lb ft^{-3}. In the metric SI system L and D are in newtons, so that ρ is in kg/m^3.)

To ensure that the hypothetical forces are truly comparable with the measured ones, it is necessary that they shall act in the same direction as their respective measured forces. This is done by projecting the cross section of the body in the same direction as the drag to find A_1, and as the lift to find A_2. Any pressure acting on such an area gives a force acting in the required direction. Thus, since

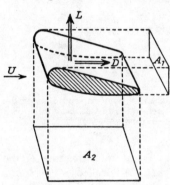

Fig 8.10 Perspective view of a solid body placed asymmetrically in a fluid flow and therefore producing a lift force L and drag force D. The projected areas A_1, A_2 appropriate to the drag and lift coefficients are shown.

a drag force is always by definition in the direction of the undisturbed motion, then A_1 is the area of the projection of the body concerned on a plane at right angles to the direction of motion; and A_2 is the area of the projection on a plane parallel to the motion. For example, both A_1 and A_2 for a sphere of radius r are πr^2; for a cylinder of length l across the flow, $A_1 = 2lr$; for a streamlined shape the area A_1 is that of the maximum cross-sectional area at right angles to the flow (see fig 8.10).*

* The definition of C_{drag} above is for the general case of a 'bluff' body which is not specifically designed to create a lift force, though it may incidentally do so. In the special case of an aerofoil which is primarily designed to give lift, it is usual to define

$$C_{\text{drag}} = \frac{D}{A_2 \rho U^2/2},$$

that is, the relevant area for drag is taken as the one which is truly appropriate to the *lift* force, the plan area of the aerofoil. This somewhat illogical definition

In Chapter 6 it is shown how a force exerted by a moving fluid is always proportionate to $\rho A u^2$ (where A is an area related in some way to the arrangement in question, and u a velocity somewhere in the system). It is therefore evident that both numerator and denominator of the fraction expressing C_{drag} or C_{lift} have the same dimensions. C_{drag} and C_{lift} are therefore dimensionless and so have the same value whatever system of units is used. It is not to be expected that either C_{drag} or C_{lift} is a constant value even for one shape ; both coefficients vary widely under different conditions. As a general rule, well streamlined shapes, leaving little wake behind them, have low values of C_{drag}, perhaps of the order of 0·1, but bluff bodies giving

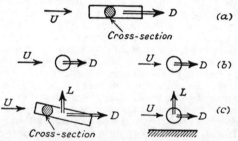

Fig 8.11   (a) A cylinder end-on to the flow gives drag force D only, no lift. (b) Cylinders and spheres held symmetrically to the flow give drag forces only. (c) Cylinders held asymmetrically to the flow, or having a fixed boundary near by, give both drag and lift forces.

rise to large eddies behind them may have a C_{drag} as high as 1·5 or so. For a given shape of body, C_{drag} may vary for different speeds, or viscosities of the fluid, and size of the body, and there is considerable evidence (to be discussed in a later chapter) that the combination of variables $uA^{\frac{1}{2}}/\nu$ is important in deciding the value of C_{drag} for any shape. The way in which C_{drag} varies with $uA^{\frac{1}{2}}/\nu$ is not the same for all shapes.

The coefficient of lift is essentially concerned with bodies which are not symmetrical about a line in the direction of the undisturbed flow. Thus, unless there is some asymmetry in the flow itself, such as may exist when there is a solid boundary near the body, the symmetrical shapes such as the sphere and cylinder shown in fig 8.11 (a) and (b)

is defensible only because the aeronautical engineer is mainly concerned with the variation of C_{lift} and C_{drag} as the angle of incidence θ changes (see fig. 8.10). Since the projected area A_1 in the direction of motion will change with θ, then A_1 will not be a constant for a given aerofoil. It is much more convenient to have a constant area for expressing C_{drag}, and the *chord* area A_2 (i.e. that appropriate to C_{lift}) is the one usually taken.

do not produce any lift at all (and consequently $C_{lift} = 0$). An asymmetrical body such as an aerofoil, fig 8.10, or a symmetrical body held asymmetrically to the flow, fig 8.11 (c), does produce a lift force, depending on the degree of asymmetry of the flow. It is found in fact that the coefficient of lift of an aerofoil increases with the angle of incidence (i.e. the angle between the axis of the aerofoil and the direction of the oncoming stream) until a position occurs when breakaway takes place on the upper surface.

Appendix : Other methods of flow measurement

Pitot tubes, Venturi meters and orifice plates are not the only methods available for continuously measuring velocities or discharges of fluids. There are many others, some of which use dynamic forces and pressures (and so involve Bernoulli's equation), and some which do not.

There are arrangements which distort a flow in a more complicated way than the simple ones shown in this Chapter, and which therefore give a pressure change proportional to the square of the velocity. Pressures across a diameter of a pipe bend (see Chapter 11), or near any change of pipe section, or indeed due to the friction in a length of pipe, may all be used. In open channels, wall distortions may be used to create a difference of water level : these are discussed in Chapter 14.

Among devices which use the flow pressures directly are meters which change their internal geometry as the flow increases, thus giving a direct indication. Pistons or discs may move through apertures, or aerofoil section blades change incidence against a spring system, and such devices are well known in industrial practice. Another group of devices is concerned with the kinematics of the flow ; these do not measure forces or pressures directly. They include rotary meters of several sorts, propellers, paddle wheels (see Plate 2), anemometers and similar instruments designed to give the minimum resisting force to the flow. All such instruments require calibration before use.

A laboratory device is the hot-wire (and hot-film) method, where a wire is heated by an electric current but the heat is removed by the passing fluid. The wire temperature depends on the velocity, though not by a linear law, and this in turn controls the electrical resistance, which is measured. An electromagnetic device is now frequently used in industrial work, and it has the advantage that there are no obstructions in the pipe. A magnetic field is produced across the pipe, and the fluid, acting as a moving conductor, creates an electromotive force between electrodes at right-angles to the field. The disadvantage lies in the complexities of the electronics.

Much more detailed accounts of these methods are to be found in the following :

H. Addison, *Hydraulic Measurements* (Chapman & Hall).

A. Linford, *Flow Measurements and Meters* (Spon).

G. P. Katys, *Continuous Measurement of Unsteady Flows* (Pergamon).

PROBLEMS

1. A large pipe, carrying water at a pressure of 30 kN/m² gauge, leads to an orifice near the top of an airtight tank in which initially there is perfect vacuum. The orifice diameter is 5 cm and $C_d = 0.65$. Find the time required for 6000 litres to flow into the tank. Vapour pressure of water is 1·2 m absolute. *Ans.* 429 s.

2. A 20 cm water pipe has in it a Venturi meter of throat diameter 12·5 cm, which is connected to a mercury manometer showing a difference of 87·8 cm. Find the velocity in the throat and the discharge. If the upstream pressure is 690 kN/m², what power would be given up by the water if it was allowed to discharge to atmospheric pressure.
Ans. 16 m/s: 0·197 m³/s: 136 kW.

3. An aerofoil is so shaped that the velocities along the upper and lower surfaces are respectively 25 per cent greater than, and 25 per cent smaller than, the velocity of the oncoming stream. What is the lift force on such a wing, 15 m long and 3 m chord, at 320 km/h? What is the lift coefficient? How nearly can such conditions be achieved in practice? Air density $\frac{1}{800}$ of water density.
Ans. 222 kN $C_{\text{lift}} = 1·0$.

4. A 30 cm diameter axial flow fan supplies 2 m³/s of air drawn from the atmosphere to a 60 cm diameter pipe by means of a well-designed diffuser fitted between the fan and the pipe. A manometer connected across the fan indicates a pressure rise equivalent to 5 cm of water.

Assuming both the friction losses and the tangential component of velocity downstream of the fan to be negligible, calculate

(a) the gauge pressure at the entry to the 60 cm diameter pipe;
(b) the longitudinal force transmitted by the fan to its driving motor;
(c) the longitudinal force exerted at the flange between the 60 cm pipe and the diffuser.

Assume the density of air constant and equal to 1·25 kg/m².
Ans. 4·69 cm water: 34·7 N: 83·2 N.

5. At a place in a pipeline, the bore changes suddenly from one cross-sectional area to another larger one downstream. If the pressure intensity on the annular area between the two bores is found experimentally to be the same as the pressure in the smaller bore, show that the change of pressure between places upstream and downstream of the enlargement is

$$p_1 - p_2 = \rho u_2(u_1 - u_2)$$

and the energy degradation is $E = \dfrac{(u_1 - u_2)^2}{2g}$,

where u_1 and u_2 are the velocities in the smaller and larger bores respectively.

Hint Use momentum theorem for pressure forces: at the expansion eddies form, so Bernoulli's equation must have an unknown degradation E.

6. Find the time to empty a tank 6 m square and 2 m deep through a 20 cm diameter faired orifice which is 1 m below the tank bottom.
Ans. 6 m, 21 s.

9

COMPRESSIBILITY IN MOVING FLUIDS— GAS FLOW

by G. JACKSON, M.A.

9.1 Basic equations for the steady flow of a gas

In the preceding chapters the discussion has for the most part been about liquids such as water, for which the density can be regarded as constant. Many engineering tasks require a study of the flow of gases such as air, as when designing buildings to withstand winds, in the design of engines and of vehicles of all kinds—cars, yachts, trains and aeroplanes. A gas differs from a liquid in its response to pressure. Although quite a large change in pressure does not appreciably alter the volume of a mass of liquid, a gas is readily compressed to a higher density or expanded to a lower. Because in general the pressure varies from point to point within a flowing fluid, the discussion of gas flows begins with a reconsideration of the constant-density assumption. It will be shown, perhaps surprisingly, that density changes are negligible and hence exactly the same methods of calculation can be used for gases as for liquids provided that the speed is low compared with the speed of sound. Very few land or water vehicles achieve speeds at which air is appreciably compressed by their motion. Compressibility becomes important within steam or gas turbines, around high speed fans and propellers and in the vicinity of fast aircraft. Some of the earliest examples of compressibility phenomena were in the field of gunnery.

Consider, as an illustration of the way in which the compressibility of a fluid can affect its behaviour, the problem of finding the change in velocity when a fluid in steady flow passes through a stream-tube the cross-sectional area of which changes from a_1 to a_2. The mass of fluid flowing in through a_1 in unit time must equal the mass of fluid flowing out through a_2 in unit time,

i.e. $$\rho_1 a_1 u_1 = \rho_2 a_2 u_2 \quad . \qquad . \qquad . \qquad . \quad (9.1)$$

If the fluid is a liquid, then for most practical purposes it is safe to say that the density does not alter and hence

$$\rho_1 = \rho_2$$

so that $$a_1 u_1 = a_2 u_2 ,$$

and when the stream-tube expands ($a_1 < a_2$) it follows that the flow slows down ($u_1 > u_2$). If on the other hand the fluid is a gas a change in area causes a change in speed, a change in speed causes a change in pressure and a change in pressure causes a change in density. It is possible for an expansion in area to accelerate the flow. This acceleration would be accompanied by a decrease in density, satisfying equation 9.1. Just such an acceleration occurs in the flared nozzle of a rocket motor. Thus the ability of a gas to be compressed or expanded may cause it to behave in a markedly different manner from a liquid.

Changes in pressure p and density ρ of a gas are usually accompanied by changes in temperature. To proceed with the analysis of gas flows, it is helpful to have equations connecting pressure, density and temperature. One such equation, previously mentioned on page 13, is the equation of state for a perfect gas,

$$\frac{p}{\rho T} = R . \qquad . \qquad . \qquad . \qquad . \quad (9.2)$$

This equation will be used throughout this chapter. Provided the absolute temperature T is considerably greater than that for liquefaction, equation 9.2 is a close approximation to the behaviour of real gases and its use simplifies the calculation of changes in p, ρ and T. The gas-constant R can be shown to be equal to the difference between the specific heats of the gas at constant pressure and at constant volume, both of which are constant for a perfect gas,

i.e. $$R = c_p - c_v$$
$$= \text{constant throughout the gas.}$$

The two equations 9.1 and 9.2 so far introduced contain five variables —p, ρ, T, u and a—several of which will in general be initially unknown so that more information must be sought. The Bernoulli equation cannot be used because it was obtained by assuming the density did not change; a counterpart must be found, which is an energy-balance equation. The energy concept in its generalized form is called the First Law of Thermodynamics. This law equates the inflow of heat and of work to the gain of energy. In this chapter the only problems considered will concern the steady flow of a perfect gas in which every stream-tube is heat-insulated, no work is done (e.g. by driving a turbine) and no energy is added (e.g. by burning fuel in the gas stream). The law then becomes an energy-conservation law, stating that the sum of the enthalpy, the kinetic energy and the potential energy of a mass of gas remains unchanged as it flows along. Since the enthalpy of unit mass of a perfect gas is equal to $c_p T$, the energy equation takes the form

$$\frac{u^2}{2} + c_p T + gz = \text{constant along a stream-tube.}$$

This equation can at the outset be simplified by the omission of the new variable z, the height, since in most problems involving gas flow, for example in the flow of air relative to an aeroplane, the changes in height cause only trivial changes in potential energy. The energy equation will therefore be written

$$\frac{u^2}{2} + c_p T = \text{constant along a stream-tube.} \qquad . \quad (9.3)$$

It should be noted that, whereas the Bernoulli equation is subject to the restriction that there shall be no degradation of energy, there is no such limitation in the use of the energy equation. An irreversible process such as friction in a real fluid or, anticipating a result obtained later in this chapter, the formation of a shock-wave, will cause a temperature rise in the gas. Provided each stream-tube is thermally insulated, the energy equation 9.3 is none the less valid since the degraded energy is retained within the gas and is included in the term $c_p T$.

If it should happen in addition that the perfect gas in heat-insulated (i.e. adiabatic) flow can be regarded as an ideal frictionless fluid, and if no irreversible change, such as at a shock-wave, takes place, then it can be shown that changes in pressure and density are related by the equation

$$p/\rho^\gamma = \text{constant along a stream-tube} \qquad . \qquad . \quad (9.4)$$

where $\qquad \qquad \gamma = c_p/c_v.$

The flow of a perfect gas under these conditions is called *isentropic*.*

A further useful relation between the variables may often be obtained by applying the momentum theorem (Chapter 6). Finally the data of each particular problem will include values of some of the variables for particular regions of the flow.

9.2 Comparison of the Bernoulli and energy equations

Equation 9.3 can be rewritten in several ways. For example, the term $c_p T$ can be written, using the relation $R = c_p - c_v$ and equation 9.2.

$$c_p T = (R + c_v)T$$
$$= \frac{p}{\rho} + c_v T$$

---

* For a full discussion of the thermodynamic concepts referred to in section 9.1, see *Engineering Thermodynamics*, Spalding and Cole (Edward Arnold, 3rd ed., 1973).

and the energy equation stated as

$$\frac{u^2}{2} + \frac{p}{\rho} + c_v T = \text{constant along a stream-tube in a gas.}$$

The Bernoulli equation (Chapter 7), omitting the potential energy term gz, is

$$\frac{u^2}{2} + \frac{p}{\rho} = \text{constant along a stream-tube in a liquid.}$$

These two equations would clearly be identical if $c_v T$ were constant; putting this remark another way, a compressible fluid can be reckoned as incompressible if the term $c_v T$ does not change by very much, i.e. compressibility effects will be unimportant if

$$\Delta T/T \ll 1\cdot 0,$$

where ΔT is the amount by which the absolute temperature T is changed in the course of the flow. Consider a flow in which a gas is brought to rest at a stagnation point, the temperature rising to the stagnation temperature. The temperature rise can then be deduced from equation 9.3

viz.
$$\frac{u^2}{2} + c_p T = 0 + c_p(T + \Delta T).$$

Therefore
$$\Delta T = u^2/2c_p$$

and
$$\Delta T/T = u^2/2c_p T$$

$$= \frac{u^2}{\gamma RT}(\gamma - 1)/2,$$

since $R = c_p - c_v$ and $\gamma = c_p/c_v$.

Thus
$$\Delta T/T = M^2(\gamma - 1)/2, \text{ say,}$$

where
$$M = u/\sqrt{(\gamma RT)}.$$

Hence compressibility effects, measured by $\Delta T/T$, will be small if the speed u is small compared with $\sqrt{(\gamma RT)}$, i.e. if M is small. For air $\gamma = 1\cdot 4$ and if $M = 0\cdot 2$ it follows that

$$\frac{\Delta T}{T} = 0\cdot 008,$$

which is small enough to be neglected in comparison with unity for most practical purposes. If T had the normal atmospheric value, the stagnation-point temperature-rise would be approximately two kelvins (2K).

The greatest temperature rise in a heat-insulated flow will be to the stagnation temperature ; the greatest temperature drop is unlikely to be numerically much greater than this. It is generally true to say that *if M is everywhere less than 0·2 in a moving gas the changes in density are negligible.*

This is a very valuable simplification. It means that a slow-moving gas follows the same laws as a liquid and that all the conclusions founded on the assumption of constant density in other chapters of this book apply equally to a liquid and to a gas, provided that M is everywhere small in the gas. The larger M becomes, the more important become changes in density and in temperature and the more does the character of the flow change. To decide whether compressibility has to be taken into account, it is preferable to consider the magnitude of the ratio M rather than the speed u. M, which is dimensionless, is called the *Mach number.*

To conclude these remarks on the two equations, it is interesting to note that in an isentropic flow the energy equation can, as was the Bernoulli equation, be derived from Newton's law. The latter was shown in Chapter 7 to lead to the relation

$$u^2/2 + \int \mathrm{d}p/\rho = \text{constant along a stream-tube,}$$

omitting the gravity term as before. In isentropic flow $p \propto \rho^\gamma$ so that then

$$\int \frac{\mathrm{d}p}{\rho} = \frac{\gamma}{\gamma - 1} \frac{p}{\rho}$$

$$= \frac{\gamma}{\gamma - 1} RT, \text{ from } (9.2)$$

$$= c_p T, \text{ from the definitions of } R \text{ and } \gamma.$$

Therefore $\dfrac{u^2}{2} + c_p T = \text{constant along a stream-tube.}$

This is a proof of the energy equation which was introduced without proof on p. 99.   It is not a general proof, for this equation is valid also for some flows which are not isentropic.

9.3 The speed of propagation of a weak pressure-wave in a gas

The aim of this paragraph is to show that the denominator $\sqrt{(\gamma RT)}$ in the expression for the Mach number is equal to the speed of sound in the gas. The Mach number is therefore the ratio of the speed of the gas to the speed of sound. To appreciate the relevance of the speed of sound, imagine yourself shouting into the wind. You shout by generating small pressure changes in your throat. Your friend upwind will hear you unless the wind is blowing faster than sound can travel; the critical wind speed is equal to the speed of sound. This *sonic* speed is a critical speed for gas flow problems in general, because any obstacle or deviation in a gas stream causes pressure changes. The influence of very small changes in pressure travels at the speed of sound. Large pressure changes spread faster. The importance of compressibility depends on the ratio of the gas flow speed u to the propagation speed of the slightest change in pressure.

To estimate this speed, consider the state of affairs which would arise at a particular instant some time after a solid body had been suddenly introduced at O, on the right hand side of Fig 9.1, into a gas stream moving with a uniform velocity u at a pressure p. The obstacle fixed at O would cause various changes in pressure around its profile;

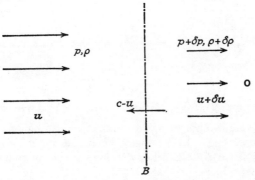

Fig 9.1 A very weak pressure-wave travelling into a moving gas.

for example, at some point (a stagnation point) the velocity would be reduced to zero with a corresponding rise in pressure. Such a pressure change would react on the adjacent oncoming fluid, changing its pressure and velocity in such a way as to provide the centripetal forces necessary to push apart the streamlines and deflect the fluid past the obstacle. The pressure disturbance, transmitting itself further and further from O, affects progressively greater amounts of fluid and in consequence the pressure jump which is being propagated outwards becomes progressively weaker. By the time the presence of the obstacle has made itself felt at B, a great distance ahead of O, the pressure change has reduced to a very small value δp and the disturbance is advancing on a front of so large a radius that it can be considered plane. This plane

wave of pressure, analogous to the ripple that would spread upstream
along the surface of a slowly-flowing river if a stick were dipped into it,
is transmitting itself away from O at a speed c relative to the fluid and
therefore at a speed $(c - u)$ relative to O, which is fixed.   The pressure-
wave is represented in fig. 9.1 as a line across which the pressure rises
from p to $p + \delta p$; the density ρ and velocity u change accordingly by
small amounts.

The pressure-wave is sweeping across from right to left with a speed
$(c - u)$: bring it to rest by superimposing a speed $(c - u)$ from left to
right on the whole system and consider a stream-tube of the resulting
steady flow (fig 9.2).   The equations for steady flow, developed earlier
in this book, can now be used in order to find c.

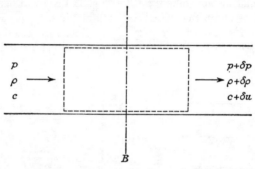

Fig 9.2   The flow relative to a very weak pressure-wave.

All the stream-tubes being identical, none can suffer a change in
cross-sectional area.   Let this area be a and apply the momentum
theorem (Chapter 6) to the flow through the control volume enclosed
by the broken line in fig 9.2.

$$a[p - (p + \delta p)] = (\rho + \delta p)a(c + \delta u)^2 - \rho ac^2$$

Therefore $-\delta p = 2\rho c\delta u + c^2\,\delta \rho$.   .   .   (9.5)

neglecting second-order terms.

Also, from the equation of continuity of mass flow, equation 9.1,

$$\rho ca = (\rho + \delta p)(c + \delta u)a$$

$$\therefore \ \rho\delta u = -c\delta \rho$$.   .   .   .   (9.6)

Combining 9.5 and 9.6 to eliminate δu,

$$c^2 = \delta p/\delta \rho.$$

For vanishingly small values of the pressure rise,

$$\delta p \rightarrow o,$$

whereupon $c^2 \rightarrow \mathrm{d}p/\mathrm{d}\rho.$

Finally assuming the compression to be isentropic then

$$\mathrm{d}p/\mathrm{d}\rho = \gamma p/\rho \text{ from equation 9.4}$$

and hence $\quad\quad\quad\quad c = \sqrt{(\gamma p/\rho)}$

or from 9.2 $\quad\quad\quad\quad c = \sqrt{(\gamma RT)}$ . . . . (9.7)

The assumption of isentropic compression is justified by the close agreement between measurements of the speed of sound and values calculated from 9.7. The assumption will be referred to again later, at the end of section **9.5**.

For air, $\gamma = 1\cdot4$ and $R = 287$ J/(kg K) so that if $T = 288$ K, then

$$c = 340 \text{ m/s}$$

This is a representative value for the earth's atmosphere at sea-level. At an altitude of 11 km it falls to approximately 300 m/s, on account of the reduced temperature. Observe that for a particular gas c depends only on the absolute temperature.

The Mach number commonly referred to in connection with aircraft is the ratio of the true speed of the aircraft to the sonic speed in the atmosphere at the height of the aircraft. Having earlier concluded that compressibility is unimportant if the Mach number is less than 0·2, it follows that the constant-density assumption and the Bernoulli equation can be used for aircraft travelling at speeds up to 60 or 70 m/s. In Plate 4 (*a*), which shows significant compressibility effects, the Mach number is 0·8 and the air speed is approximately 270 m/s.

The Mach number is by no means constant throughout the air surrounding an aeroplane. For example the flow speed u increases across the upper surface of the wing ; if $u^2/2 + c_\mathrm{p}T$ is constant, it follows that T decreases and therefore c decreases. Hence the local value of the Mach number M increases. In Plate 4 (*a*) air approaches a wing at $M = 0\cdot8$. In this illustration the local values of M near the upper surface become greater than unity, evidenced by the formation of a shock wave. A shock wave, the border-line between regions of markedly different density, forms only when the speed exceeds the speed of sound. Taking advantage of the change in refraction of light which accompanies a change in density, optical techniques can be used to make shock waves visible. Shock waves appear as dark lines in Plate 4.

9.4 Supersonic flow and shock waves

When a gas is flowing steadily past a fixed slender symmetrical blunt-nosed solid body such as the wing in Plate 4 (*b*) at a speed in excess of the speed of sound in the gas before it is affected by the body (i.e. at supersonic speed), the flow in the neighbourhood of the nose

is found to exhibit a steady pattern similar to fig. 9.3. The flow
relative to the body is identical if the body is travelling at supersonic
speed through a stationary gas.

There is an abrupt rise of density and of pressure across a line DEF.

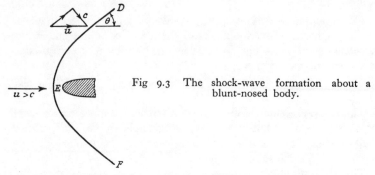

Fig 9.3   The   shock-wave   formation   about   a
blunt-nosed body.

The pressure rise is greatest at E, getting smaller towards D or F.
The slope θ of the line becomes constant at some distance from the
nose.   From these experimental facts can be deduced two important
results :

  (i) a strong pressure-wave propagates itself at a speed greater than
       the speed of sound ;

 (ii) if the pressure in a supersonic stream is rising, it will generally
       rise suddenly ; a fall in pressure will never be sudden.

Conclusion (i) follows from the observed flow around E.   There
the pressure jumps by an amount by no means infinitesimal.   The
wave front at E which maintains a fixed distance from the body is
necessarily travelling at the supersonic speed u relative to the oncoming stream.   Moving from E towards D (or F) the pressure
jump diminishes and the velocity of propagation of each segment of
DE, being equal to the component of u in the direction perpendicular
to the segment, diminishes also. Thus a small pressure change propagates itself at the speed of sound and a large pressure change propagates
itself at a speed greater than the speed of sound.

Far from E the pressure rise is very small, and the speed of propagation is the sonic speed c so that the wave front trails downstream behind
the body at an inclination θ given by

$$\sin \theta = c/u$$
$$= 1/M$$

This value of θ is called the *Mach angle*.   In passing it may be noted
that if θ is observed then M can be deduced and this provides a method
of measuring a supersonic speed.   In the caption to Plate 3 it is pointed

out that a $45°$ angle corresponds to $M = 1·4$, because sin $45°$ is $1/\sqrt{2}$ and $\sqrt{2}$ is approximately $1·4$.

Conclusion (ii) follows from conclusion (i). An infinitesimal pressure change cannot possibly spread at its sonic speed of propagation directly into a flow which is itself supersonic. Small pressure changes must accumulate into a finite pressure jump (i.e. a *shock-wave*) large enough for its augmented speed of propagation to be able to hold its position against the supersonic oncoming flow.

On a streamline passing close to a solid body in a liquid or in a low-Mach-number gas, the pressure begins to rise a long way ahead of the body. The pressure might rise slowly ahead of the body, fall adjacent to the body and rise again to its original value as in fig 9.4 (*a*).

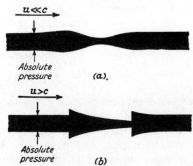

Fig 9.4 (*a*) and (*b*) Diagrammatic representations of the pressure changes along a streamline in (*a*) subsonic flow and (*b*) supersonic flow involving shock-waves.

Fig 9.4 (*b*) illustrates the corresponding pressure distribution in a supersonic flow. The approaching fluid is quite uninfluenced by the solid body until it reaches a shock-wave, whereupon it suffers a rise in pressure which is so sudden (it takes place within a distance of approximately 10^{-4} cm) that it can be taken as discontinuous. The weak 'tail' of falling pressure is attentuated and is shown as being more gradual in fig 9.4 (*b*) than in 9.4 (*a*). If a flow accelerates up through the speed of sound a pressure rise which starts by being gradual will become sudden when the flow becomes supersonic; a pressure decrease will always take place gradually. There are sudden increases of pressure across the dark lines and gradual decreases of pressure through the light-coloured zones in Plate 4 (*c*).

9.5 The change in conditions across a normal shock-wave

To examine in more detail the flow in the neighbourhood of a shock-wave, the simplest case to consider is the flow at E in fig 9.3. There, on the axis of symmetry, the sudden pressure rise occurs across a line

normal to the flow. Such a *normal shock* involves, as has been pointed
out, a larger pressure jump than an *oblique shock* (such as between
E and D) in the same stream.

The analysis of the conditions in the neighbourhood of a strong
pressure-wave starts in the same way as the previous analysis of a weak

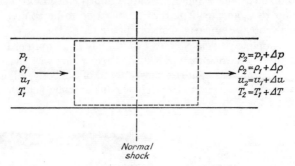

p_1
ρ_1 $\longrightarrow$
u_1
T_1

$p_2=p_1+\Delta p$
$\rho_2=\rho_1+\Delta\rho$ $\longrightarrow$
$u_2=u_1+\Delta u$
$T_2=T_1+\Delta T$

*Normal
shock*

Fig 9.5   The flow relative to a normal shock-wave.

pressure-wave, so that fig 9.5 is similar to fig 9.2 except in so far as
the changes in pressure, density and velocity are no longer small.

Assuming that the flow in each stream-tube is adiabatic (which would
certainly be true for a normal shock-wave of infinite extent since all
the stream-tubes are identical) and assuming the gas is a perfect gas,
then

$$\rho_1 u_1 = \rho_2 u_2 \qquad . \qquad . \qquad . \qquad . \qquad (9.1)$$

$$\frac{p_1}{\rho_1 T_1} = \frac{p_2}{\rho_2 T_2} = R \qquad . \qquad . \qquad . \qquad (9.2)$$

and
$$\frac{u^2_1}{2} + c_p T_1 = \frac{u^2_2}{2} + c_p T_2 \qquad . \qquad . \qquad . \qquad (9.3)$$

with
$$R = c_p - c_v.$$

Note that the relation $p \propto \rho^\gamma$ cannot be used since there is no reason
to suppose that the compression from p_1 to p_2 is isentropic.   Indeed,
the conclusion in the previous paragraph that a shock-wave can only
exist if the pressure is rising in the flow direction, not if it is falling,
is linked with the fact that the flow process is irreversible.   A further
relation can, however, be obtained by applying the momentum theorem,
i.e.
$$p_1 - p_2 = \rho_2 u_2{}^2 - \rho_1 u_1{}^2 \qquad . \qquad . \qquad . \qquad (9.8)$$
Given u_1, ρ_1, p_1 and T_1, the four unknowns u_2, ρ_2, p_2 and T_2 are
now determinate.

To find Δu $(= u_2 - u_1)$ eliminate T_1 and T_2 from *9.3* by using *9.2* and then p_2 by using *9.8* and ρ_2 by using *9.1* : write

$$M^2{}_1 = \frac{\rho_1 u_1{}^2}{\gamma p_1} \quad \text{where} \quad \gamma = c_p/c_v.$$

The algebra, which the reader should work through for himself, leads to a result which can be put in the form

$$\frac{\Delta u}{u_1} = - \frac{2}{\gamma + 1} \frac{M_1{}^2 - 1}{M_1{}^2}.$$

Similarly

$$\frac{\Delta \rho}{\rho_1} = \frac{2(M_1{}^2 - 1)}{(\gamma M_1{}^2 + 1) - (M_1{}^2 - 1)},$$

$$\frac{\Delta p}{p_1} = \frac{2\gamma}{\gamma + 1}(M_1{}^2 - 1)$$

and

$$\frac{\Delta T}{T_1} = \left(\frac{2}{\gamma + 1}\right)\left(\frac{\gamma - 1}{\gamma + 1}\right)\left(\frac{M_1{}^2 - 1}{M_1{}^2}\right)(\gamma M_1{}^2 + 1).$$

These results are illustrated in figs 9.6 (*a*) and 9.6 (*b*) for two representative values of γ. The flow velocity drops and the temperature, density and pressure all rise behind a shock wave. It may be seen that the pressure rise is not very sensitive to a change in γ; the temperature rise is more strongly affected. Another quantity, required for the next paragraph, is the Mach number behind a normal shock-wave, which is

$$M_2 = M_1(u_2/u_1)(T_1/T_2)^{1/2}$$

and which on substitution and simplification becomes

$$M_2 = \sqrt{\left(\frac{(\gamma M_1{}^2 + 1) - (M_1{}^2 - 1)}{2(\gamma M_1{}^2 + 1) - (\gamma + 1)}\right)}$$

Plotting this result in fig 9.7, it may be seen that M_2 is never greater than unity, that is to say, the flow behind a normal shock-wave is never supersonic. This is true for all gases.

Finally, it is to be noted that the relation between the pressure rise Δp and the density rise $\Delta \rho$ across a normal shock-wave, obtained by eliminating M_1 from the foregoing expressions for Δp and $\Delta \rho$, is

$$\frac{\Delta \rho}{\rho_1} = \left(\frac{1}{\gamma}\frac{\Delta p}{p_1}\right) \Big/ \left(1 + \frac{\gamma - 1}{2\gamma}\frac{\Delta p}{p_1}\right).$$

In fig 9.8 this is compared with the density rise corresponding to an isentropic compression which, since p is then proportional to ρ^γ, is

$$\frac{\Delta \rho}{\rho_1} = \left(1 + \frac{\Delta p}{p_1}\right)^{1/\gamma} - 1.$$

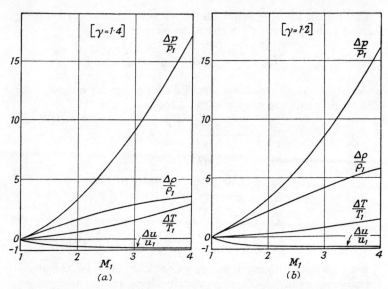

Fig 9.6 (a) and (b) The changes of pressure, density, temperature and flow velocity across normal shock-waves in fluids for which (a) $\gamma = 1\cdot4$, (b) $\gamma = 1\cdot2$.

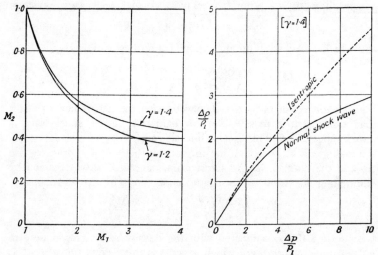

Fig 9.7 Mach numbers upstream (M_1) and downstream (M_2) of normal shock-waves.

Fig 9.8 Comparison between the pressure-density relations for isentropic compression and for compression across a normal shock-wave.

This comparison shows that only very weak pressure-waves achieve an isentropic compression. It would be quite wrong therefore to suppose that across all shock-waves

$$p_2/p_1 = (\rho_2/\rho_1)^\gamma.$$

This would only be true if the shock-wave were very weak, i.e. if $\Delta p[= (p_2 - p_1)]$ were very small in comparison with p_1, as is the case for a sound-wave.

9.6 The Pitot tube in a gas stream

To illustrate how the ideas introduced so far can be used for solving practical problems, consider how to estimate the stagnation pressure p_0 which would be generated when a gas-stream originally at a pressure p is brought to rest in an open-ended tube (a Pitot tube) pointing into the stream. A Mach meter operates by taking to ratio of p_0 to p and indicating the result on a dial calibrated in M, the calibration curve being the full line in Fig 9.10.

There are three cases to be considered :

(i) $0 < M < 0\cdot2$ (ii) $0\cdot2 < M < 1\cdot0$ (iii) $M > 1\cdot0$.

Case (i) can be taken as identical with that for an incompressible fluid. This problem was discussed in Chapter 8, where it was shown, from Bernoulli's equation, that

$$p_0 = p + \tfrac{1}{2}\rho u^2.$$

This can be rewritten

$$\frac{p_0}{p} = 1 + \tfrac{1}{2}\gamma M^2 . \qquad . \qquad . \qquad . \qquad (9.9\,(i))$$

Case (ii) can be solved in the same way, except that the energy equation must be used instead of Bernoulli's equation,

i.e. $$c_p T_0 = \frac{u^2}{2} + c_p T.$$

Therefore $T_0/T = 1 + (u^2/2c_p T)$,

i.e. $(p_0/p)(\rho/\rho_0) = 1 + (u^2/2c_p)(\rho R/p)$ for a perfect gas,

i.e. $(p_0/p)^{(\gamma-1)/\gamma} = 1 + ((\gamma - 1)/2)M^2$ for isentropic compression from p to p_0.

Note that no shock-wave can form since the flow is subsonic and so it is reasonable to assume isentropic flow.

It follows that

$$\frac{p_0}{p} = \left(1 + \frac{\gamma - 1}{2}M^2\right)^{\gamma/(\gamma-1)} \qquad\qquad (9.9\,(ii))$$

which is the required result. In passing, it is worth noticing that for small values of M equation 9.9 (ii) can be expanded to give

$$\frac{p_0}{p} = 1 + \tfrac{1}{2}\gamma M^2(1 + \tfrac{1}{4}M^2 + \ldots),$$

which shows that it is not until M exceeds 0·2 that the difference between the values of p_0 from 9.9 (i) and (ii) exceeds 1 per cent of $\tfrac{1}{2}\rho u^2$, a result similar to the one obtained on p. 101.

Case (iii), a Pitot tube in a supersonic stream, involves a shock-wave lying upstream of the tube, shown diagrammatically in fig 9.9.

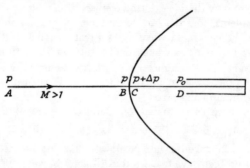

Fig 9.9   The shock-wave formation and the pressure changes ahead of a Pitot tube.

Along the central streamline ABCD there is no change of pressure from A to B, a sudden increase in pressure as the speed drops to a subsonic speed at C and thereafter the pressure increases continuously from C to D where the velocity is zero.

The pressure and the Mach number at C are, from section **9.5**, given by

$$\frac{p_c}{p} = 1 + \frac{2\gamma}{\gamma + 1}(M^2 - 1)$$

and

$$M_c = \sqrt{\left(\frac{(\gamma M^2 + 1) - (M^2 - 1)}{2(\gamma M^2 + 1) - (\gamma + 1)}\right)}$$

and the pressure at D therefore, following equation 9.9 (ii) above, is given by

$$\frac{p_0}{p_c} = \left(1 + \frac{\gamma - 1}{2}M_c^2\right)^{\gamma/(\gamma-1)}$$

Therefore

$$\frac{p_0}{p} = \left[\frac{(\gamma + 1)[(\gamma + 1)M^2/2]^\gamma}{2(\gamma M^2 + 1) - (\gamma + 1)}\right]^{1/(\gamma-1)} \qquad . \qquad (9.9\,(iii))$$

If p_0 is measured and if p, the undisturbed pressure, is also known, then M can be deduced from the appropriate equation 9.9 (i), (ii), or (iii).

In fig 9.10 the three curves 9.9 (i), (ii) and (iii) have been plotted to show the extent to which the estimate of p_0 would be in error if compressibility or the formation of a shock-wave were neglected at high speeds.

Flow processes of this kind and the calculations that go with them are of interest not only in connection with the use of a Pitot tube to

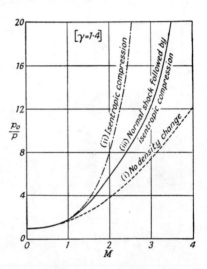

Fig 9.10 Calculated values of the stagnation — or Pitot — pressure (p_0) based on three different hypotheses. Curve (iii) corresponds to the actual flow about a Pitot tube.

help in the measurement of speed or of Mach number. In the neighbourhood of the intake to a turbo-jet or a ram-jet engine in flight a similar state of affairs is reproduced if the air-flow through the engine is small; for large flow velocities through the engine the shock-wave is drawn inside with other shock-waves probably forming outside the nacelle. Again, on the wing of an aeroplane near the leading edge there is a stagnation point where the flow divides into two streams, one passing under and one over the wing, and the conditions at this point are the same as those within a Pitot tube. If the leading edge is rounded (e.g. Plate 4 (b)) the shock-wave formation is the same and the comparison is exact for all Mach numbers.

It is a simple matter to estimate the absolute temperature T_0 of the air at the stagnation point. It is not necessary to subdivide the speed range since the energy equation

$$u^2/2 + c_p T = c_p T_0$$

applies whether or not a shock-wave is formed. Thus for any Mach number

$$T_0/T = 1 + \frac{\gamma - 1}{2}M^2.$$

This curve is plotted for air in fig 9.11. If the Mach number is less than 0·2 the change in temperature is insignificant; if an aeroplane is travelling at 1 km/s, the temperature rise at the stagnation point is 500 K. In a real gas where viscous action brings to zero the relative

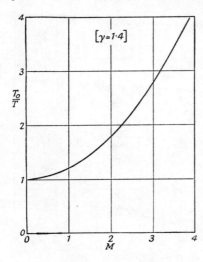

Fig 9.11   The stagnation temperature (T_0) of a gas.

speed between any solid surface and the fluid in immediate contact with it, it might be expected that the same temperature rise would be experienced over the whole surface and not only at the stagnation point. This is not quite correct, but none the less the rise in temperature of a real gas in contact with a flat heat-insulated surface is approximately $\frac{7}{8}(u^2/2c_p)$, e.g. about 440 K at 1 km/s in air. It is left to the reader to contemplate the consequences of a temperature rise of this magnitude in relation to the design of the structure and of the air conditioning system for a supersonic aircraft, or of the heat shield for a vehicle re-entering the earth's atmosphere.

9.7 Oblique shock-waves and sharp noses

Returning to fig 9.3, showing the shock-wave around the blunt nose of, say, a bullet, the flow immediately ahead of the nose and the flow far

from the bullet are now both understood. The former involves a
normal shock-wave followed by a subsonic compression with a gradual
dividing of the streamlines past the bullet; the latter involves a vanishingly weak pressure-wave (a *Mach wave*), lying at the Mach angle
($\sin^{-1} 1/M$) to the flow direction. Between the two extremes a shock-
wave varying in strength (i.e. the magnitude of the pressure rise across
it) from that of a normal shock-wave to zero lies at an oblique angle to
the flow direction, the angle varying from 90° ahead of the nose to the
Mach angle at a remote distance. To complete an understanding of
the picture, it therefore remains to study the flow through an oblique
shock-wave of finite strength. Plane oblique shock waves can be seen
springing from the sharply-pointed leading and trailing edges of the
wing in Plate 4 (*c*).

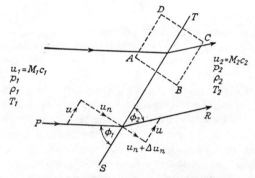

Fig 9.12   The flow relative to an oblique shock-wave.

Fig 9.12 represents a part of a shock-wave ST, for simplicity of
infinite extent, upstream of which the streamlines of the approaching
uniform supersonic flow make an angle ϕ_1 with ST. Consider the
flow through a control volume such as ABCD. The pressure is
uniform at p_1 over that half of the control volume which lies upstream
of ST and uniform, at a higher pressure p_2, over the downstream half.
Therefore there is no resultant pressure force in the direction ST and
hence, by the momentum theorem, no change in momentum in that
direction. Since the mass flow rates into and out of ABCD are the
same, the velocity component u in the direction ST must be the same
on either side of the shock-wave. Thus an oblique shock-wave reduces
to a normal shock the properties of which depend on

$$M_n = u_n/c_1$$

which can be written $\qquad M_n = (u_1/c_1) \sin \phi_1$

or $\qquad M_n = M_1 \sin \phi_1 .$

These properties can be calculated from section **9.5** or read off from fig 9.6 using M_n instead of M_1. Superimposed on the normal shock is the velocity u in the direction ST. Since Δu_n is negative,

viz.
$$\Delta u_n / u_n = -\frac{2}{\gamma + 1}\left(\frac{M_n{}^2 - 1}{M_n{}^2}\right),$$

it follows that the streamlines passing through the shock-wave are deflected *away* from the normal to the shock and that the resultant velocity is diminished. This velocity u_2 may or may not be less than c_2. The normal component $(u_n + \Delta u_n)$ is of course less than c_2, where

$$c_2 = \surd(\gamma R T_2)$$

$$= c_1 \bigg/ \sqrt{\left(1 + \frac{\Delta T}{T_1}\right)}$$

and $\Delta T / T_1$ is obtained from fig 9.6, using M_n instead of M_1. The size of the component u then determines whether or not u_2 is super-sonic. M_2 is always less than M_1 but M_2 may be either less or greater than unity.

In this way it is readily possible, given M_1 and ϕ_1, to calculate M_2 and ϕ_2 and thereby to gain some insight into the flow immediately behind plane oblique shock-waves. The restriction to plane shock-waves is noteworthy. If the shock-wave is plane and of infinite extent as postulated for fig 9.12, then the deflected flow is uniform behind the shock-wave, is subject to no further modifying influence, and the flow is completely determined by the foregoing analysis. This is also true if the flow is bounded by a solid boundary having as its cross-section one of the streamlines, say PR, in fig 9.12 and stretching out to infinity beyond P, beyond R and perpendicular to the paper. If however the oblique shock is formed as part of the flow about the blunt leading edge of an aeroplane wing, the flow behind the nearly-normal parts of the shock-wave will be subsonic and will therefore be affected by the shape of the wing section ; the oblique parts of the shock-wave system near the leading edge will vary from point to point in both strength and obliquity and the downstream streamlines will have to adapt themselves to one another as well as to the bounding surface. The oblique shock-wave formed around the nose of a bullet or a similar missile will not be plane either ; it will be conical.

Returning to the flow for which a complete solution has been outlined above, the flow past a sharp concave corner such as PR (fig 9.12), it is worth remarking that the device whereby one thinks of a flow, plots the streamlines and then chooses one streamline to represent a solid surface is often used in the theory of fluid mechanics. The definition of a streamline is that no fluid crosses it and this is also the definition of a solid surface. Another useful artifice is to combine one such streamline with its mirror image to produce the solution to yet another problem. In particular, the foregoing analysis solves the problem of what happens when an infinite wedge, shown in cross section in fig 9.13 (*a*), is held in a supersonic flow. The significance

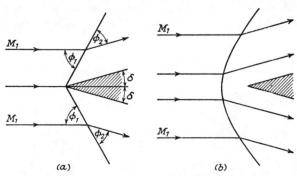

Fig 9.13 (*a*) and (*b*)   The shock-wave formation about a body with a pointed nose, showing (*a*) attached and (*b*) detached shock-waves.

of this problem is that the same kind of flow pattern would be obtained around the sharp leading edge of an aeroplane wing in the region away from the influence of the wing-tips, as may be seen in Plate 4 (*c*). Around the pointed nose of a missile or of a supersonic aeroplane the flow could be of similar appearance.

The following question immediately presents itself : is the shock-wave system attached to the body as in fig 9.13 (*a*) or is it detached like that for a blunt nose as in fig 9.13 (*b*) ? The answer, again based on experiment, is that the shock is attached whenever possible. Limitations on the combinations of M_1, ϕ_1, and δ for which the attached flow is possible must exist since the flow normal to the shock-wave must always be supersonic (otherwise the shock-wave would not exist) and in addition, for a wedge, the flow must be deflected into a direction parallel with the surface. Thus if, for a given combination of M_1 and δ, a shock-wave inclination ϕ_1 can be chosen, bearing in mind that

$$M_1 \sin \phi_1 > 1$$

i.e.
$$\phi_1 > \sin^{-1} 1/M_1,$$

i.e. ϕ_1 is at least as large as the Mach angle, and if the chosen value of ϕ_1 leads to a deflection

$$\phi_1 - \phi_2 = \delta,$$

then the shock-wave will be attached. For each value of M_1 there is a certain nose angle below which the shock is attached and above which it is detached. Alternatively for a given nose angle, as the Mach number of the approaching flow rises through unity a detached wave moves towards the nose and attaches at a particular Mach number. Further increase in speed causes the attached shock to become more and more oblique. The calculated limiting values for a wedge are shown in fig 9.14 ; the numerical values are different for a conical nose.

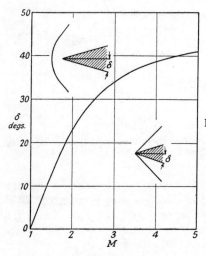

Fig 9.14   Shock-attachment angles for a wedge in air.

Because the pressure rise across an oblique shock-wave is derived from the component of velocity perpendicular to the wave front the pressures acting on the nose of a body behind an attached wave are not as great as those behind a detached, and therefore more nearly normal, wave. This means that the force in the downstream direction acting on the body—the drag force—associated with the formation of shock-waves is less for a given free stream Mach number M_1 if the leading-edge, or nose, shock is attached. A diagram such as fig 9.14 is therefore of assistance in the selection of a suitable nose-angle for an obstacle in a supersonic flow.

9.8 High-speed flow past a thin wing

Thus far in this chapter a detailed examination has been made of the flow around the front of a body. The details of the flow about the after-parts depend naturally on the shape of the body, but if the body is of a smooth and slender profile a number of general statements can be built up on the basis of the already established features of high-speed gas-flow. A representative body of this kind is the cross-section of a long unswept uniform wing of an aeroplane, the section considered being remote from the influence of the modified flow around a wing-tip, engine nacelle or fuselage. Broadly similar remarks will also apply to missiles and to bullets except in so far as these have exhaust jets or blunt ends instead of tapering gently to a point. The same considerations can also provide a starting point for a discussion of the flow around the blades of a compressor or of a gas-turbine. These blades resemble small wings, seldom more than about a metre long, projecting radially from the circumference of a rotating disc. They present additional problems by being twisted, being spaced closely together and, in the case of a steam turbine, using a fluid which cannot be regarded as a perfect gas.

Restricting ourselves to the relatively simple example of a long thin straight wing moving through air, at a low subsonic speed the flow does not differ from the flow of an incompressible fluid described in Chapter 8. The streamline pattern that goes with it is sketched again in fig. 9.15 (a). When the Mach number M is increased but the flow speed nowhere reaches the local sonic speed, no shock-waves can be formed and the flow-pattern does not change very much, although just as the stagnation pressure was shown in section 9.6 to become more intense as compressibility effects became more significant, so do the pressures on the wing surface generally become more intense. Expressing the pressure change at a particular point as a non-dimensional pressure coefficient and so taking into consideration changes due to the increase of velocity alone as opposed to changes due to the increase of Mach number, it can be shown that the pressure coefficient increases in inverse proportion to $\sqrt{(1 - M^2)}$. The lift coefficient (Chapter 8) accordingly increases in the same way and the lift force therefore increases more rapidly than the square of the speed. It must be borne in mind that, in the subsequent as in the foregoing discussion, the angle of incidence of the wing is assumed constant, a condition which is not representative of an aeroplane in free flight for which the resultant force and not the attitude is specified. The state of affairs discussed in this paragraph would be reproduced at the centre of a fixed uniform wing completely spanning a wind tunnel in which the flow speed is gradually increased, the wall fixing taking whatever force is imposed on the wing.

In fig 9.15 (a) consider how conditions change as an element of air moves from left to right along the streamline passing close above the wing. The pressure first rises in the neighbourhood of the stagnation point at the leading edge, then falls as the flow velocity is increased past the thickest part of the wing, falling below atmospheric pressure and rising again as the element passes towards the trailing edge, fig 9.4 (a). Similar changes occur along a streamline passing under the wing except that the changes in velocity and pressure are generally smaller. The nett force, to provide which the wing exists, is upward. The velocity then is highest and consequently the temperature and the sonic speed lowest, therefore the local Mach number highest, somewhere near the middle of the upper surface of the wing. Furthermore, air leaving this region suffers a rise in pressure. Thus for a fairly high but still subsonic free-stream Mach number (i.e. ratio of aeroplane speed to speed of sound in undisturbed atmosphere at altitude of aeroplane) the local flow over the wing may become supersonic in a region of rising pressure—the very combination of circumstances which give rise to the formation of a shock-wave. This type of flow is shown in Plate 4 (a) and illustrated diagrammatically in fig 9.15 (b), where only the shock-

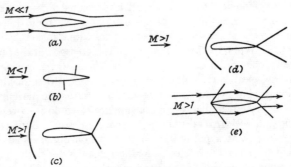

Fig 9.15   The flow past a wing for various subsonic and supersonic speeds.

waves are shown. Where shock-waves are formed, it is more illuminating to sketch their positions than to sketch the streamlines of the flow. In passing, it will be recalled that the streamline-plotting method of Chapter 5 is only applicable to an incompressible flow: it will also be recalled from the beginning of the present chapter that diverging streamlines do not necessarily imply increasing pressure in a compressible fluid. In fact, it will be shown later in this chapter that diverging streamlines in a supersonic flow, such as might be expected immediately ahead of the shock-wave in fig 9.15 (b), imply a falling pressure. Across the shock-wave there is a sudden rise in pressure and, in fig 9.15 (b), a return to subsonic flow over the rear of the wing.

In a real fluid, characterized by the presence of a boundary layer around the wing profile, a rising pressure in the flow direction always brings with it a risk of breakaway of the boundary layer from the surface. This phenomenon takes place at low speed on the upper surface when the inclination of the wing and hence the gradient of pressure is sufficiently large ; the breakaway of the flow causes a loss of lift, an increase of drag, gives rise to a broad eddying wake and is referred to as the low-speed stall (see fig 6.9). The sudden pressure rise when a shock-wave is formed near the surface may for the same reasons give rise to very similar effects at high speed, even though the wing presents but a small angle to the flow. This circumstance is then referred to as a *shock stall*. The interaction of a shock-wave and a boundary layer is somewhat complex ; the fluid near the surface is travelling at a subsonic speed (the relative speed at the surface is zero) so that the shock-wave cannot continue up to the surface itself, and furthermore, via this subsonic part of the boundary layer, down-stream flow changes can influence the upstream flow, although the latter is supersonic and would otherwise be immune to such an influence.

Leaving aside these considerations, a further increase in speed intensifies the pressure changes. In particular the pressure rise across the shock-wave has to become greater, so that the upper-surface shock occurs after the flow has speeded up to a higher local supersonic speed— i.e. further towards the trailing edge. Meanwhile a shock-wave forms in the region of (less steeply) rising pressure on the under surface. Increasing the free-stream speed causes both upper- and lower-surface shock-waves to move rearwards. These are the only shock-waves present until the free-stream speed becomes supersonic. Then, when the other region of rising pressure, near the nose, is also a region of supersonic flow, a shock-wave forms there (fig. 9.15 (c)). Finally, the shock-wave pattern at a fairly high supersonic speed settles down* to the configuration of fig 9.15 (d) with a leading-edge shock-wave such as discussed earlier and two oblique shock-waves springing from near the trailing edge. The obliquity of the shock-waves depends on the free-stream Mach number. The local Mach number would exceed unity everywhere except in the region of the rounded nose which lies behind a normal or nearly-normal shock-wave. If the nose were pointed and the free-stream Mach number high enough, the leading-edge wave would be attached as shown in the final figure (9.15 (e)) or Plate 4 (c) and the whole of the flow field about the wing would then be supersonic. The shock waves from a supersonic aeroplane are trailed across the ground as the aeroplane passes above. Ahead of the shock-

---

* The general pattern remains the same until the Mach number increases to so high a value (beyond 5, say) that the leading-edge shock-wave lies very close to the wing surface. *Hypersonic* flows of this kind are not considered in this book.

waves the presence of the aircraft has no influence whatsoever. An observer on the ground hears nothing until the shock-waves reach him, when the sudden pressure rise causes a bang like a thunder clap. There are legal restrictions on the production of sonic bangs in populated areas.

Comparing fig 9.15 (a) and (d), the flow pattern is different, so the lift coefficient also changes differently with Mach number. When the latter considerably exceeds unity, an approximate theoretical rule is that the lift coefficient varies in inverse proportion to $\sqrt{(M^2 - 1)}$. The effects of compressibility on the lift of a long thin wing can be summarized in a diagram showing how C_L varies with M, as in fig 9.16.

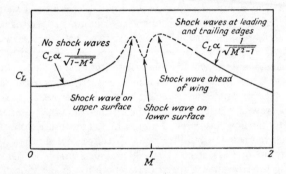

Fig 9.16   The lift coefficient of a two-dimensional wing at constant incidence in subsonic and supersonic flow.

That part of the curve covering the range of Mach numbers between the first appearance of a local patch of supersonic flow on the upper surface of the wing and the formation of the leading-edge shock-wave is shown as a broken line. Where the flow is entirely subsonic or entirely supersonic the forces obey relatively straightforward rules; where the flow contains both supersonic and subsonic regions, the forces naturally depend on the extent and location of the various regions so that in this *transonic* range the shape of the curve depends very much on the shape of the wing section and on its attitude to the flow; in some cases the lift force may temporarily change sign. Unless it can accelerate very quickly through the transonic speed range, a supersonic vehicle must be carefully designed to minimize these force fluctuations.

The prediction of the flow pattern about a given body in the transonic range is beyond the scope of this book, although the next paragraph of this chapter concerns a much simpler problem which in some aspects bears a resemblance to the flow described above and in which partly subsonic and partly supersonic flows are amenable to simple calculation.

9.9 Flow in a convergent-divergent nozzle

The flow of a liquid through a passage which first converges and then slowly diverges has been discussed in Chapter 8. The flow speed increases and the pressure decreases in the converging part with a subsequent reduction of speed and increase of pressure in the diverging part. There is thus a maximum speed and minimum pressure at the narrowest section (the *throat*). Such an arrangement is called a Venturi tube. If a Venturi tube is attached to the bottom of the wall of a tank containing a liquid, then this qualitative description of the flow applies whatever the depth of liquid in the tank and whatever the size of the Venturi, provided that the pressure at the throat never falls so much that cavitation occurs.

The corresponding situation for a gas can be constructed by fitting a convergent-divergent nozzle at the outlet from a pressure vessel containing a gas at a pressure exceeding that of the atmosphere. For a small excess pressure the outward flow is slow, and if the local Mach number everywhere is small in comparison with unity the gas behaves exactly as a liquid. Increasing the pressure in the vessel causes the flow to speed up and the Mach number at the throat to rise. It is shown below that, once the throat flow has become sonic, then a sufficiently large pressure difference across the nozzle will cause the flow to continue to accelerate and the pressure to continue to fall right up to the exit, even where the nozzle is diverging. The falling pressure means that breakaway of the flow is unlikely. Such behaviour is very different from that of a liquid in a Venturi tube and a convergent-divergent nozzle designed to eject a gas at high speed is for that reason called a Laval nozzle. Typical pressure distributions along a Venturi tube and a Laval nozzle are shown in fig 9.17. C. G. P. de Laval used convergent-divergent nozzles to produce high-speed jets of steam for driving a steam-turbine, applying the same principle as the Pelton wheel (Chapter 15).

The flow in a Laval nozzle is of interest for many reasons. Perhaps the simplest application is to a rocket motor in which (by the momentum theorem) the greater the jet velocity the greater is the thrust for a given fuel consumption. Burning fuel in a combustion chamber provides a source of high-pressure gas which can be accelerated to a supersonic speed by passing it out to the atmosphere through a Laval nozzle. Calculation of the velocity at the nozzle exit enables the propulsive thrust to be estimated, or conversely a study of the flow enables a

PLATE 3　Air flowing through a Laval nozzle.　Flow direction from left to right.　The optical system used (Schlieren method) makes regions of changing air density show up as regions of altered light intensity.　Streamlines are not shown up.

The photographs are, top to bottom, in the order of progressively decreasing pressure outside the nozzles, the upstream conditions remaining constant.　In the top two photographs the external pressure is greater than, in the third just equal to, and in the bottom photograph less than the design exit pressure for the nozzle.

Strong shock-waves are to be seen in the first two. The 45° inclination of the very weak waves (Mach waves) in the parallel jet in the third picture shows that the exit Mach number is 1·4.　In the bottom picture the flow expands gradually through expansion waves at the exit to a pressure lower than that of the surrounding air and is recompressed by a shock-wave near the right-hand edge of the picture.

*Reproduced by permission of the
National Physical Laboratory.*
(Crown copyright reserved)

PLATE 3

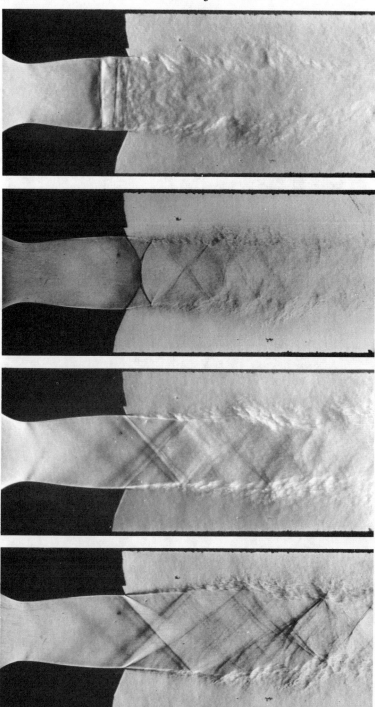

PLATE 4

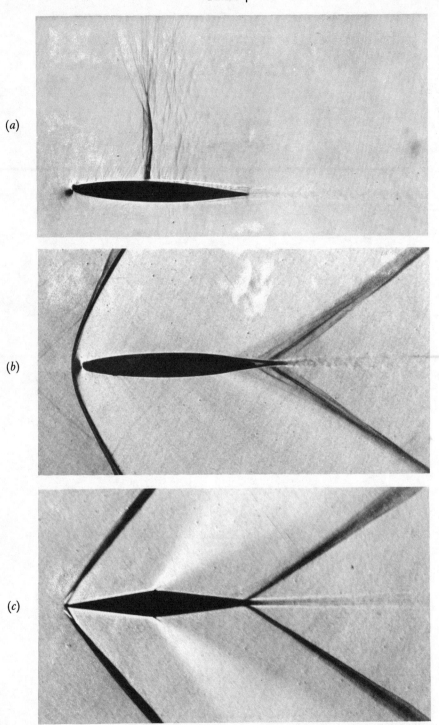

(a)

(b)

(c)

PLATE 4 High speed air-flow past aerofoils, showing shock-wave formation.

(a) A blunt-nosed aerofoil (section RAE 104) at 3½° incidence, Mach number $M = 0.8$.

(b) A blunt-nosed aerofoil (section EC 1250) at zero incidence, Mach number $M = 1.6$. The leading edge shock-wave is detached from the aerofoil.

(c) A double-wedge aerofoil (thickness/chord ratio 12½ per cent) at zero incidence, $M = 1.6$. The leading-edge shock-wave is attached to the aerofoil. Note that shock-waves (dark lines) form when the flow is compressed but that the expansion at mid-chord (shown by light-coloured zones) is gradual.

*Reproduced by permission of the
National Physical Laboratory.
(Crown copyright reserved)*

suitable nozzle to be designed to produce a required force. Similarly the supersonic flow in a wind-tunnel is produced after air has
been accelerated through a convergent-divergent nozzle. Again, the
passage between closely-spaced blades of a turbine is convergent-
divergent. If the spacing of a row of turbine blades is increased until
each blade is so far from its neighbours that it can be considered as
isolated the resulting flow is like that about a wing, leading to the idea

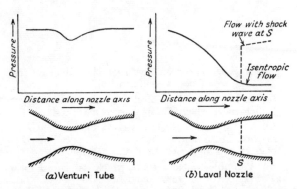

Fig 9.17   The pressure distribution for gas flow along a convergent-divergent
duct with (a) a small pressure difference between its ends, (b) a large
pressure difference between its ends.

that nozzle flow should reproduce some of the features of the flow past
a wing.   In this way the discussion links with the remarks on wings in
the previous paragraph.   It will in fact be found that for the Laval
nozzle a gradually increasing upstream pressure will cause a shock-wave
to form first at the throat and later to move back to the exit in the same
way that a shock-wave forms on the surface of a wing and moves back to
the trailing edge.   The leading-edge shock ahead of a wing and the subsequent isentropic compression to the stagnation pressure perform the
same functions as a compressor providing compressed gas for a Laval
nozzle.   There is no shock upstream of the nozzle for the particular
flow envisaged here since, in a flow starting from rest and accelerating
along a converging passage, neither supersonic flow nor a rising pressure are present, both of which conditions are essential before a shock-
wave can be formed.

The following analysis, like the analysis of the flow in a Venturi
tube, assumes that the pressure and velocity of the gas are uniform
over any cross section in a Laval nozzle and depend only on the value
of the cross-sectional area a.   It is a good approximation to the flow of a
real fluid in a carefully designed nozzle.   Assuming further that the

flow is thermally insulated (i.e. adiabatic) and that the pressure vessel is so large that the velocity within it can be taken as zero,* and denoting by a subscript ' o ' the conditions in the vessel, then the basic equations become

$$\rho a u = \text{constant along the nozzle} \qquad . \qquad . \qquad (9.1)$$

$$p/\rho T = p_0/\rho_0 T_0 = R . \qquad . \qquad . \qquad . \qquad . \qquad (9.2)$$

$$\frac{u^2}{2} + c_p T = c_p T_0 \qquad . \qquad . \qquad . \qquad . \qquad . \qquad (9.3)$$

where $R = c_p - c_v$.

First, solutions will be found for which

$$p/\rho^\gamma = p_0/\rho_0{}^\gamma \qquad . \qquad . \qquad . \qquad . \qquad . \qquad (9.4)$$

where $\gamma = c_p/c_v$.

The use of equation 9.4 implies that the flow is free from shock-waves.

These four equations determine p, ρ, u and T for any value of a. The constant in equation 9.1 is the mass flow rate through the nozzle measured in, say, kg/s ; for example if the nozzle were the propelling nozzle of a rocket motor, the constant would be the fuel consumption including the oxidant. Representing the mass flow rate by m, equation 9.1 becomes

$$\rho a u = m \qquad . \qquad . \qquad . \qquad . \qquad . \qquad (9.1a)$$

and m can be calculated once the conditions at any one cross section have been determined. To meet the objection that there are, including m, five unknown quantities and but four equations wherewith to find them, it must be pointed out that there is a fifth piece of information available, namely that the pressure outside the nozzle has a specified value. This pressure will be written p_a, the suffix denoting atmospheric pressure.

To find the pressure p at a section of the nozzle where the area is a, proceed as follows :

Substituting $u = Mc$ and $c = \sqrt{(\gamma p/\rho)}$ into equation 9.1a,

$$m = \rho a M \sqrt{(\gamma p/\rho)}$$

and from 9.4, $= a M (p/p_0)^{(\gamma+1)/2\gamma} \sqrt{(\gamma p_0 \rho_0)}$

i.e. $a' = (p/p_0)^{-(\gamma+1)/2\gamma}/M\sqrt{\gamma} \qquad . \qquad . \qquad (9.10)$

where $a' = a(p_0 \rho_0)^{1/2}/m$

which is a convenient dimensionless group representing the area a.

---

* If the velocity through the pressure vessel is appreciable the suffix ' o ' can be read as meaning the stagnation conditions which would be produced by bringing the gas isentropically to rest.

From 9.2, a' can alternatively be written as

$$a' = a[p_0/m\sqrt{(RT_0)}].$$

It was pointed out on p. 111 that equation 9.3 may be written

$$p/p_0 = \left(1 + \frac{\gamma - 1}{2}M^2\right)^{-\gamma/(\gamma-1)} \qquad . \qquad . \qquad (9.11)$$

From 9.10 and 9.11 it is easy to construct the curve BDE in fig 9.18. For example if γ is 1·4, as for air, the coordinates of the point just above E where the local Mach number is marked as 2·0 are calculated as follows.

From 9.11, $\qquad p/p_0 \quad = (1·8)^{-3·5}$
$\qquad\qquad\qquad\qquad\quad = 0·128.$

From 9.10 $\qquad a' \quad = (0·128)^{-0·857}/2\sqrt{1·4}$
$\qquad\qquad\qquad\qquad = 2·464$

and $\qquad\qquad \log_{10}a' = 0·392$

The drudgery of calculations like these is entirely removed by a pocket electronic calculator with the facility for computing x^y at the touch of a button.

The line BDE shows the pressure changes that can be produced isentropically (i.e. without shock-waves) in nozzles. On the same diagram

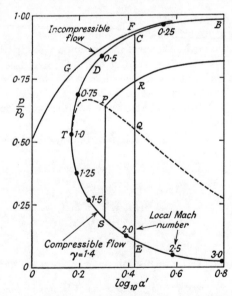

Fig 9.18 Pressure as a function of cross-sectional area for flow in a Laval nozzle.

is plotted for comparison the corresponding curve BFG for the flow of a liquid, which, from the continuity and Bernoulli equations, is

$$p/p_0 = 1 - 1/2a'^2.$$

For very slow flows (small m and therefore large a'), the two curves become coincident.

Consider the problem of finding m for a given nozzle with given values of p_0 and ρ_0. For a liquid, m is completely determined when p_a is selected. For example, p_a/p_0 might have a value at the level of F; this fixes a value of a' on the curve BFG and hence, via the area a of the nozzle at its exit, fixes the mass flow. The pressure along a Venturi tube would then fall from p_0 far upstream to a minimum near G, say, at a point determined by the throat area and then rise to F at the exit. The curve BFG continues indefinitely in either direction beyond that range of a' covered by the diagram, the pressure always falling as a' decreases, and the foregoing description of the flow in a Venturi applies wherever the points F and G may lie.

For a gas, provided that the throat pressure does not fall as low as the value at T, where a' is a minimum, precisely the same remarks apply to a Laval nozzle. That is to say, the pressure along a Laval nozzle may fall from B, following the curve BDE, to a minimum at D (the throat) and then rise to C at the exit, the point C and hence the mass flow being determined by the exit pressure for a gas in the same way as for a liquid. This state of affairs can only exist, however, so long as D does not reach T. Since each point on the curve corresponds to a particular value of the local Mach number, it is not surprising to find that at T the local Mach number is unity and that the character of the flow changes as soon as the flow speed at the throat reaches the local sonic speed. The co-ordinates of the minimum point can be found by putting $M = 1$ in *9.10* and *9.11*,

viz.
$$(p/p_0)_T = (1 + (\gamma - 1)/2)^{-\gamma/(\gamma-1)}$$
$$= (2/(\gamma + 1))^{\gamma/(\gamma-1)}$$

and
$$(a')_T = \sqrt{\left(\frac{1}{\gamma}\left(\frac{\gamma + 1}{2}\right)^{\frac{\gamma+1}{\gamma-1}}\right)}.$$

If the gas is air so that $\gamma = 1\cdot4$, then

$$(p/p_0)_T = 0\cdot528 \quad . \quad . \quad . \quad . \quad . \quad (9.12)$$
and
$$(a')_T = 1\cdot461 \quad . \quad . \quad . \quad . \quad (9.13)$$

Once this critical point has been reached, then the *throat* area and the *upstream* conditions, not as before the *exit* area and the *downstream* conditions, determine the mass flow rate and

$$((p_0\rho_0)^{\frac{1}{2}}/m)a_T = 1\cdot461$$

$$\therefore\ m = a_T(p_0\rho_0)^{\frac{1}{2}}/1\cdot461\ .\qquad .\qquad .\qquad .\qquad (9.14)$$

Thus if for given values of p_0 and ρ_0 the external pressure p_a is progressively reduced, then the mass flow increases to this maximum value, reached when the throat Mach number becomes unity. Thereafter no change of conditions at the throat is possible, no further reduction of p_a will affect m and the nozzle is said to be *choked*.

The exit area a_E of the nozzle now corresponds to a particular a' given by

$$(a')_E = \frac{a_E}{a_T}(a')_T$$

$$= 1\cdot461\frac{a_E}{a_T}\quad \text{if}\quad \gamma = 1\cdot4\qquad .\qquad .\ (9.15)$$

which may be at E, say. If it should be that the external pressure p_a is just equal to the value of p corresponding to this point on the curve, then the emerging jet will have the same pressure as its surroundings and the Mach number in the jet will have the value appropriate to the particular point, about 2·1 for the example chosen. The ratio p_0/p_a defined in this way is called the *design pressure-ratio* of the nozzle ; it depends only on a_E/a_T and on γ. Fig 9.18, together with equations 9.14 and 9.15, provide a means of selecting the throat and exit areas of a nozzle which is required to discharge a specified mass-flow at a specified supersonic Mach number under given pressure conditions.

The pressure distribution along a given nozzle is now known if the nozzle is running at its design pressure-ratio ; the pressure falls along BC to the critical pressure at T, the throat, and continues to fall until the exit is reached, the flow velocity and the Mach number increasing continuously along the whole length of the nozzle. There is subsonic flow in the converging part and supersonic flow in the diverging part. It remains to discuss the flow when the exit pressure differs from the design pressure. The throat and exit areas, from equation 9.15, define a'_E represented, say, by the line EQC, but the exit pressure may have any value above or below the design pressure at E, subject only to the restriction that the exit pressure must be lower than the pressure at a'_E on the upper half of the curve, i.e. the pressure at C, to ensure that the nozzle is choked.

If p_a lies below E then further expansion must take place beyond the confines of the nozzle, the nozzle being capable of reducing the pressure no further than to the design pressure. If on the other hand

p_a lies above E, then a supersonic stream must accept a rise in pressure, a change which can be brought about only by a shock-wave. The pressure rise that can be brought about by a normal shock-wave across the exit depends on the exit Mach number. The locus for the various Mach numbers represented by points on TE is shown as the broken line TPQ. The ordinate at Q of this curve corresponding to the particular example considered before is

$$(p/p_0)_E(1 + \Delta p/p),$$

where $\Delta p/p$ is read off from fig 9.6 (a) at the Mach number of 2·1. If, then, p_a lies between E and Q, shock-waves weaker than a normal shock, that is to say oblique shock-waves, will spring from the end of the nozzle. If p_a lies at Q itself, then a normal shock lies across the exit plane. If, finally, p_a lies between Q and C a normal shock at the exit is insufficient. What happens then is that a normal shock forms within the diverging part of the nozzle at a point so positioned between the throat and the exit that the subsequent isentropic pressure rise in the subsonic flow downstream of the shock-wave, this pressure rise taking place along a line comparable with DCB, is just sufficient to bring the exit pressure up to p_a. From each point on TPQ can be drawn a line such as PR plotted in the same way as DCB, bearing in mind that the normal shock-wave SP entails a decrease of stagnation pressure, represented by the gap between the upper two curves on fig 9.10. There is a corresponding decrease of stagnation density, the stagnation density being in fact proportional to the stagnation pressure since the stagnation temperature is constant throughout the flow, even though a shock-wave is present. A complete set of such lines as PR, filling the space between the curves TPQ and TDB, enables the position of the shock-wave to be estimated. Thus if the exit pressure and exit area define a point R, a normal shock-wave lies across the flow in the nozzle at a point where the area corresponds to the point S. The pressure distribution along the nozzle in this case, also shown in fig 9.17 (b), would consist of a fall in pressure along BCDS with a discontinuous pressure rise to P and then a further gradual rise along PR.

The process for investigating the flow in a given nozzle can be summarized as follows:

(i) Draw the curves BDE and TPQ for the appropriate value of γ, using equations 9.10 and 9.11.

(ii) Draw a line CE to represent the nozzle exit area, using equation 9.15, and plot a point on CE where $p = p_a$, the pressure outside the nozzle.

(iii) If the point representing p_a lies above C, then the nozzle is not choked and the flow is subsonic everywhere and similar to the flow in a Venturi tube. The intersection of a horizontal line at p_a with the curve CB will determine the mass flow.

(iv) If the point representing p_a is below C, the nozzle is choked and the mass flow is given by equation *9.14*.

(v) If the point representing p_a is between C and Q, a shock-wave forms in the diverging part of the nozzle and the exit flow is subsonic.

(vi) If the point representing p_a is between Q and E, oblique shock-waves form outside the nozzle and the exit flow is supersonic, the exit Mach number being read off at the intersection of CE and the curve TSE.

(vii) If the point representing p_a is below E then the exit Mach number is as in (vi) and the flow expands outside the nozzle. If in so doing the jet expands to a pressure below p_a then shock-waves may subsequently be formed some way downstream of the nozzle exit before the jet pressure equals that of the surroundings.

Notice that no mention has been made of the profile of the nozzle so that if on this basis a nozzle were being designed for a particular function it would be possible to go no further than the selection of throat and exit areas. The design could be completed if, for example, the pressure were required to have a stated value at each position along the nozzle axis. At the same time the assumptions of one-dimensional frictionless adiabatic flow must not be violated by rapid changes of area or by an excessive length of nozzle which might, in practice, permit considerable escape of heat.

The adiabatic flow of a real gas along a Laval nozzle follows closely the above pattern, the most noticeable departure being likely when a shock-wave lies in the nozzle ; the rise in pressure may then cause breakaway of the flow from the walls. Since this particular flow gives a subsonic exit velocity a Laval nozzle, regarded as a device for producing a high-speed jet, is inefficient when it contains a shock-wave so that this condition, corresponding to exit pressures above TPQ, is in any case best avoided.

Some photographs of the various types of flow are shown in Plate 3.

9.10 Choking in pipes

When sucking a gas out from a large pressure-vessel through a nozzle, the phenomenon of choking sets a limit to the number of kilograms that can be withdrawn per second. If the gas is air and if the pressure and density in the pressure vessel are p_0 and ρ_0 and if the cross-sectional area at the narrowest part of the nozzle is a_T, air cannot be withdrawn at a rate faster than the value of m given in equation 9.14, no matter how low a sucking pressure is applied. The phenomenon of choking is not confined to convergent–divergent nozzles. It can occur in the flow of gas through a pipe of constant diameter if frictional heating or heating by combustion causes the gas to expand sufficiently. The mass flow rate is given by the product of density, speed and area. If the area is constant, when the gas expands the speed must change inversely as the density. The gas therefore accelerates as it flows along the pipe. Any attempt to increase the mass flow rate succeeds only up to the point when the speed of the gas becomes as high as the speed of sound in the gas. Thereafter no further reduction of outlet pressure is of any avail—the request cannot be ' heard ' upstream.

When pipe flow is discussed later in this book (Chapter 13) the analysis will be restricted to flows in which frictional heating is small, to the flow of liquids or the flow of gases at low subsonic speeds, and to flows without combustion and without significant heat transfer across the pipe walls. The study of the response of a fast-flowing gas to the burning of fuel in an engine, the investigation of heat exchange in gas-cooled nuclear reactors and the exploration of many other gas-flow problems of great engineering interest must be left to another occasion.

PROBLEMS

1. Show that for air the stagnation temperature-rise on the Kelvin scale of temperature is approximately
$$5 \times (\text{speed in hundreds of metres per second})^2$$
Note that for air $\gamma = 1\cdot4$ and the gas constant is $R = 287$ J/(kg K)

2. An aeroplane is flying at a speed of 185 m/s at a height where the air pressure is 30 kN/m² and the air temperature is 228 K.
What pressure will be developed between its Pitot and static tubes ? Give two answers, one neglecting compressibility and the other taking it into account.

Ans. $7\cdot8$ kN/m², $8\cdot7$ kN/m².

3. A Laval nozzle has a throat area A_t. Prove that the cross-section at area A required to produce a local Mach number M is given by the relation
$$\frac{A}{A_t} = \frac{1}{M}\left[\frac{2}{\gamma + 1}\left(1 + \frac{\gamma - 1}{2}M^2\right)\right]^{\frac{\gamma+1}{2(\gamma-1)}}$$
Hence show that for the flow of air
$$A \propto \frac{1}{M}(M^2 + 5)^3$$

4. Air at 300 kN m^{-2} absolute, 287 K is released from a pressure-vessel at a rate of 0·5 kg s^{-1}. The nozzle through which it is released is to be 8 cm long and the pressure is required to fall linearly with distance along the nozzle down to a pressure of 100 kN m^{-2} absolute at the exit. Plot a curve showing how the cross-sectional area of the nozzle must vary along its length. Indicate on this graph how the flow speed, the local sonic speed and the local Mach number would vary along the nozzle.

Ans. Throat area 7 cm^2 at 2·34 cm from exit :
exit area 7·65 cm^2.

5. An aircraft is flying at a Mach number of 1·2. If the air temperature is 233° K calculate the temperature at the stagnation point on the leading edge of the wing and also at a point just outside the boundary layer where the local Mach number is 1·3.

Ans. 300 K : 224 K.

6. A convergent-divergent nozzle is supplied with compressed air from a reservoir at a pressure of 1 MN m^{-2} absolute. The throat has a cross-sectional area of 8 cm^2 and the nozzle expands to a parallel section of area 13·5 cm^2 before discharging into a region where the absolute pressure is 100 kN m^{-2}. Calculate the exit Mach number.

Ans. 2·0.

7. Show that the energy equation for the adiabatic flow of air can be written in the form

$$T_0 = T(1 + 0·2M^2)$$

or
$$c_0 = c(1 + 0·2M^2)^{0·5}.$$

If the flow is isentropic, show that

$$\rho_0 = \rho(1 + 0·2M^2)^{2·5}$$

and
$$p_0 = p(1 + 0·2M^2)^{3·5}.$$

Here p, ρ, T and c are measured at a point where the local Mach number is M; the suffix ' 0 ' denotes stagnation conditions.

8. An aerofoil with a chord of 0·2 m is tested in a high-speed wind-tunnel working at a Mach number of 0·8. Upstream of the working section, where the cross-sectional area of the tunnel is greater, the Mach number is 0·05, the absolute pressure is 101·3 kN m^{-2} and the temperature is 295 K. Find the Reynolds number of the test. Assume μ proportional to (absolute temperature)$^{\frac{1}{2}}$, taking the value of μ at 293 K as 1·82 × 10^{-5} kg/(ms).

Ans. 2·7 × 10^6.

9. Air initially at standard sea-level temperature and pressure flows into an evacuated tank through a convergent streamlined orifice contracting to a diameter of 4 cm. What pressure must be maintained in the tank to produce a sonic jet ? What is the mass flow through the nozzle ?

Ans. 53·5 kN/m^2 : 0·3 kg s^{-1}.

10. Show that if the Mach number upstream of a normal shock-wave in air is large then the density ratio across the shock-wave is 6 and the downstream Mach number is 0·378.

11. A rocket-propelled missile is travelling horizontally through air at a pressure of $71\cdot4\,\text{kN m}^{-2}$. The motor burns fuel at a constant rate of $3\,\text{kgs}^{-1}$ and discharges the propellant gases at a pressure of $61\cdot2\,\text{kN m}^{-2}$ and a speed of $2\,\text{km s}^{-1}$ relative to the missile through a nozzle of exit diameter $0\cdot25\,\text{m}$. Calculate the propulsive thrust of the motor.

Ans. $5\cdot5$ kN.

12. On p. 339 it is shown that the speed of propagation of a compression wave through a fluid is $c = \sqrt{(K/\rho)}$ where K is the coefficient of compressibility (bulk modulus) of the fluid defined on p. 4. Prove that if the compression during the passage of a wave through a perfect gas is assumed to be isentropic, then

$$K = \gamma p$$

and hence $c = \sqrt{(\gamma RT)}$ as was shown by a different argument on p. 105.

CALCULATIONS CONCERNING FORCES ON AND PRESSURES AND VELOCITIES IN MOVING FLUIDS

There are two ways of calculating the interaction of velocities, forces and pressures in moving fluids. The first is the momentum theorem (Chapter 6): and the second is the Bernoulli equation (Chapter 7), or energy equation for compressible fluids (Chapter 9). Both these ways are essentially derived from Newton's Second Law of Motion and so deal with the same variable, namely the forces on, and the consequent motion of an element of fluid, but the information required and the results obtained are not the same for both these two ways. The momentum theorem is applied to the conditions at the boundaries of a ' control ' volume fixed relative to solid surfaces, and the changes of momentum arriving and leaving the volume are assessed to find the total forces applied to the fluid. In the Bernoulli equation (or energy equation for compressible fluids) the changes of energy along a stream-tube in steady motion are used to relate the velocity and pressure changes within the flow. The pressure intensity at the solid surfaces bounding the flow may then be integrated to find the forces normal to them. The table overleaf shows the similarities and differences of the two methods, and the following examples show how one or the other methods may be used according to the circumstances.

Example (a) *Flow through an orifice* (Chapter 8, p. 85)

Due to the convergence of the flow, the energy conditions are known —the total energy is constant throughout, so the Bernoulli equation is applicable. The momentum theorem cannot be used because the total force in the direction of motion is not known. Thus, at the boundaries of the control volume ABCD in fig S.1, the pressure intensity all over the side CD is known, so the pressure force on this side is also known. But the pressure intensity distribution on the side AB is not known, for it falls towards atmospheric pressure at the orifice as the fluid accelerates. Consequently the pressure force on AB is not known unless experiments are specifically made to find the

CAPABILITIES OF THE MOMENTUM THEOREM AND THE ENERGY EQUATION

	Momentum Theorem	Bernoulli or Energy Equation
Applicable	To any fluid flow, providing an acceleration term is considered when flow is non-steady	To steady flows in which the energy changes are zero or are known independently
Information required	Velocity distribution in the stream at one end of a control volume and either velocity distribution at other end of control volume or total forces (pressure and shear) on boundaries of control volume	Velocity and pressure at one point on streamline, with independent knowledge of energy changes and either pressure variation along streamline or velocity variation along streamline
Solution gives	Average final velocity of stream or Total force	Velocity variation along streamline or Pressure variation along streamline
Solution will not give	Actual velocity distribution within control volume or at the boundaries or Distribution of pressure and shear forces	Tangential forces due to friction
Best application	When energy changes are unknown and only an overall knowledge of the flow is required, e.g. total resultant forces, mean velocities	When energy changes are known and detailed information on the flow is required, e.g. velocity and pressure distributions

Notes

1. If the flow is compressible, separate information is required to find the density changes.
2. If both energy changes and total forces are known, both methods are applicable and give the same results to any given set of data. *Alternatively*, the two equations can be used simultaneously to determine another unknown variable which would otherwise be found purely by experiment.

pressure intensity there. Thus the total force in the direction of the jet, the difference between the force on CD and on AB, is not known, so the momentum theorem cannot be used.

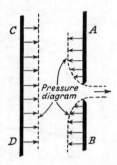

Fig S.1   Flow through a sharp-edged orifice in the side of a tank in which the total energy of the fluid is kept constant. The increase of velocity near the orifice decreases the pressure intensity there so that the total pressure force on the jet by the tank walls is unknown. The 'control' volume is the rectangle ABCD.

Example (b)   *Flow through a boundary layer* (Chapter 6, p. 66)

Since a boundary layer is caused by a tangential shear force on the fluid, there is a degradation of energy into heat within the fluid. Alternatively, since more and more fluid is slowed down by this force while the pressure remains constant, the total energy, $z + p/\rho g + u^2/2g$ steadily falls within the layer, the energy going to heat. The Bernoulli equation cannot therefore be used unless this energy degradation is known from independent evidence. The momentum theorem can, however, be used to find the sum of the forces on the fluid (pressure plus shear forces) if the changes of velocity in the layer are known.

Example (c)   *Flow in a conical nozzle*

A convergent nozzle on the end of a pipe accelerates the fluid, and in doing so has exerted on it a force F, tending to part the nozzle from

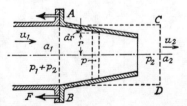

Fig S.2   Flow through a conical nozzle. A force F is exerted on the nozzle, and if this is known, the flow Q may be found by the momentum theorem as well as by the Bernoulli equation. 'Control' volume ABCD shown dotted.

the pipe. Both the momentum equation and the Bernoulli equation are applicable and can be used for finding either Q, the discharge, or F, the force tending to part the cone from the pipe. It will be assumed that the fluid in the pipe, of cross-sectional area a_1 is travelling at u_1, and has an absolute pressure $(p_2 + p_1)$, while the nozzle projects a uniform stream of velocity u_2 and cross-sectional area a_2 into an absolute pressure p_2.

In fig S.2 a cylindrical 'control' volume is shown enclosed by dotted lines. The forces at its boundaries are the pressure forces $(p_2 + p_1)$.AB and p_2.CD on the ends AB and CD of the cylinder, and the force F exerted at the flange of the nozzle and which keeps the nozzle attached to the pipe. The increase of the flow of axial momentum through the ends of the cylinder is

$$\int_C^D \rho u_2{}^2 da - \int_A^B \rho u_1{}^2 da$$

so by the momentum theorem

$$\int_C^D \rho u_2{}^2 da - \int_A^B \rho u_1{}^2 da = (p_2 + p_1)\text{AB} - p_2\text{CD} - F.$$

The left-hand side is simplified because the velocity is uniform over the areas a_1 and a_2, becoming $\rho Q(u_2 - u_1)$. On the right-hand side, the pressure p_1 is conveniently considered as a gauge pressure above p_2, which is usually atmospheric pressure.

Thus putting $\qquad\qquad p_2 = 0 \quad \text{and} \quad \text{AB} = a_1$

so $\qquad\qquad\qquad \rho Q(u_2 - u_1) = p_1 a_1 - F.$

But for an incompressible fluid $Q = u_1 a_1 = u_2 a_2$.

So $\qquad\qquad \rho Q^2\left(\frac{1}{a_2} - \frac{1}{a_1}\right) = p_1 a_1 - F \quad . \qquad . \qquad . \quad (S.1)$

Thus if ρ, a_1, a_2, p_1 and F are known, this equation may be solved for Q.

But Bernoulli's equation is quite applicable to the flow, because at a contraction the energy is constant. The equation is the same as for the Venturi meter, so that

$$Q = a_2\left\{1 - \left(\frac{a_2}{a_1}\right)^2\right\}^{-\frac{1}{2}} \sqrt{\left(2g\frac{p_1}{\rho g}\right)} \quad . \qquad . \quad (S.2)$$

Thus if ρ, a_1, a_2, p_1 and the constancy of the energy are known, the Bernoulli equation can be solved for Q, producing exactly the same result as did the momentum equation $S.1$.

Alternatively, if Q, ρ, a_1, a_2 and p_1 are known, the momentum equation $(S.1)$ is directly solved for F. But also the Bernoulli equation can be used to find F, without using the momentum equation at all, as follows. The gauge pressure on the inside of the cone is given by Bernoulli's equation as

$$p/\rho g = u_1^2/2g + p_1/\rho g - u^2/2g$$

and substituting $Q = \pi r^2 u = \pi r_1^2 u_1$

$$p = \frac{\rho Q^2}{2\pi^2 r_1^4} - \frac{\rho Q^2}{2\pi^2 r^4} + p_1$$

where r is the radius of the bore at which the pressure is p. Now the force F is the reaction of the integral of the pressure over an elementary ring of radius r, or

$$F = - \int_{r_1}^{r_2} p 2\pi r \mathrm{d}r = - \int_{r_1}^{r_2} p_1 2\pi r \mathrm{d}r - \int_{r_1}^{r_2} \frac{\rho Q^2 2\pi}{2\pi^2}\left(\frac{r}{r_1^4} - \frac{r}{r^4}\right)\mathrm{d}r$$

$$= - p_1 \pi (r_2^2 - r_1^2) - \frac{\rho Q^2}{\pi}\left(\frac{r_2^2}{2r_1^4} - \frac{1}{2r_1^2} + \frac{1}{2r_2^2} - \frac{1}{2r_1^2}\right).$$

Substituting $a_1 = \pi r_1^2$ and $a_2 = \pi r_2^2$, and collecting terms,

$$F = - p_1 a_2 - \rho \frac{u_1^2}{2} a_2 + p_1 a_1 + \frac{\rho Q^2}{a_1} - \frac{\rho Q^2}{2a_2}.$$

But $p_1 + \dfrac{\rho u_1^2}{2} = \dfrac{\rho u_2^2}{2} = \dfrac{\rho Q^2}{2a_2^2}$ by Bernoulli again.

So $F = \dfrac{-\rho Q^2}{2a_2^2}.a_2 + p_1 a_1 + \dfrac{\rho Q^2}{a_1} - \dfrac{\rho Q^2}{2a_2} = + p_1 a_1 - \rho Q^2\left(\dfrac{1}{a_2} - \dfrac{1}{a_1}\right)$

This expression *is exactly the same as was derived more shortly by the momentum theorem.* It will therefore be seen that since both the momentum and Bernoulli equations are valid, both eventually give similar answers to the problem.

Example (d)   *Flow in a Borda's mouthpiece*

A Borda's mouthpiece is a short length of pipe of cross section a_0 projecting into a tank of fluid, wherein the pressure is equivalent to a head h. A jet of fluid of cross-sectional area a_1 jumps clear of the pipe and is ejected through it. Since the flow is converging, Bernoulli's equation clearly applies, as there is little, if any, degradation of energy to heat. Also, the whole force system on the fluid is fully known : for example, on the boundaries of the ' control ' volume ABCD in fig S.3, the pressure exerted on the fluid by the tank wall CD is the same as that by AB. The projecting pipe has removed all the motion to within the tank, so that there are no fluid velocities against the surface AB, changing the pressure there, contrary to the case of an ordinary orifice. Thus the excess of pressure force on CD above that on AB is only that due to the head h on the area a_0, namely $\rho g h a_0$, and this is the force producing the flow, the fluid being accelerated from a standstill to a velocity u. The change of momentum is

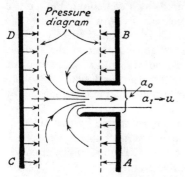

Fig S.3 Flow through a Borda's mouthpiece. Streamlines are shown, and the velocity near the wall AB is low, so the pressure intensity is sensibly the same as that on CD. The pressure force is thus known and the momentum theorem may be used to find a_1. The 'control' volume is the rectangle ABCD.

then $\rho Q u = \rho a_1 u^2$. Equating the force to the change of momentum, $\rho a_1 u^2 = \rho g h a_0$. The unknown variable a_1 can only be determined by using Bernoulli's equation, which gives the velocity in terms of the head h or $u = \sqrt{(2gh)}$, assuming that the area of the tank is large compared with a_0. Substitution of this equation for u into the momentum relation gives

$$\rho a_1\, 2gh = \rho g h a_0$$

or

$$a_1 = \tfrac{1}{2} a_0.$$

Thus

$$Q = a_1 u = 0.5 a_0 \sqrt{(2gh)}.$$

The coefficient of discharge of this special type of orifice is therefore 0·50, a value found quite without experiment, solely because both the Bernoulli equation and the momentum theorem can be applied: they have been used as simultaneous equations to determine a_1, which could only be found in the case of the sharp-edged orifice (p. 86) by experiment.

Example (e) *A jet striking a surface*

The simple case of the jet of fluid striking an extensive plane surface normal to the jet axis (fig 6.2) shows clearly the limitations and capabilities of both the momentum and Bernoulli equations. The momentum equation gives the total force exerted by the jet, providing the surface is sufficiently large to turn all the jet through 90°. It will not however give any clue about the distribution of pressure over the surface, nor anything about the internal geometry of the flow pattern;

for instance, the radius of curvature of the streamlines of the jet near the surface is neither known nor given. Only the geometry of the flow at the ends of the control volume need be known.

The Bernoulli equation gives the pressure distribution along the plate, and so also gives the total force (by integration), but only if the velocity is known at all these points. In turn the velocity can only be known from a flow pattern. It is clear that there will be a stagnation point on the axis of the jet and adjacent to the surface, but the velocities and curvatures of the streamlines elsewhere are unknown until a full internal flow pattern can be drawn. If such a pattern is known the pressure distribution can be inferred and by integration the force is again evaluated.

With one dependent variable, the force, computed by two independent methods, it is clear that another dependent variable can be solved. In essentials this can be the flow pattern, of which the radius of curvature of the free surface of the jet is one feature (see fig. S.4). This radius is thus fixed by the equivalence of the momentum flow of the incoming stream with the integrated pressure distribution along the plane. If the radius were for example larger, the point downstream where the jet again becomes parallel-sided (and so where the pressure again falls to atmospheric) will be further from the jet centreline; the area over which the pressure is to be integrated will be larger and the equivalence of the force found by such integration to the momentum flow will no longer be true.

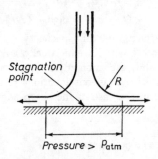

Fig. S.4 A jet of water striking a flat normal surface must satisfy the momentum equation, but the maximum pressure intensity (at the stagnation point) must satisfy Bernoulli's equation. Between these two requirements, R is fixed.

10

THE ANALYSIS OF EXPERIMENTS IN FLUID MECHANICS

10.1 It is apparent at an early stage in the study of fluid mechanics that purely theoretical analyses rarely produce correct solutions to the problems set by real fluids flowing under specified conditions. Experiment is nearly always needed to correlate the theory with the actual measurements of the variables concerned. Coefficients must be introduced to bridge the gap thus disclosed, and to account for the errors caused by incorrect or simplified assumptions in the theory. Such assumptions are necessary because the present stage of development of mathematics is inadequate to deal with the problems of real fluids so that simplification is required. In many arrangements of the boundaries of flows in which engineers are interested, the idealized theory is so clearly inadequate that recourse must be made to experiment pure and simple, with no pretence to analysis by theory.

A problem with such experiments in fluid mechanics is the large number of variables, all of which are interrelated, and all of which may affect the measurements being studied. Experiments cannot always be arranged so that only two variables are changed at a time, with the other variables temporarily kept constant. It is only this method that allows the effect of each variable to be studied separately. It is much more often found that circumstances force experiments to be arranged so that a greater number of variables must change at the same time, so that the effect of each variable cannot be separately studied. It is highly desirable, however, to present the results of these experiments so that the effect of each can be seen. A way of finding the correct way of presenting the information, and of arranging the variables, is by using the Method of Dimensions. This method uses the axiom that the units of all the terms of any physically correct equation must all be the same. For example, if one term of an equation is measured in units of a velocity (in, say, metres per second), then *all* other terms in the equation must be measured in units of velocity (metres per second). To ensure that this is so, it is necessary to break down all units of measurement into the three primary dimensions, those of Mass M, Length L, and Time T. Thus a velocity has the dimensions (length/time) $= LT^{-1}$: an acceleration is LT^{-2}:

force, being the product of mass and acceleration, is MLT^{-2} : density, being a mass per unit volume, is ML^{-3} : velocity gradient, being a velocity per unit length, is T^{-1} : the coefficient of viscosity, being a force per unit area per unit velocity gradient, is $ML^{-1}T^{-1}$: and so on. All measurements can be expressed in terms of M, L and T.

10.2 Now consider a phenomenon where one variable (the *dependent* variable) might be controlled by several others. These others are called *independent* variables because any one of them can be changed, and while affecting the dependent, does not affect any of the other independents. An example is the force F produced by a jet of fluid striking a large flat surface normal to the jet axis (the direct analysis of this phenomenon is given in Chapter 6). Clearly F might change when the velocity U of the jet changes ; when the viscosity μ and the density ρ of the fluid changes ; or when the size of the jet changes. The last variable may be expressed as the diameter d of a circular jet of the same cross-sectional area as the actual jet. This assumes that the shape of the jet does not affect F ; a preliminary experiment could be carried out to show that this assumption is indeed true. Notice that although the variable μ was not considered in the direct analysis of Chapter 6, it is included here as one variable that might affect F. Experiment will eventually decide if it is indeed relevant or not.

Now the dependence of F on the other variables can be conveniently expressed as

$$F = \phi(u, \ d, \ \rho, \ \mu)$$

the symbol ϕ meaning solely ' a function of ' and not implying anything about the form of the function. It does not imply that F varies linearly with the product $ud\rho\mu$, for instance. But any function can be expressed as a series comprised of a number of terms each being made up of the product of the variables brought to suitable powers. That is,

$$F = u^{a_1}d^{b_1}\rho^{c_1}\mu^{d_1} + u^{a_2}d^{b_2}\rho^{c_2}\mu^{d_2} + \ldots$$

where a_1, a_2, a_3, $\ldots$: b_1, b_2, b_3, $\ldots$: c_1, c_2, c_3 $\ldots$ are indices. Dividing both sides of the equation by the first term on the right-hand side

$$F/u^{a_1}d^{b_1}\rho^{c_1}\mu^{d_1} = 1 + u^{a_2-a_1}d^{b_2-b_1}\rho^{c_2-c_1}\mu^{d_2-d_1} + \ldots$$

Since the first term on the right-hand side is a number, it is dimensionless, so that by the axiom already mentioned, *all* terms are dimensionless. In particular, the term on the left-hand side can be written

$$[F/u^a d^b \rho^c \mu^d] = 0$$

the sign [ ] meaning ' the dimensions of '.

Thus
$$[F] \equiv [u^a d^b \rho^c \mu^d]$$

and by inserting the dimensions of each variable, an equation in M, L and T is found,

$$MLT^{-2} \equiv (LT^{-1})^a \ (L)^b \ (ML^{-3})^c \ (ML^{-1}T^{-1})^d$$
$$= L^a T^{-a} \ L^b \ M^c L^{-3c} \ M^d L^{-d} T^{-d}$$

The indices for each of the three primary dimensions M, L, and T may now be collected to form three equations

for M, $\ 1 = c + d$
for L, $\ 1 = a + b - 3c - d$
for T, $-2 = -a - d$

These three simultaneous equations have four unknown quantities in them, only three of which can be determined in terms of the fourth. There are not enough equations to solve for all four unknowns, and it is purely a matter of experience (and intuition) to know for which three unknowns the equations are to be solved. In this case it is convenient (and a well-known form of the solution is found) if a, b, and c are solved in terms of d : and so by the usual methods of solution of simultaneous equations

$$a = 2 - d : b = 2 - d : c = 1 - d,$$

so that

$$F = u^{2-d} d^{2-d} \rho^{1-d} \mu^d + \text{other terms all involving } u, \ d, \ \rho \text{ and } \mu.$$

The 'other' terms on the right-hand side all involve u, d, ρ and μ; since the same dimensional argument can be put to each term, they will all come out into the form

$$u^{2-d'} d^{2-d'} \rho^{1-d'} \mu^d$$

the index d' being a different value for each term. It will be seen that the product $u^2 d^2 \rho$ is common to all terms and that the difference between the terms lies in the value of $(u^{-1}\rho^{-1}d^{-1}\mu)^d$. The whole expression for F may therefore be rewritten

$$\frac{F}{u^2 d^2 \rho} = \left(\frac{\mu}{u\rho d}\right)^{d_1} + \left(\frac{\mu}{u\rho d}\right)^{d_2} + \left(\frac{\mu}{u\rho d}\right)^{d_3} + \ldots$$

or, replacing the series by the symbol ϕ again,

$$\frac{F}{u^2 d^2 \rho} = \phi \frac{ud}{\nu} \quad \text{where} \quad \nu = \mu/\rho$$

or
$$F = u^2 d^2 \rho \ \phi\left(\frac{ud}{\nu}\right) \qquad . \qquad . \qquad . \qquad . \quad (10.1)$$

It will therefore be seen that the non-dimensional quantity $F/u^2d^2\rho$ is a function of (ud/ν), and this conclusion is based solely upon the axiom that an equation for F in terms of the four variables u, d, ρ and μ must be dimensionally homogeneous.

10.3 Here, then, is a clue to one way of presenting the results of experiments on this particular phenomenon. Having changed u, d, ρ and μ in a number of tests, and in each one having measured F, a graph may be drawn up of $F/u^2d^2\rho$ plotted against (ud/ν). All the data will fall on one curve (experimental error excluded), which is the graph of the function ϕ. In this way the effect of every variable is easily seen on one diagram only. If, of course, the data all fall on a straight line parallel to the axis of (ud/ν) in a certain range of values of (ud/ν), the quantity $F/u^2d^2\rho$ does not depend at all on (ud/ν). This is what occurs in the simple case of the jet striking a flat surface ($F = u^2a\rho \sin\theta \cos\theta$: see Chapter 6), when F does not depend on ν except when ud/ν is small (treacle, thick oil, at low speeds and small jet diameters), for which conditions the assumptions of Chapter 6 do not hold (no shear forces, fluid leaves surface tangentially).

The method of analysis is shown above as applied to the phenomenon of a jet striking a flat surface. Precisely the same analysis results if the phenomenon to be investigated is that of a force caused by any fluid motion past a solid surface, for example, the drag of a cylinder immersed in an extensive stream, or the drag due to the boundary layer caused by a stream passing tangentially along a plate. The only difference will be in the method of defining the length measurement corresponding to the jet diameter d. In the former case the cylinder diameter d fixes the scale of the fluid phenomenon ; in the latter case the distance x from the leading edge of the plate fixes the thickness of the boundary layer and so the drag force. The dimensional analysis will give $F/u^2d^2\rho = \phi_2(ud/\nu)$ and $F/u^2x^2\rho = \phi_3(ux/\nu)$ respectively. The variables in both these expressions are essentially the same as that for the first case taken, but the functions ϕ_2 or ϕ_3 will be quite different from ϕ. *Thus the method of dimensional analysis is valid only for comparing the same phenomenon at different scales and speeds*, but not valid at all for comparing two different phenomena. A change in the geometry of the boundaries changes the phenomenon to be considered, and the function determined experimentally for one set of boundaries is of no use in predicting the function for another set.

10.4 Omission of variables

It may be argued that the result of the above method depends on the variables chosen to start with, and upon the choice of the three variables whose indices are solved by the simultaneous equations. So it does. If a variable has been omitted at the beginning which is in fact a relevant one for the phenomenon, then the final experimental plot of ϕ will show a scatter of the points which is not due to experimental error. A search must then be made for the omitted variable, a new dimensional analysis made and a revised method of plotting found. If, on the other hand, a variable is included that is really not important to the problem, then the analysis will show finally two groups of variables from which the function ϕ is produced. Both groups would therefore appear to control the phenomenon. In the preceding example, if the surface tension T (force per unit length) had been included as a possible variable, a non-dimensional group $u^2 d\rho/T$ would have appeared in the analysis thus,

$$\frac{F}{u^2 d^2 \rho} = \phi\left(\frac{ud}{\nu}, \frac{u^2 d\rho}{T}\right)$$

A set of experiments could now be carried out to determine if T really affected the phenomenon. For this purpose (ud/ν) must be kept constant while $u^2 d\rho/T$ is varied. A plot of $F/u^2 d^2 \rho$ against $u^2 d\rho/T$ would then show a straight line parallel to the axis of $u^2 d\rho/T$ showing that in fact T was irrelevant to the problem. Alternatively, if a large number of experiments were carried out and all the variables, u, d, ρ, μ and T changed, then a plot of $F/u^2 d^2 \rho$ against (ud/ν) would show all the points on one graph, no matter how T changed. If, of course, T was really important, then such a plot would show several graph lines, one for each value of $u^2 d\rho/T$. The plot would thus be one of $F/u^2 d^2 \rho$ against ud/ν, with 'contours' of $u^2 d\rho/T$. It will therefore be seen that the method of dimensional analysis does not give any clue as to the correctness of the assumptions about the relevant variables. It merely tells how the variables should be grouped so that experiments will decide which are the important ones.

10.5 The choice of variables to be solved by the simultaneous equations must also affect the non-dimensional groups (like ud/ν and $u^2 d\rho/T$) in the final result. In the example of section **10.2**, the equations could have been solved for b, c and d in terms of a, for instance, instead of a, b and c in terms of d. That is b = a, c = a − 1, d = 2 − a, so that $F = u^a d^a \rho^{a-1} \mu^{2-a}$ + other terms

PLATE 5 Examples of flow visualization.

(a) Flow of water from right to left in a bed of sand, under an impermeable vertical wall. Photograph was taken in a glass-sided laboratory tank, the streamlines being shown by coloured trails from crystals of potassium permanganate. The water is taken off along the surface of the sand to the left.

(b) Water motions under a train of waves produced in a glass-sided laboratory channel. Particles of aluminium, strongly illuminated, are photographed with a time exposure equal to the period of the wave, thus showing the orbital motions near the surface, which become elliptical and finally straight lines at the bottom. The wave on the surface is not photographed because at any one place the surface has moved through the whole height of the wave in the time of exposure, and is therefore fogged and indistinguishable on the photographic plate.

Photo by F. Ruellan and M. Wallet : reproduced by permission of SOGREAH, Grenoble, France

(c) Streamlines of the very slow flow of water around a cylinder sandwiched between the two glass sides of a tank only 1 mm apart. This small gap and the low velocity prevents eddy formation in the water so that the flow around the cylinder is wholly laminar ; there is no breakaway and the flow pattern is similar to that predicted by streamline theory (Chapter 5). The flow pattern is also similar to that around cylinders in streams which are not confined so closely, provided that the Reynolds number $\mathbf{R} = Ud/v$ is less than about 1·0 (U = undisturbed stream velocity, d = cylinder diameter). The streamlines are made visible by streaks of coloured water from potassium permanganate crystals. Notice that the laminar flow ensures that there is very little diffusion of the dye.

PLATE 5

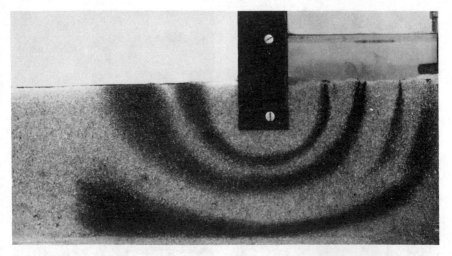

(a)

(b)

(c)

PLATE 6

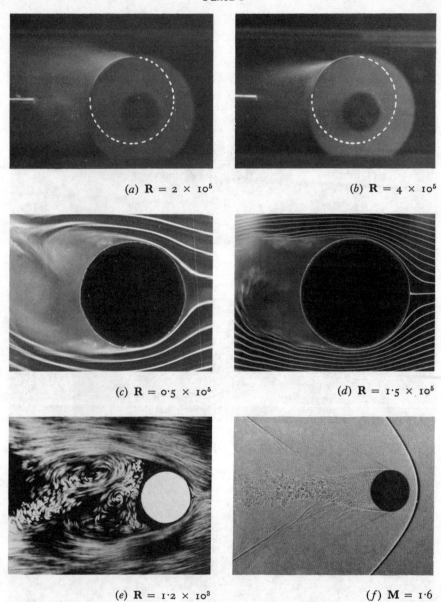

(a) $R = 2 \times 10^5$

(b) $R = 4 \times 10^5$

(c) $R = 0.5 \times 10^5$

(d) $R = 1.5 \times 10^5$

(e) $R = 1.2 \times 10^3$

(f) $M = 1.6$

PLATE 6   Examples of flow visualization.

The Plate shows several examples of flow around a simple shape: (a), (b), (c) and (d) show air flowing past a circular cylinder in a wind tunnel; (e) shows the flow past a circular cylinder standing in a water stream; (f) shows a sphere travelling at supersonic speed through still air. The flow relative to the cylinder or sphere is from right to left in every case.

In (a), aluminium dust is fed into the airstream downwind of the cylinder through the tube shown. The wake is illuminated from above by a plane beam of light, the outline of the cylinder in this plane being shown by the dotted circle. Allowance has been made for perspective effects. Within the wake, where the velocities are low, each particle of dust circulates for a long period before it is picked up by the fast flow at the edge of the wake and blown away downstream. Thus with a moderately long exposure the breakaway points and the wake can be seen.

In (b), the same cylinder is used as in (a) but the speed of the air has been doubled. Observe that the breakaway points have moved further back and the wake is narrower than in (a).

In (c), filaments of smoke have been introduced into the air upstream of the cylinder. In addition to showing the breakaway points and the wake, filament lines outside the wake and ahead of the cylinder can now be seen.

In (d), the air speed is the same as in (c) but the diameter of the cylinder is three times as big. Compare (c) and (d) with (a) and (b). Observe that the rearward movement of the breakaway points and the narrowing of the wake can be produced either by increasing the speed of the air or by increasing the size of the cylinder.

In (e), the cylinder projects from the surface of a stream of water. The movement of aluminium dust particles floating on the surface of the water is revealed by a time photograph. The flow pattern for water in (e) is comparable with the flow for air in (a) and (c).

Whatever the fluid and whatever the speed or the size of the cylinder, if the Reynolds number is kept constant the flow pattern will not change unless the velocity becomes so high that compressibility effects become important. Changes in air density are then large enough to produce optical effects due to changes in refractive index. In (f) a sphere is photographed by the shadowgraph method while it is travelling at $1 \cdot 6$ times the speed of sound, i.e. $M = 1 \cdot 6$. The breakaway points are as in (b) but with a weak shock wave springing from each. Strong shock waves ahead of and behind the sphere appear as black and white lines. Compare (f) with Plate 4 (b), which uses a different method of flow visualization (the Schlieren method) to illustrate supersonic flow past a streamlined aerofoil.

Refer also to pages 120 and 202 for further explanations.

Photograph (f) by U.S. Army Ballistic Research Laboratories, Aberdeen Proving Ground, Maryland

PLATE 7

Opposite (*a*) A Venturi flume being used to measure the flow in a sewage treatment plant. It is photographed from the downstream side, and the hut contains a water-level recorder. Notice the disturbed flow downstream where a hydraulic jump occurs, and the standing waves at the throat, where critical depth occurs.   *Photo by G. Kent Ltd.*

Opposite (*b*) A hydraulic jump in a 10 cm wide glass-sided channel.   Fast flow is produced by a sluice (*right*) and the flow in the jump is observed by a time photograph ($\frac{1}{50}$ second) of the air bubbles entrained in the water.   The tremendous turbulence is clearly seen. Flow from right to left.

Below (*c*) A hydraulic jump downstream of a weir on a river in flood.   The jump is caused by a raised concrete sill across the river downstream of the weir crest.   Observe the smooth surface of the water over the weir, where the flow is accelerating, and the rough, air-entraining surface of the jump where there is deceleration (see Chapter 14).

(c)

PLATE 7

(a)

(b)

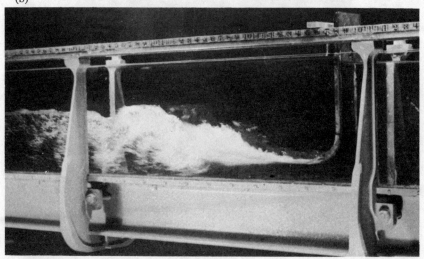

PLATE 8

PLATE 8   The flow over Bendora Dam, Australia

(*above*) A 1 : 40 scale model in the Snowy River Commission's hydraulic laboratory.
(*Below*) The bottom of the jet of water at Bendora, with a flood corresponding to that of the model study.

The value of such a model is in its good reproduction of discharge coefficient, the trajectory of the nappe, and the pressure loading and energy dissipation conditions at the base of the dam. An interesting and noteworthy feature which the pair of photographs illustrate is the inability of the model to reproduce the air entrainment characteristics of the prototype nappe—the ' white water '—which, although an unimportant factor in a model study of this type, is an example of ' scale effect ' which can be troublesome when more than one law has a significant governing influence on the flow behaviour.

Photos by Snowy Mountain Hydro-Electric Authority

or
$$F = \frac{\mu^2}{\rho}\phi_1\left(\frac{ud\rho}{\mu}\right) \qquad . \qquad . \qquad . \qquad . \quad (10.2)$$

This answer, though different from the previous one, *is just as correct.* It only presents the variables in another way. Experimental data could be just as well expressed by plotting $F\rho/\mu^2$ against $ud\rho/\mu$ as by the previous way. The experimental points would still all lie on one curve, but it would be a quite different curve from that found by the other way of plotting. It is only convention, and experience, that makes the presentation of data by certain non-dimensional groups more common than by others. The common forms of non-dimensional groups used in fluid mechanics are

$\dfrac{ud}{\nu}$ (often called the Reynolds number : d is a length measurement, not necessarily a diameter).

$\dfrac{u^2}{dg}$ (often called the Froude number : g is the acceleration due to gravity).

$\dfrac{u}{\sqrt{(K/\rho)}}$ (often called the Mach number : K is the coefficient of compressibility).

$\dfrac{T}{u^2d\rho}$ (often called the Weber number : T is the surface tension)

Sometimes unusual groups are needed for special purposes. For example, consider the terminal velocity u of a sphere of diameter d falling through a fluid of density ρ and viscosity μ. If the density of the material of the sphere is ρ', then the downward weight force acting on the sphere is $\frac{\pi}{6}d^3(\rho' - \rho)g$ (for by Archimedes' principle there is an upthrust equal to the weight of fluid displaced). Now at the steady terminal velocity the downward force exactly equals F, the hydrodynamic drag force caused by the motion. But the dependence of F can be investigated by dimensional analysis, which for this case is exactly the same as for the jet hitting a plate, equation *10.1*.

That is
$$F = \frac{\pi}{6}d^3(\rho' - \rho)g = u^2d^2\rho\phi\left(\frac{ud}{\nu}\right)$$

or
$$\frac{dg}{u^2}\left(\frac{\rho' - \rho}{\rho}\right) = \phi_1\left(\frac{ud}{\nu}\right).$$

The experimental data for spheres falling through a fluid could therefore be correctly presented by plotting $\dfrac{dg}{u^2}\left(\dfrac{\rho' - \rho}{\rho}\right)$ against $\left(\dfrac{ud}{\nu}\right)$. One curve would result for all experiments, but it would be an inconvenient one to use later if it was desired to find, in advance of experiment, what speed would result from given values of d, ρ, ρ' and μ : the unknown variable u features in the quantities on both axes and a trial and error method would be necessary to determine a value of u.

It is much more convenient to use the unusual dimensional analysis (equation _10.2_) already given above as a second way of finding F,

that is
$$F = \frac{\mu^2}{\rho}\phi\left(\frac{ud}{\nu}\right)$$

But
$$F \propto d^3(\rho' - \rho)g$$

so that
$$\frac{d^3 g}{\mu^2}\rho(\rho' - \rho) = \phi_2\left(\frac{ud}{\nu}\right),$$

and the corresponding method of plotting is $\dfrac{d^3 g}{\mu^2}\rho(\rho' - \rho)$ against ud/ν.

In this method u only occurs in the quantities on one axis so that by putting the given values of d, μ, ρ and ρ' into one variable, a value can be instantly read from the curve of ud/ν, and u found directly.

10.6 Use of dimensional analysis in experiments

Having performed a dimensional analysis of the possible variables for a phenomenon, the result can be used in the organization of experiments which will illustrate every aspect of the phenomenon. Suppose it has been found by the analysis that four variables A, B, C, D are interconnected by several non-dimensional groups N_1, N_2, N_3, etc., each of which may contain some of the variables A, B, C, D and also other variables such as μ, T, K, etc.

That is
$$A/B^x C^y D^z = \phi(N_1)(N_2)(N_3).$$

From the examples given it will be seen that N_1, N_2, N_3 might be Reynolds, Mach or Weber numbers or any other non-dimensional group. The experimental data may therefore be presented as shown in fig 10.1, as a set of graphs of $A/B^x C^y D^z$ against N_1, with ' contour curves' of N_2, each graph being for a certain value of N_3. In this way the effect of every group is presented separately, though of course there will be many graphs if the number of relevant non-dimensional groups N is large. If one group, N_2 say, is in fact irrelevant, then all the curves of each graph will coincide, leaving only N_1 and N_3 as relevant groups. Notice that the effect of grouping the variables is that three fewer graphs are necessary to present the data than would be necessary if non-dimensional grouping were not used at all. For example, in the case that has already been described of a force F depending on u, d, ρ and μ, *four* graphs would be necessary to show a complete set of experimental data in the direct way. That is, F against u, with d, ρ and u remaining constant: F against d, with u, ρ and u constant: F against ρ: and F against μ. Contrast these four graphs with the one non-dimensional plot of $F/\rho d^2 u^2$ against $ud\rho/\mu$ which shows all that the four graphs show.

It is a long and tedious job to investigate fully a phenomenon in this way, if there are many variables concerned, and it is often impossible to select fluids which have the requisite properties so that tests can be made by changing one group, N_1, without changing another, N_2. Technical advances slowly make it more possible to make full analyses of problems of fluid mechanics ; for example, the advent of

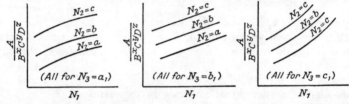

Fig 10.1   The way in which 4 variables, A, B, C, and D can be expressed as functions of 3 non-dimensional groups N_1, N_2, and N_3 each composed of other variables. The phenomenon to which these curves refer is entirely imaginary. Dimensional Analysis has given the indices x, y, z : a, b, c are numerical values of N_2 : a_1, b_1, c_1 are numerical values of N_3.

detergents has permitted control to be exerted over the surface tension, without greatly changing density or viscosity. The effect of the Weber number can thus now be more fully investigated and presented by the graphical method of fig 10.1. Engineers, however, can rarely wait long enough for full investigations to be made of a phenomenon, so that their data is from experiments that only cover a small range of the relevant variables. These experiments must frequently be carried out with the boundaries of the flow at a reduced scale from that which will eventually be used, so as to decrease the cost of any modifications which may be necessary. For example, it would be too expensive and risky to carry out experiments on full-size aeroplanes : reduced-scale models are held stationary exposed to an air current in wind tunnels. But it is now necessary to relate the measurements on a model to the corresponding ones on the full-size aeroplane (*prototype*). Having measured the force F_m on a model of size l_m, exposed to a flow of speed u_m in a fluid of density ρ_m and viscosity μ_m, what will be the force F_p on the prototype at speed u_p ?

The corresponding forces F_m and F_p can be very easily found if the numerical values of the non-dimensional groups N_1, N_2, N_3 ... are the same for both model and prototype. In this way $\phi(N_1, N_2, N_3 ...)$ for the model must be the same as $\phi(N_1, N_2, N_3 ...)$ for the prototype, and the other variables are then simply related, with no further experimental data. For example, take the case of an aeroplane to be tested to find the drag force F. Clearly the velocity u through still air, the size l (exemplified for instance by the wing span), the fluid density ρ and viscosity μ are of importance in finding F. The surface tension T is not of importance (because there is no liquid-gas interface involved), and it is assumed that the speed is low compared with the velocity of sound so that compressibility effects are negligible, and K the coefficient of compressibility can be ignored.

A dimensional analysis then gives

$$F/u^2 l^2 \rho = \phi(ul\rho/\mu).$$

Notice here that $F/u^2 l^2 \rho$ is a dimensionless quantity itself and is in fact of the same form as the drag coefficient of Chapter 7. Now relate both the model condition (suffix m) and prototype condition (suffix p). That is,

$$F_m/u^2{}_m l^2{}_m \rho_m = \phi(u_m l_m \rho_m/\mu_m)$$

and
$$F_p/u^2{}_p l^2{}_p \rho_p = \phi(u_p l_p \rho_p/\mu_p).$$

The model must be of course exactly the same geometrical shape as the prototype so that the fluid boundaries are the same ; if this is so, then the curve of the function ϕ is the same for both prototype and model. The numerical value of ϕ can however only be the same in the two cases if

$$u_m l_m \rho_m/\mu_m = u_p l_p \rho_p/\mu_p$$

or
$$\frac{u_m}{u_p} = \frac{l_p}{l_m} \cdot \frac{\rho_p}{\rho_m} \cdot \frac{\mu_m}{\mu_p} \qquad . \qquad . \qquad . \qquad . \quad (10.3)$$

If u_m and u_p are so connected, then

$$F_m/u^2{}_m l^2{}_m \rho_m = F_p/u^2{}_p l^2{}_p \rho_p$$

or
$$F_p = F_m \left(\frac{u_p}{u_m}\right)^2 \left(\frac{l_p}{l_m}\right)^2 \left(\frac{\rho_p}{\rho_m}\right) \qquad . \qquad . \qquad . \quad (10.4)$$

Substituting for u_m from above,

$$F_p = F_m \left(\frac{l_m}{l_p} \cdot \frac{\rho_m}{\rho_p} \cdot \frac{\mu_p}{\mu_m}\right)^2 \left(\frac{l_p}{l_m}\right)^2 \frac{\rho_p}{\rho_m}$$

$$= F_m \frac{\rho_m}{\rho_p} \left(\frac{\mu_p}{\mu_m}\right)^2$$

Thus a simple method exists of predicting F_p from F_m *providing that u_m is the corresponding speed given by equation 10.3.* Now it will be shown in Chapter 12 that a grouping of variables such as $(ul\rho/\mu)$—the Reynolds number—is a measure of the sort of eddies present round the solid boundaries of the flow. If $ul\rho/\mu$ is the same for both model and prototype then the same sort of eddies exist round both, and the flow conditions are the same. Consequently the drag coefficient $F/u^2l^2\rho$ is the same for both model and prototype. Running the model at the corresponding speed of equation *10.3* is a guarantee that the breakaway and the eddies in the wake occur at the same position in the model as in the prototype (though of course if there are slight differences of shape or roughness then differences of flow are inevitable—a dimensional analysis is always for two precisely similarly shaped bodies).

For a small-scale model $l_p/l_m > 1\cdot0$, and if it is tested in the same fluid as the full-size aeroplane, $\rho_p/\rho_m = 1\cdot0$ and $\mu_m/\mu_p = 1\cdot0$. To achieve the corresponding speed it follows that $u_m/u_p > 1\cdot0$: the model must have a higher relative wind speed than its prototype if the flow conditions, eddy pattern and drag coefficient are to be exactly the same. For example, a $1/5$ scale model should be tested at 1000 km/h in atmospheric air if the prototype is to fly at only 200 km/h. Such high speeds cause additional phenomena to occur, due to the compressibility of the air, which have not been expected in the dimensional analysis because the compressibility K was ignored. The flow conditions around the model are therefore dissimilar to those round the prototype, and the model drag gives a misleading idea of the prototype's drag, if equation *10.4* is now used. With modern high-speed aircraft the effect is magnified, a 1000 km/h prototype needing an experiment to be carried out at 5000 km/h on a $1/5$ size model. One way of getting similarity of eddies without the drawback of such high speeds is to increase the density of the fluid in which the model is tested, by using a heavy gas in an enclosed room within which is the wind tunnel, or by compressing the air to many atmospheres pressure (fig 10.2). These arrangements are undoubtedly more complicated than the usual atmospheric wind tunnel, but they enable the Reynolds number for the model to be more nearly equal to that of the prototype. If such special tunnels are not available, then it is customary to test the model at a speed far below the corresponding speed and assume that $\phi(ul\rho/\mu)$ does not change when extrapolating from the model to the prototype. Fortunately it is found by experience that this procedure does not give large errors for well-streamlined aeroplane shapes.

If the prototype aircraft is to fly at high speeds then it is found (Chapter 9) that the compressibility K (Chapter 1) becomes important

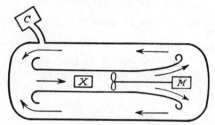

Fig 10.2 Diagram of a compressed-air wind tunnel. M is the motor driving the fan that circulates the air compressed by the compressor C. X is the model under test.

and that the flow pattern is greatly affected by compression waves. Inserting the variable K into the dimensional analysis a revised equation is found

$$\frac{F}{u^2 l^2 \rho} = \phi\left(\frac{ul\rho}{\mu}\right), \left(\frac{u}{c}\right)$$

where $c = \sqrt{(K/\rho)} = \sqrt{(\gamma RT)}$, shown in Chapter 9 to be the velocity of sound waves in the undisturbed air. To obtain true similarity of the flow conditions it would be necessary to have both

$$u_m l_m \rho_m / \mu_m = u_p l_p \rho_p / \mu_p \quad \text{and also} \quad u_m / c_m = u_p / c_p$$

That is
$$\frac{u_m}{u_p} = \frac{l_p}{l_m} \cdot \frac{\rho_p}{\rho_m} \cdot \frac{\mu_m}{\mu_p} \quad \text{and} \quad \frac{u_m}{u_p} = \sqrt{\left(\frac{K_m}{K_p} \cdot \frac{\rho_p}{\rho_m}\right)}$$

or
$$\frac{l_p}{l_m} \cdot \frac{\rho_p}{\rho_m} \cdot \frac{\mu_m}{\mu_p} = \sqrt{\left(\frac{K_m}{K_p} \cdot \frac{\rho_p}{\rho_m}\right)}.$$

It is impossible to obtain this relationship with air or any other usual gases or liquids, for which the possible range of ρ, μ and K are very limited. In the previous paragraph it is shown how difficult it is to get the eddies exactly similar by equalizing the two Reynolds numbers ; it is, however, easy to get the compressibility phenomena similar because it is only necessary to make

$$\frac{u_m}{u_p} = \frac{c_p}{c_m} = \sqrt{\left(\frac{K_m}{K_p} \cdot \frac{\rho_p}{\rho_m}\right)}$$

That is, if the model is tested in the same fluid as the prototype, $K_p = K_m$ and $\rho_m = \rho_p$ so that $u_m/u_p = 1\cdot0$. The model speed is therefore precisely the same as the prototype no matter what the scale of the model may be, if only the compressibility effects are to be made similar. The drag forces due to eddies and friction are not now in scale, but again it is found in practice that $\phi(ul\rho/\mu)$ is sufficiently constant over certain ranges of speed that $\dfrac{F_m}{F_p} = \left(\dfrac{u_m}{u_p}\right)^2 \left(\dfrac{l_m}{l_p}\right)^2 \left(\dfrac{\rho_m}{\rho_p}\right)$ as before (equation 10.4). A great deal of study has been devoted to the effects of eddies on the shock-waves, and the above engineer's approximation, though good enough for many purposes at the present, will doubtless be modified in the course of time.

10.7 The drag force of a ship

An important experimental method has been developed to find from model tests the drag force experienced by a ship. It is a matter of great economic importance to know in advance the power required to drive a ship at a given speed, and model tests are the only certain way of doing so.

Compared to the case just described of the drag of a deeply-immersed object (aeroplane or submarine), the new factor to be introduced is the production of surface waves. It is well known that a moving ship produces both a bow-wave and a stern-wave while a pattern of waves (the *wake*) streams out behind. This wave pattern is not by any means coincident with the mass of eddies (*eddy wake*) produced and left behind by the friction of the water on the ship's hull. As the waves travel away from the ship they become lower, and their energy is degraded into thermal energy by the viscosity of the water : this energy must be continuously supplied by the ship to preserve the whole wave system which does not change. The supply of this wave energy causes a drag force which is additional to the frictional drag of the ship's hull as it is being forced through the water. Now the effect of a series of waves is to raise some water above the mean sea-level and to depress other parts of the surface. Such changes of level, which are an increase of potential energy, require a quantity of energy to produce them proportional to the product gh, where h is the height of the waves. The term g must therefore be included in the dimensional analysis because the gravitational acceleration could be changed (if we had the means to do so) without changing any other of the variables u, l, ρ and μ. The term h is not included in the analysis because the height of the waves cannot be changed independently of the other variables : h is in fact a dependent variable fixed by the independent variables in the same sort of way as they fix F.

Thus the dimensional analysis is performed on the variables F, u, l, g, ρ, μ, where l is a length characterizing the size of the ship, the overall length for example. One answer is

$$F = u^2 l^2 \rho \ \phi(lg/u^2), \ (\mu/\rho u l)$$

or
$$F = u^2 l^2 \rho \; \phi_1(u/(gl)^{1/2}), \; (ul/\nu),$$

ϕ_1 merely meaning 'another function of'. The drag of a surface ship is therefore a function of both the Reynolds number ul/ν and also of the Froude number $u/(lg)^{1/2}$. The first expresses, as before, the effect of eddies on the drag force : the second expresses the effect of surface-wave formation on the drag. In most ship designs the contributions of friction and wave formation to the total drag are of the same order. It is not justifiable to neglect either, but in very high speed ships such as hydroplanes and speed boats, the friction component is relatively small.

The significance of the Reynolds number is shown in Chapter 12 to be that its numerical value indicates the type of eddy pattern caused by fluid friction. In a similar sort of way the numerical value of the Froude number indicates the type of wave pattern caused by the passage of a ship through the water. The speed C of a simple set of waves depends on the wave-length L, the distance between successive wave crests. In deep water $C = (gL/2\pi)^{1/2}$, as will be shown in Chapter 16. Now the ship causes a wave pattern which travels at the same speed u as the ship so that the wave-length of the waves in the pattern is fixed by u, a low speed giving short wave-lengths, and vice versa.* The number of waves in the pattern along the ship's length depends therefore on the speed. If there is only one wave in the ship's length, $L = l$, and if this wave still exactly follows the simple deep water speed law

$$u = C = (gl/2\pi)^{1/2} \quad \text{or} \quad u/(gl)^{1/2} = (1/2\pi)^{1/2} = 0.4.$$

Shorter waves, with more of them in the length l, give lower values of $u/(gl)^{1/2}$. Thus the numerical value of the Froude number $u/(gl)^{1/2}$ indicates the number of waves in the pattern, and indeed the type of pattern itself. The speed law for a forced pattern of waves such as this is slightly different from the simple deep-water law, but C is still proportional to $L^{1/2}$. It is found by experience that great changes come over the pattern at about $u/(gl)^{1/2} = 1.0$, and at higher values of the Froude number, the ship rides upon one wave-crest, 'planing' over it as a high speed motor-boat does. The part of the total drag force due to the wave generation undergoes a great modification because of these changes, there being a distinct decrease at about $u/(gl)^{1/2} = 1.0$. However, the part due to frictional drag is always increasing nearly proportionately to u^2 so that the combined total drag may not show this decrease, see fig 10.3. Ocean-going ships are always designed for $u/(gl)^{1/2} < 1.0$; (300 m ship at 30 knots gives

---

* The speed of the waves can be shown by suddenly stopping the ship, when the bow wave continues at the original ship's speed.

$u/(gl)^{1/2} = 0.284$: its model, which might be about 5 m in length and weigh 700 kg would travel at 1·96 m/s, a not excessive speed).

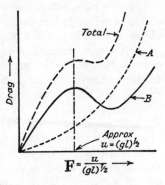

Fig 10.3 A typical drag curve for a ship which produces waves on the surface of the sea. A is the frictional drag: B is the wave drag which is greatly variable with the Froude number $\mathbf{F} = u/(gl)^{\frac{1}{2}}$. The total drag often shows a point of inflexion near $\mathbf{F} = 1$.

Because the pattern of the waves affects the drag it is essential to tow models of ships at the correct (or corresponding) speed to give the same pattern as does the full-size prototype. To do this

$$u_{\mathrm{m}}/(gl_{\mathrm{m}})^{1/2}) = u_{\mathrm{p}}/(gl_{\mathrm{p}})^{1/2} \quad \text{or} \quad u_{\mathrm{m}}/u_{\mathrm{p}} = (l_{\mathrm{m}}/l_{\mathrm{p}})^{1/2}.$$

But it is also desirable to tow at such a speed that the eddies are similar and give the same pattern of turbulence in the boundary layers on the ship's surface. That is

$$u_{\mathrm{m}}l_{\mathrm{m}}/\nu_{\mathrm{m}} = u_{\mathrm{p}}l_{\mathrm{p}}/\nu_{\mathrm{p}}$$

or
$$\frac{u_{\mathrm{m}}}{u_{\mathrm{p}}} = \left(\frac{l_{\mathrm{p}}}{l_{\mathrm{m}}}\right)\frac{\nu_{\mathrm{m}}}{\nu_{\mathrm{p}}}.$$

It will therefore be seen that the requirement of $u_{\mathrm{m}}/u_{\mathrm{p}}$ for waves to be similar is not the same for eddies to be similar. Equating the right-hand sides of the equations for $u_{\mathrm{m}}/u_{\mathrm{p}}$, the values of $\nu_{\mathrm{m}}/\nu_{\mathrm{p}}$ will be found which ensures that both the eddies and waves are similar. that is

$$\left(\frac{l_{\mathrm{m}}}{l_{\mathrm{p}}}\right)^{1/2} = \left(\frac{l_{\mathrm{p}}}{l_{\mathrm{m}}}\right)\frac{\nu_{\mathrm{m}}}{\nu_{\mathrm{p}}} \quad \text{or} \quad \frac{\nu_{\mathrm{m}}}{\nu_{\mathrm{p}}} = \left(\frac{l_{\mathrm{m}}}{l_{\mathrm{p}}}\right)^{3/2}.$$

Thus if true similarity is to be achieved for both eddies and waves, the fluid in which a small-scale model is to be tested must be less viscous than the water in which the prototype will float. For a 1 : 20 scale model (and this would be an unusually large one for the usual merchant ship),

$$\nu_{\mathrm{m}}/\nu_{\mathrm{p}} = (1/20)^{3/2} = 1/89, \quad \text{when} \quad u_{\mathrm{m}}/u_{\mathrm{p}} = (1/20)^{1/2} = 1/4.47.$$

There are, in fact, no cheap, safe fluids of so small a viscosity that complete similarity can be obtained in this manner.

The engineer is therefore forced to compromise, in a somewhat similar manner to that used in the case of high-speed aircraft. He tests the model by towing it in water at the correct Froude number for the scale used, and measures the total drag F_m. The wave pattern is therefore correctly formed because $u_m/u_p = \sqrt{(l_m/l_p)}$. The friction drag F_{fm} of the model is estimated by assuming that it is the same as would occur if a flat surface of the same area is towed end on at the same speed u_m. The usual friction equation (Chapter 12) of the form $F_{fm} = C_f A u^2_m/2g$ is used where C_f is found from boundary layer theory and experiment. The wave drag of the model F_{Wm} is then found as

$$F_{Wm} = F_m - F_{fm}.$$

The wave drag of the prototype ship, F_{Wp}, can now be scaled up from F_{Wm} by the scaling law.

$$F_{Wm}/F_{Wp} = u^2_m l^2_m \rho_m/u_p^2 l_p^2 \rho_p$$

Because usually u_p and l_p are much larger than u_m and l_m, $F_{Wm} \ll F_{Wp}$. Having found F_{Wp}, the friction drag F_{fp} is calculated for the ship by the same friction equation, though C_f for the prototype is almost certainly different from that for the model as the surface of a prototype ship is much rougher than that of the model. Finally the two components F_{fp} and F_{Wp} are added to form the total drag F_p of the ship.

It is usually admitted that the division of the total drag of aeroplanes and ships into two additive and therefore independent portions is quite arbitrary, and that probably the shock-wave or surface-wave resistance is affected by the frictional resistance, and vice versa. Much more advanced research is needed to elucidate these problems for any particular aeroplane or ship form. However, the errors of the above simplified method are thought to be sufficiently small, and are at any rate less than the errors involved in attempting to measure the total drag of prototype ships and aeroplanes and thus to prove the validity of these admittedly crude methods.

10.8 Flow over a weir

The engineer often desires to know the discharge of fluid over a weir (a wall across a stream) and the way in which it depends on the height h (or *head*) of the upstream surface above the top of the weir. In one special case, that of the broad-crested weir, a direct analytical solution can be worked out, depending on Bernoulli's equation (see Chapter 14). Another sort of weir is a sharp-crested wall, an elevation of which is shown in fig 10.4. A proof of the law connecting Q

with h can again be made using Bernoulli's equation. This proof is unsatisfactory, because greatly erroneous assumptions must now be made in order to solve Bernoulli's equation to obtain the discharge. Experimentally determined coefficients must be introduced to account for the errors introduced by these assumptions, and these coefficients are so large that it seems quite unreal to have employed such a precise statement of hydrodynamics as Bernoulli's equation for a starting-point. It is far more satisfying to treat the problem from the outset as an experimental one, and to use dimensional analysis to see how the variables should be grouped.

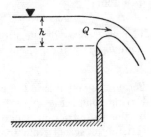

Fig 10.4   Definition sketch for flow over a weir.

Consider then a uniform sharp-crested weir across a stream of width b. The discharge per unit width, Q/b is the same for all points along the weir and will depend upon the head h of the undisturbed stream above weir crest, upon viscosity μ, density ρ and surface tension T. In addition, the gravitational acceleration g must also be included because gravitational forces are responsible for the falling of the jet over the weir, causing a deformation of the surface. This is exactly the same reason as was used for including g in the dimensional analysis for ship drag forces. Thus Q/b depends on h, g, ρ, T, μ and dimensional analysis gives one possible grouping of the variables as

$$Q/b = h^{3/2}g^{1/2}\phi(\mu/\rho h\sqrt{gh}),\ (T/\rho gh^2)$$

or $$Q = bg^{1/2}h^{3/2}\phi(\mathbf{R}),\ (\mathbf{T})$$

where $\mathbf{R}$ is the form of the Reynolds number applicable to a weir and $\mathbf{T}$ is the surface tension (Weber) number.

Experiments should therefore be made changing all the variables and the results could be plotted as curves of $Q/b\,g^{1/2}\,h^{3/2}$ against the Reynolds number $\mathbf{R} = \mu/\rho\,h\,\sqrt{(gh)}$, each curve for a different $\mathbf{T} = T/\rho gh^2$. This method of plotting is illustrated in fig 10.5. Experiments such as these have been carried out many times, and it has been found that all curves are coincident whatever the value of $\mathbf{T}$, except when h is less than about 1·3 cm. For most purposes, then, the

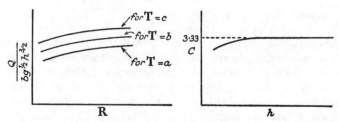

Fig 10.5   The result of dimensional analysis and experiment on the discharge Q over a sharp-edged weir. (*Left*) Schematic diagram of how the results might be presented if the surface tension number **T** is an important variable. (*Right*) Since experiment shows **T** does not affect $C = Q/bh^{3/2}$, and since a function of $\mathbf{R} = (v/h^{3/2}\sqrt{(2g)})$ can be simplified to a function of h, if v and $\sqrt{(2g)}$ are constants, the simplified presentation of C against h is the one usually employed.

flow over a sharp-edged weir is unaffected by the surface tension of the fluid. Further, over a wide range of **R**, $Q/b\,g^{1/2}\,h^{3/2}$ is nearly constant at a value of $3\cdot33/g^{1/2}$ for this shape of weir crest. Other shapes of weir crest have also been tested, but the value of $Q/b\,h^{3/2}$ (g is usually omitted as it always has the same value) is different from that found for the sharp edge. As will be described in Chapter 14, a value of $1\cdot68$ m$^{1/2}$/s is found for a broad-crested weir providing h is sufficiently small that the flow becomes parallel to the crest. For many designs of curved or *ogee* weirs which are often used in engineering work, $Q/bh^{3/2}$ may be as high as about $2\cdot35$ m$^{1/2}$/s though it is not constant at this value : such weirs are therefore not suitable as flow-measuring devices unless they have been previously calibrated (see fig 10.6).

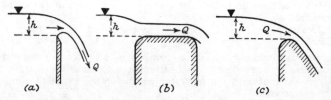

Fig 10.6   The effect of the shape of the weir on the value of the coefficient $C = Q/bh^{3/2}$. (*a*) A sharp-crested weir gives $C = 1\cdot81$ m$^{1/2}$/s, if h is greater than about $1\cdot2$ cm. (*b*) A broad-crested weir gives $C = 1\cdot70$ if it is long enough to create parallel flow over its crest (see Chapter 14). (*c*) An ogee weir may give C up to $2\cdot35$, but this value usually changes considerably with h.

Conclusion

The method of dimensional analysis of the variables of a physical phenomenon enables the effect of many variables to be studied together. It is not necessary to make any assumptions about the relevance of any particular variable as only experiment will show if such a variable should have been included or not. The method merely suggests the grouping of variables in order to show their effect, but gives no hint of whether any variable is in fact of importance or not. Thus dimensional analysis is peculiarly suited to problems in fluid mechanics which is pre-eminently an experimental science.

PROBLEMS

1. Define the Coefficient of Drag of a solid object in a fluid stream. With what variables does it change ? What weight must a 13 cm diameter sphere have, if it is to fall in air at N.T.P. at the same speed as a 1 cm sphere falling in water, and weighing 0·01 N in air ?

(v for air = 13 v for water)

Ans. 0·9 × 10⁻⁴ N.

2. Particles of stone, density 2650 kg/m³, fall freely at the following speeds in water at 20 °C, $\mu = $ 0·010 poise.

Particle diameter : mm	0·2	0·5	1·0	2·0	5·0	10
Speed : cm/s	1·8	2·5	10·2	17	30	42

Plot a curve of speeds for similarly shaped particles of ' Perspex ', density 1200 kg/m³, falling in water at 10 °C, $\mu = $ 0·013 poise. Why should Perspex sand be considered for the bed of civil engineering models of rivers ?

Ans. First pair of data gives $d = $ 0·48 mm and $u = $ 1·0 cm/s for Perspex.

3. When tested with water, a metering nozzle 2·54 cm in diameter gave

Pressure Difference :	1·08	3·24	5·38	6·47	m of water
Flow :	2·32	4·01	5·20	5·66	× 10⁻³ m³/s.

A similar nozzle but 7·6 cm in diameter is to be used to measure air discharging to atmosphere. Tabulate the air discharges (m³/s), and pressure differences in cm of water gauge for the range of similarity of the water tests.

Water density $\rho = $ 1000 kg/m³, $\mu = $ 0·0114 poise
Air $\rho = $ 1·25 kg/m³, $v = $ 0·146 stokes

Ans. 2·5 cm W.G. gives 0·0906 m³/s, etc.

4. What is the ratio of the windage torques of an electrical alternator running at constant speed in an atmosphere of (a) air, (b) hydrogen, if the flow in the clearance passages is fully turbulent ? Derive an expression for the torque T by dimensional analysis on the variables diameter D, speed N, clearance C, viscosity μ, and density ρ.

Density of hydrogen is $1/14$ density of air, and viscosity of hydrogen is 0.51 the viscosity of air.

$Ans.$ $T = N^2 D^5 \rho \, \phi\Big(\dfrac{C}{D}\Big)\Big(\dfrac{\mu}{\rho N D^2}\Big)$ is one grouping : $1/14$.

5. A model is to be made of the tail race of a hydro-electric power house. The largest pump available in the laboratory has a maximum flow of 4200 l/min and the maximum flood discharge in the actual tail race is 320 cumecs. What is the largest undistorted scale that can be used for the model? What is the ratio of the Reynolds numbers for the flow in full-size and model tail race.

$Ans.$ $1/28 : 149$ to 1.

6. A one-fourteenth scale model of an aircraft is to be tested in a wind-tunnel, under conditions dynamically similar to those encountered by the full-scale prototype flying at a true speed of 350 m/s at an altitude of 12 km (where the temperature and pressure are 216.5 K and 18.25 kN/m^2). In the wind-tunnel the temperature is always 288 K, but the pressure can be varied. What tunnel pressure will be required? Assume the viscosity of air varies with temperature $T^{3/4}$ approximately.

Show that the forces on the model will be 10% of the corresponding forces on the prototype. Is the experiment likely to be practicable?

$Ans.$ 365 kN/m^2.

$Hint.$ Consider both Mach and Reynolds numbers (see Chapter 9).

11

CURVATURE OF STREAMLINES

11.1 The simple applications of Bernoulli's equation in Chapter 8 were made on the assumption that the total energy H of a flow is the same for every streamline, and the same along every streamline. Such a situation is nearly true in a number of cases, but in others there is a change of H across the flow. One important case is that of straight-line flow with friction applied at one of its boundaries so that there is a boundary layer wherein the fluid is slowed down : the pressure is constant all over planes normal to the flow so that the total energy $H = u^2/2g + p/\rho g$ decreases near the boundary. Properties of this sort of flow will be discussed later.

Another important case is when a flow is constrained to turn a corner.

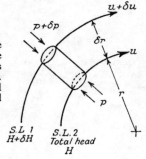

Fig 11.1 Plan view of a flow of which the streamlines are bent round a common centre of curvature. The cylinder of fluid shown is in equilibrium with the pressure system shown. The fluid at the two streamlines S.L.1 and S.L.2 has neither the same velocity nor total head.

Centrifugal forces are now brought to bear upon the fluid and these are balanced by an increase of pressure in the radial direction (a *radial pressure gradient*). Consider then the general case of the forces on a cylinder of fluid of cross section area a, whose axis is normal to a number of streamlines bent round a common centre of curvature X (see fig 11.1). All variables will be made to increase in the outward direction so that the circumferential velocity increases from u to $u + \delta u$ when going outwards from radius r to $r + \delta r$; the pressure intensity increases from p to $p + \delta p$, and the total head from H to $H + \delta H$. For simplicity it is assumed that the plane of the motion is horizontal ; the height z will therefore be the same everywhere and can be ignored. If the flow is two-dimensional (that is, the rotation is the same at all

166

levels in the axial direction) the fluid in the cylinder cannot be moving radially at all, because all cylinders at the same radius have the same force system on them and so must have the same motion ; if there was outward motion in one place, then there would have to be a return inward motion somewhere else. Thus the cylinder is in equilibrium, with the centrifugal force just balancing the pressure forces on the ends. The centrifugal force is the product of the mass of the cylinder and the mean centrifugal acceleration, while the pressure force is the product of δp and the cross-sectional area.

That is,
$$a\,\delta p = \rho a\,\delta r \frac{(u + \frac{1}{2}\delta u)^2}{r + \frac{1}{2}\delta r}$$

where $(u + \frac{1}{2}\delta u)$ is the mean circumferential velocity of the fluid in the cylinder.

Simplifying,
$$\frac{\delta p}{\delta r} = \rho \frac{u^2 + u\delta u}{r + \frac{1}{2}\delta r} = \rho u^2/r \quad . \qquad . \qquad . \quad (11.1)$$

if $\delta u \ll u$ and $\delta r \ll r$.

11.2 The Bernoulli energy equations may now be written for each streamline,

so $H = u^2/2g + p/\rho g$ and $H + \delta H = (u + \delta u)^2/2g + (p + \delta p)/g\rho$.

Subtracting these, and ignoring second order terms,
$$\delta H = 2u\,\delta u/2g + \delta p/g\rho$$

or
$$\frac{\delta H}{\delta r} = \frac{u}{g}\frac{\delta u}{\delta r} + \frac{\delta p}{g\rho\delta r}$$

Substituting for $\delta p/\delta r$ above
$$\frac{\delta H}{\delta r} = \frac{u}{g}\frac{\delta u}{\delta r} + \frac{\rho}{g\rho}\frac{u^2}{r}$$

If δr is now made infinitesimal the expression becomes
$$dH/dr = (u/g)\,(du/dr + u/r) \quad . \qquad . \qquad . \quad (11.2)$$

This general equation makes no assumption about the energy dissipation along the streamlines as it is only concerned with the radial gradient of H. Consequently it may be used for real fluids with accuracy and without any experimental coefficients being used. There are three principal cases of the equation.

11.3 *Case I.* A flow wherein $r = \infty$ and $du/dr = 0$

The restriction of $r = \infty$ implies straight-line flow, and that of $du/dr = 0$ implies uniform velocity at all places in one cross section of the flow. Substitution in the general equation *11.2* gives $dH/dr = 0$, that is, H is a constant for all streamlines in the cross section concerned. This is precisely the result that common sense indicates, for if the velocity is constant in a straight-line flow, there is no reason for H being different in one streamline than another. Provided that there is no energy degradation along the streamlines (i.e. no friction forces), then H is the same along any one streamline, as well as the same for each streamline. Thus in this sort of flow H is the same everywhere, and Bernoulli's equation can be applied between any two points in the flow even if they are not on the same streamline.

11.4 *Case II.* A flow wherein $u \propto 1/r$

There is now no restriction at all upon the curvature as in Case I, and the streamlines of this flow are therefore circles of any radius up to infinity.

If $$u = K/r$$
then, differentiating, $$du = -Kr^{-2}\,dr\;;$$
and substituting for K above, so $du/dr = -u/r$,
and the general equation *11.2* becomes

$$\frac{dH}{dr} = \frac{u}{g}\left(\frac{u}{r} + \left(-\frac{u}{r}\right)\right) = 0.$$

Thus, in this special sort of circular flow, the total head H is constant at all places, and the Bernoulli equation may thus be applied with the same H for all points. The speed must be infinite at $r = 0$.

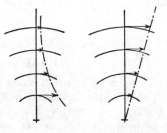

Fig 11.2 Comparison of the velocity distribution across the diameters of (*left*) a free vortex and (*right*) a forced vortex. The streamlines in each case are arcs of circles.

The flow is called a *free vortex* or *potential vortex*, since it was shown in Chapter 5 that equipotential lines may be drawn if the rotation is restricted to that when $u \propto 1/r$. Many circular flows do indeed closely approximate to free vortices, including those occurring when a swirl occurs at an outlet to a tank (e.g. the vortex when a bath plug is removed), although the speed is far from infinite in the centre. In this central core the free vortex condition does not apply; if it did apply at the centre there would be infinite velocities in opposite directions and consequently an infinite velocity gradient. An infinite shear stress would therefore be developed in a real fluid; this is impossible, so free vortex flow does not occur at the centre.

When a straight-line flow is diverted round a corner by its walls, such as at a pipe bend, a close approximation to a free vortex motion is set up in the fluid. The motion is somewhat modified near the inner wall, near where there is often a decrease of velocity (due to the boundary layer) instead of the rise predicted by a free vortex. Ignoring this slight modification, and assuming that free vortex motion extends from radius r_1 to radius r_2, where $r_2 < r_1$

then
$$H_1 = H_2$$

or
$$u_1{}^2/2g + p_1/\rho g = u_2{}^2/2g + p_2/\rho g.$$

Writing
$$u_1 = K/r_1 \quad \text{and} \quad u_2 = K/r_2$$

$$\frac{p_1 - p_2}{g\rho} = \frac{K^2}{2g}\left(\frac{1}{r_2{}^2} - \frac{1}{r_1{}^2}\right) = \frac{K^2}{2g}\left(\frac{r_1{}^2 - r_2{}^2}{r_1{}^2 r_2{}^2}\right).$$

Thus the pressure increases outwards. Since the velocity distribution is known, $u = K/r$, the discharge Q can be computed for any given cross section of pipe (see Chapter 4) and can be expressed in terms of the pressure rise $\dfrac{p_1 - p_2}{\rho g}$. A free vortex may therefore be used as a method of measuring the flow of the fluid, without introducing any additional equipment. The method is, however, approximate, unless the bend is experimentally calibrated, because of the boundary layer effect ignored in the above analysis.

11.5 *Case III.* A flow wherein $u \propto r$

This case is again one of circular flow but the velocity increases proportionally with the radius so that all the fluid has the same angular velocity ω.

Thus
$$u = \omega r \quad \text{or} \quad u/r = \omega \quad \text{and} \quad \mathrm{d}u/\mathrm{d}r = \omega.$$

The general equation *11.2* therefore becomes
$$\mathrm{d}H/\mathrm{d}r = u/g(\omega + \omega) = 2\,\omega u/g.$$

Between two radii r_1 and r_2 the total head of the fluid thus increases by
$$\int_{H_2}^{H_2} \mathrm{d}H = \int_{r_1}^{r_2} \frac{2\,\omega u}{g}\,\mathrm{d}r = \frac{2\omega^2}{g}\int r\,\mathrm{d}r$$

or
$$H_2 - H_1 = \frac{\omega^2}{g}(r_2^2 - r_1^2).$$

This sort of circular flow is called a *forced* or *flywheel* vortex (see also Chapter 5). It can be generated by the fluid being whirled around in a container so that every part has the same angular velocity; or it exists when a paddle rotates in a large mass of fluid, though outside the paddle the conditions are more nearly those of a free vortex (fig 11.3).

Fig 11.3 A paddle rotating in a fluid creates a forced vortex within its diameter and a free vortex outside it. In both vortices there is a rise of pressure in an outward radial direction.

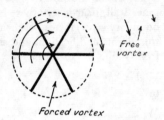

Forced vortex

In the forced vortex the total energy of each streamline is different, so that although Bernoulli's equation could be applied along each streamline, it cannot be applied to points on different streamlines.

The increase of pressure $(p - p_0)$ between the centre and a certain radius r of a forced vortex can be found by considering the increase of H from the centre to that radius, that is

$$H - H_0 = \frac{\omega^2 r^2}{g}$$

where H_0 is the total head at the centre.

But since
$$u = 0 \text{ at } r = 0,$$
$$H_0 = p_0/\rho g$$

and
$$H = \frac{p}{g\rho} + \frac{u^2}{2g} = \frac{p}{g\rho} + \frac{\omega^2 r^2}{2g},$$

thus
$$\frac{p}{g\rho} + \frac{\omega^2 r^2}{2g} - \frac{p_0}{g\rho} = \frac{\omega^2 r^2}{g} \quad \text{or} \quad \frac{p - p_0}{g\rho} = \frac{\omega^2 r^2}{2g}.$$

It will therefore be seen that large pressure differences can be set up in forced vortices if they are of large enough radius. In fact, they are excellent devices for increasing the total energy of a fluid. Fluid at low pressure can be fed into the centre of a suitable vortex where it is whirled around and ejected at the periphery with a much-enhanced pressure. This is the principle of a centrifugal pump. In the other direction, high-pressure fluid can be made to do work in a forced vortex, being ejected at low pressure at the centre, having given up its energy; this is the principle of water turbines.

11.6 Secondary circulations

An important secondary effect is produced when flows contained between solid boundaries are bent round a corner. Water moving round a bend in a river, and air round a bend in a wind tunnel or in a duct of a ventilating system, are examples. Against the boundary corresponding to the bottom of a river, or the sides of a pipe bend, the fluid is slowed down, producing a boundary layer (see fig 11.4).

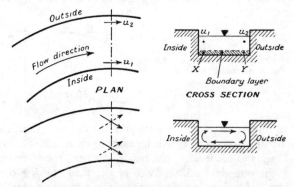

Fig 11.4 The flow of water in a bend of a river. (*Above*) The velocities u_1 and u_2 form part of a free vortex motion caused by the bending of the streamlines and so cause a radial pressure gradient. The velocities in the boundary layer on the bottom are less than u_1 and u_2 on the surface so the radial pressure gradient on the bottom is less than that on the top. (*Below*) Consequently a spiral secondary motion is set up as shown in the cross section, and also on the plan where the dotted arrows show the surface water movement, and the full arrows the bottom movement.

The whole flow is now *not* two-dimensional as was assumed in 11.1, because the rotation is less in the boundary layer than in the centre of the stream. The bending of the streamlines causes a free vortex so that there is a radial increase of pressure everywhere of

$$\Delta p = (u_1{}^2 - u_2{}^2)/2g,$$

where u_1 is the velocity at the inner wall and u_2 is that at the outer wall (see fig 11.4). But the velocities u_1' and u_2' in the boundary layer at X and Y are less than u_1 and u_2 in the main stream above, so that the pressure rise $\Delta p' = (u'_1{}^2 - u'_2{}^2)/2g$ in the boundary layer is less than the rise $\Delta p = (u_1{}^2 - u_2{}^2)/2g$ in the main stream. If the pressures in boundary layer and main stream are the same at the middle of the river, then at the outer wall the pressure in the boundary layer will be less than the pressure higher in the stream by an amount $\frac{1}{2}(\Delta p - \Delta p')$. At the inner wall the pressure difference is reversed.

A current is therefore set up by these pressure differences that gives velocities down the outer wall, inwards across the bottom, up the inner wall and outwards across the top. This current, together with the main stream, gives a spiral combined flow, as shown in fig 11.4, where full arrows show bottom boundary layer flow, dotted arrows show surface flow. The effect is very noticeable in a cup of tea, for the tea-leaves are brought to the centre of the cup when it is stirred. Very similar spiral or *secondary* flows occur in closed ducts, where there are usually two spirals in opposite directions (see fig 11.5).

Fig 11.5   Secondary flows in a bend of a rectangular pipe or duct. Dotted arrows show centre movement, full arrows the movement against the sides.

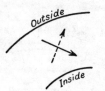

These secondary flows create problems for the hydraulic engineer in rivers, for the bottom flow will be carrying sand and silt from the outside of bends to the inside ; the inside of a bend therefore becomes shoal and the outside bank tends to erode, thus making the bend more abrupt. If a river is to supply water to a canal or pipeline, the intake should be placed, if at all possible, on the outside of a bend, where the sand tends to move inwards, so as to reduce the quantity of sand taken in. In pipes and wind tunnels secondary flow is objectionable because the spiral persists well downstream of the bend that produces it. If it is desired to have uniform straight-line flow (as in the working section of wind tunnels), then it is essential to suppress this effect, or to work an unacceptably large distance downstream of the bend. One way of suppressing secondaries is to guide the main

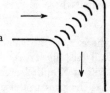

Fig 11.6   Guide vanes in a pipe bend or corner of a wind tunnel.

flow around corners by closely spaced guide vanes (fig 11.6). Small-scale secondaries are set up between the vanes, but these are dissipated in a much shorter distance than is a large secondary from a bend without guide vanes.

PROBLEMS

1. A tube 50 cm long and closed at one end is half full of mercury ($\rho = 13 \cdot 6 \times 10^3$ kg/m^3). If the tube is rotated about the open end in a horizontal plane at a constant rate of 180 rev/min, what pressure will exist at the closed end ?

Ans. 458 kN/m^2.

2. Find the maximum speed at which an open canister 25 cm diameter and 25 cm high can be rotated without spilling, if at rest it has been half filled with water.

Hint. The volume of a paraboloid of revolution is half the volume of the circumscribing cylinder.

Ans. 168 rev/min.

3. If the tangential velocity of a free vortex in water is 10 cm/s at a radius of 0·5 m, what will be the surface elevation (*a*) there and (*b*) at a radius of 3 cm, relative to the surface elevation at a very large radius ?

Ans. (*a*) 1·02 mm : (*b*) 28·3 cm.

4. Estimate whether a secondary flow would be prevented in a bend of a river, radius 600 m, cross-section triangular 100 m wide, max. depth 7·5 m, if a layer of heavily silt charged water, s.g. 1·04, existed on the bottom. The mean speed is 1 m/s.

Ans.   Secondary prevented : free vortex gives press. difference less than that required to create a slope of the heavy fluid equal to the bed slope.

5. Eddies often cause temporary local depressions in the surface of a stream. The form of these eddies may be approximated by a forced vortex of radius R within a concentric free vortex. Compute the depth of the depression, H, of the surface if the central angular velocity of the vortex is ω. Show that the flow of angular momentum across a radial plane between $r = 0$ and $r = \infty$ is $4/3 \, \rho R^3 \, \omega^2 D$, where D is the depth of the stream and $D \gg H$. Briefly discuss the effect on the central angular velocity if the stream carries the vortex into a region where the depth is $D/2$.

Ans. $H = R^2 \, \omega^2/g$.

12

THE PRODUCTION OF SHEAR FORCES IN BOUNDARY LAYERS

12.1 In several preceding chapters reference has been made to the effects that boundary layers have on other characteristics of a fluid flow. It is now appropriate to describe the properties of the fluid inside the layer and, in particular, to find the shear stress which has caused the layer to form on the solid surface.

The concept of the boundary layer is due to Prandtl who, in 1904, first realized that the whole of the effect of the friction on a solid surface is confined within a thin layer of fluid adjacent to the surface, unless the flow breaks away and leaves a large patch of dead fluid (p. 40). Outside this layer the friction has no effect, and any changes in velocity there are due solely to the distortion of streamlines by the solid surface, as given by the theoretical methods of Chapter 5. This idea now seems simple and obvious, and it has enabled a link to be made between theoretical ideal fluid hydrodynamics, which ignores frictional shear forces, and experimental evidence with real fluids.

The essential assumption made in the theory of the boundary layer is that in a viscous fluid a shear stress at a point always produces a rate of strain there. As was shown in Chapter 1, a rate of strain is equivalent to a gradient of velocity in the stream, the direction of the gradient being across the direction of the stream (and of the stress). If there is no velocity gradient present, then there is no stress. If the flow is purely laminar, then there is a simple linear relationship between the stress τ and the velocity gradient du/dy : the constant of proportionality is called the coefficient of viscosity, μ, for the fluid, where $\tau = \mu \, du/dy$. More complicated relations hold good for turbulent flow but the restriction still remains that velocity gradients cannot exist where there is no stress. Solid objects, of course, distort the streamlines of flow around them as has been described in Chapter 5, in which case there may be a velocity gradient, with an accompanying stress, if the fluid is not ideal ; the stresses and velocity gradients due to boundary layer effect would be additional to those caused in this way by the distortions of the streamlines.

12.2 The boundary layer on a plane surface

A boundary layer on a plane surface parallel to the direction of the undisturbed flow is the simplest case to study. Such a surface, if exposed to a flow of ideal fluid, would not cause any velocity gradients at all. With real fluids, the flow is decelerated near the surface because of the fluid friction, and the velocity gradients which result are due solely to that friction.

The main properties of a boundary layer on a flat surface with a uniform pressure at every place on it are shown in fig 12.1. If the

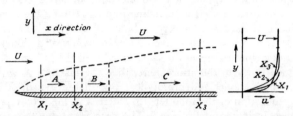

Fig 12.1 Development of a boundary layer on a flat surface parallel to the undisturbed flow. Dotted line shows outer limit of boundary layer, outside of which the velocity is constant. Curves on right show the velocity distribution at several places.

pressure is not uniform, the properties of the velocity in the layer are different. The boundary layer commences at the leading edge of the surface and grows thicker in a downstream direction. Within the first part, A in the figure, the flow is observed to be entirely laminar, whatever the roughness of the surface may be, or whether the oncoming, undisturbed, stream is laminar or turbulent. Apparently the random movements of turbulent motion (i.e. eddies) cannot exist in a thin boundary layer which has a large mean value of the velocity gradient du/dy in it. After some distance in the laminar boundary layer the fluid motion becomes unsteady to some extent, and if sensitive velocity measuring instruments are placed there they show a periodic wavering of the velocity. These oscillations quickly degenerate into irregular motions, that is, fully developed turbulence. The short region B in which this change takes place is called the *transition boundary layer*. The thickness of the layer rapidly increases in this region. At all places downstream of the transition the flow in the boundary layer is turbulent, with the thickness of the layer increasing. There is no limit to the thickness of the layer so long as there is no breakaway, the conditions for which will be examined later : part C, the *turbulent boundary layer*, continues indefinitely, providing the surface remains the same.

For engineering work the properties of the turbulent boundary layer C are most often required. However, the laminar layer A, which has quite different properties, is sometimes of predominant importance, particularly when models are being tested in wind tunnels, in ship-testing tanks, or for civil engineering work. It has been observed that the laminar flow breaks down into the transition B at a distance X from the leading edge, where

$$XU/\nu = 5 \times 10^5 \quad \text{to} \quad 2 \times 10^6$$

(ν is the kinematic viscosity of the fluid ; U is the undisturbed velocity). The higher value is applicable if the oncoming stream is non-turbulent, or when the surface itself is travelling into still fluid ; the lower value is applicable if the stream is very turbulent, but XU/ν is never smaller than 5×10^5 on a smooth surface. Consequently, if a model aircraft is tested in a wind tunnel at the same speed U as the full-size prototype is designed to fly in the atmosphere, then the distance X will be the same for both model and prototype. But in the model, X may be a large proportion of the total length, whereas in the prototype it may be only an insignificant fraction. The drag force due to a turbulent boundary layer is quite different from that due to a laminar one, so a misleading result may be obtained from such tests. As the atmosphere is usually in a less turbulent state than the air in a wind tunnel, the value of UX/ν will be rather higher for the prototype than for the model, that is, X will be rather greater in the prototype ; but it would be purely fortuitous if the increase of X for this reason put the transition point B at the same relative place on the prototype as was observed on the model. An early transition may be artificially produced on a model by putting roughness on the surface, such as a series of wires stretched across the flow. Eddies are produced behind each wire which produce drag forces more nearly that of the naturally formed turbulent boundary layer.

12.3 Growth of boundary layers

As a boundary layer grows thicker, more fluid is decelerated from its original undisturbed velocity, so that the momentum of the fluid in a direction parallel to the solid surface is steadily decreased. Such a decrease of momentum can only be caused by retarding forces, and these are the tangential drag force on the surface and the pressure forces in the direction parallel to the surface caused by changes of pressure intensity (if any). But there are also important changes of the velocity component in the direction normal to the surface. Since the boundary layer grows thicker downstream, the total quantity of fluid passing into a layer of fixed depth above the surface is greater than the quantity leaving the same layer further downstream, where the mean speed of the fluid is less (see fig 12.2). There can be no velocity component normal to the surface at the surface, so the surplus fluid entering the fixed depth layer h must leave through its top. Thus there will be a velocity component normal to the surface at the top of the layer and a consequent flow of momentum in this direction. An outward acting pressure force must therefore exist to provide this momentum so that there is an outward pressure gradient in the fluid.

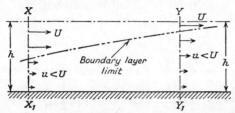

Fig 12.2 Growth of a boundary layer. Since the mean speed across YY_1 is less than that across the same height XX_1, more fluid enters the boundary layer at XX_1 than leaves it at YY. Thus there must be an outward component of velocity across XY. Pressures at X, X_1, Y, Y_2 are not all necessarily the same.

The outward pressure gradient interacts with the pressure gradients along the surface to form a complicated system of forces and velocities which can only be explained by more advanced mathematical methods than will be given in this volume (they are however given in full in *Modern Developments in Fluid Mechanics*, ed. S. Goldstein). A simpler (and far less rigorous) description will be given here, which ignores the outward components of velocity and momentum, and assumes that the pressure is uniform everywhere in the undisturbed stream, in the boundary layer, and on the surface. These assumptions are tantamount to restricting the argument to fluids of low viscosity, which produce relatively thin boundary layers growing but slowly in thickness. Consequently the outward velocities and pressure gradients are small, and the pressure outside the boundary layer is sensibly the same as that at the surface concerned.

12.4 Properties of the laminar boundary layer

Though in normal circumstances the laminar boundary layer is so short,* its properties will be discussed in detail to demonstrate the general method of calculation for all boundary layers.

* For example, in air at 320 km/h, the laminar boundary layer exists for a minimum of about 6 cm; in water at 3 m/s the corresponding distance is 17 cm. In each case, under favourable conditions the layer may be about four times these lengths.

In any laminar flow the relation between stress τ and velocity u is given by the equation $\tau = \mu \, du/dy$, where y is measured in the direction at right angles to the direction of u. A prediction of the velocity distribution involves knowing or predicting how τ varies from the value τ_0 at the solid surface to zero at the outer edge of the boundary layer. In turn, it is τ_0, the drag of the fluid on the surface, that the engineer essentially desires to know. There is no known method whereby τ can be measured directly so that an indirect approach must be made. A distribution of τ will be assumed, the corresponding velocity distribution calculated and then compared with experiment.

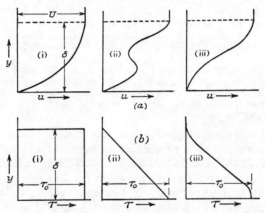

Fig 12.3   (a) Possible velocity distributions at a place in a laminar boundary layer at constant pressure : (i) observed ; (ii) and (iii) not observed. (b) Possible stress distribution in a laminar boundary layer. Stress cannot be directly observed so that all distributions are conjectural, but (i) is unlikely due to discontinuity and (ii) or (iii) more likely.

The simplest and crudest measurements within a boundary layer on a flat surface indicate that the velocity decreases towards the surface with a smooth distribution curve, see fig 12.3 (a) : there is no evidence at all of a point of inflexion, which would imply that the gradient du/dy, and therefore τ, first increases to a maximum, then decreases again. Such a behaviour of τ is unlikely : it is far more likely that τ should increase to a maximum, τ_0, at the surface, though not necessarily at a uniform rate. It is also unlikely that τ should be constant over the whole of the boundary layer thickness δ, falling off to zero suddenly at $y = \delta$. As a first approximation, it will be assumed that τ is varying at a constant rate throughout the layer so that

$\tau = \tau_0(1 - y/\delta)$. As the condition $\tau = \mu \, du/dy$ is inherent to any wholly laminar flow, the stress equation is then

$$\mu \frac{du}{dy} = \tau_0(1 - y/\delta).$$

Integrating each side, $u = \dfrac{\tau_0}{\mu}\left(y - \dfrac{y^2}{2\delta}\right) + \text{Constant.}$

The boundary conditions $y = 0$ when $u = 0$ gives Constant $= 0$; and the condition $y = \delta$ when $u = U$ gives $U = \dfrac{\tau_0}{\mu}\dfrac{\delta}{2}$

Thus
$$U - u = \frac{\tau_0\delta}{2\mu} - \frac{\tau_0}{\mu}\left(y - \frac{y^2}{2\delta}\right)$$

or
$$(U - u) = \frac{\tau_0}{2\mu\delta}(\delta - y)^2 \qquad . \qquad . \qquad . \quad (12.1)$$

This equation shows that the velocity distribution at a given cross section of a laminar boundary layer is a parabola, *if the stress varies linearly*. Since the boundary condition gave $U = \dfrac{\tau_0}{\mu}\dfrac{\delta}{2}$, the all-important stress at the surface is

$$\tau_0 = 2\mu U/\delta \qquad . \qquad . \qquad . \quad (12.2)$$

The velocity distribution and thickness δ can be used now to determine the drag force on the flat surface, which has caused the slowing of the fluid : the momentum of the fluid passing through the boundary layer has been reduced, and the change of this momentum is the force responsible for that reduction. The full reasoning has been given in Chapter 6, where it appears that the force F per unit width of the surface across the direction of flow is

$$F = \int_0^\delta \rho u(U - u) \, dy \qquad . \qquad . \qquad . \quad (6.5)$$

Substituting for u from equation *12.1* it is found that

$$F = \frac{2}{15}\rho U^2\delta \qquad . \qquad . \qquad . \quad (12.3)$$

This total force F is applied by the boundary layer over all the surface from the leading edge back to the point under consideration where the boundary layer thickness is δ, but it should not be thought that F is uniformly distributed along this distance X; in fact, the stress (force per unit area) τ_0 changes along X so that F must be written

as the integral of the elementary forces $\tau_0 dx$, from $x = 0$ at the leading
edge to $x = X$.

That is
$$F = \frac{2}{15}\rho U^2 \delta = \int_{x=0}^{x=X} \tau_0 \, dx$$

Substituting $\tau_0 = 2\mu U/\delta$ this equation can be solved by separation
of the variables δ and x giving

$$X = \rho U \delta^2/30\mu$$

or
$$\delta^2 = 30 \frac{\mu}{\rho} \frac{X}{U}$$

or
$$\delta/X = \sqrt{30}\,(UX/\nu)^{-\frac{1}{2}} = 5\cdot 48(UX/\nu)^{-\frac{1}{2}} \qquad . \qquad . \ (12.4)$$

where $\nu = \mu/\rho$ is the kinematic viscosity of the fluid, see Chapter 1.

An expression has thus been derived for the thickness of a laminar
boundary layer as depending on the distance from the leading edge,
the undisturbed velocity, and the kinematic viscosity of the fluid.
An experimental check of this theoretical equation, by determining
δ at a number of places X, would show whether or not the initial
assumption of the linear distribution of τ with y is correct. This is
a difficult experiment to do because it involves finding where the
velocity first becomes less than U. The parabola of the velocity
distribution curve shows that the slope du/dy is small near $y = \delta$ so
that small errors in determining u give large errors in y.* However,
careful experiments have at least shown that the above expression is
not gravely in error.

A much better test of the validity of the stress assumption is the
experimental determination of the drag force F, which is then compared
with the theoretical values. It is convenient, as was described in
Chapter 8, to express drag forces as Coefficients of Drag, which in this
case of tangential stress on surfaces is commonly called the *Coefficient
of friction C_f*. This is defined as

$$C_f = \frac{\text{Measured drag}}{\frac{1}{2}\rho U^2 \times \text{Area}} = \frac{F}{\frac{1}{2}\rho U^2 X}.$$

The theoretical values of C_f are determined by substituting

$$F = \frac{2}{15}\rho U^2 \delta \quad \text{and} \quad \delta = 5\cdot 48\, X \left(\frac{UX}{\nu}\right)^{-\frac{1}{2}}$$

---

* Not only is the accurate measurement of δ made difficult by the small
slope of the velocity curve at the outside of the boundary layer, but δ itself is
so small that instruments for measuring u take up so much space that inaccuracies
result. For example, with air at 320 km/h the maximum thickness of the
laminar boundary layer (at $X = 6$ cm) is only 0·047 cm. With water at 3 m/s
the corresponding value is 0·13 at $X = 17$ cm. Very fine instruments, such
as small-diameter Pitot tubes, must be used.

which give $$C_f = 1.46 \left(\frac{UX}{\nu}\right)^{-\frac{1}{2}} \qquad . \qquad . \qquad . \quad (12.5)$$

This equation is shown plotted in fig 12.4.

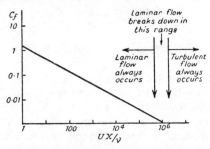

Fig 12.4   Variation of Coefficient of Friction C_f with UX/ν for a laminar boundary layer.   *Note the logarithmic scale*   Laminar flow *may* exist for $5 \times 10^5 < UX/\nu < 2 \times 10^6$, see p. 176.

It is comparatively easy to measure F (and therefore C_f) experimentally, even if it is difficult to make direct measurements of the thickness of the boundary layer.   A flat thin plate with a sharpened leading edge is suspended in an air or water flow in such a way that the drag force F can be measured directly by some sort of weighing machine.   The kinetic pressure $\frac{1}{2}\rho U^2$ is measured by a Pitot tube exposed to the undisturbed stream.   Providing the plate is so short in the direction of the flow that $UX/\nu < 5 \times 10^5$, the laminar boundary layer entirely covers the plate and the values of C_f obtained from the experiment are immediately comparable to the computed ones of equation *12.5*.   Such experiments show that C_f is indeed very close to the theoretical value $1.46\,(UX/\nu)^{-\frac{1}{2}}$.   This good agreement might be taken as indicating that all the assumptions made in the analysis are correct, notably that the linear distribution of stress through the layer $(\tau_0 - \tau \propto y)$ is true.   Unfortunately, however, the situation is not so clear cut as this : other assumptions can be made about the way in which τ varies, and the resulting expressions for C_f are so close to the one already derived that the inevitable experimental errors in the observed values of C_f completely obscure the difference between the theoretical values on the several assumptions.   For example, the unlikely assumption that τ is constant throughout a cross section of the boundary layer (i.e. $\tau = \tau_0$) gives a theoretical value of $C_f = 1.155\,(UX/\nu)^{-\frac{1}{2}}$, which is close to the value already derived for the much more likely linear increase of τ.   Thus measurements of C_f cannot determine critically how the stress varies : any more or less likely stress distribution gives nearly the same value of C_f.   From the engineer's point of view, however, this is a fortunate occurrence, for though it is not conclusive evidence, it is probable that the stress distribution in the more important turbulent boundary layer also makes little difference to the value of C_f. A simple stress distribution can therefore be assumed for the computations that follow.

12.5 Properties of the transition boundary layer

At some distance from the leading edge of a flat surface, the laminar flow in the boundary layer breaks down to give unsteady or oscillating velocities. Velocity measuring instruments in this part of the boundary layer show that the flow is steady for some time, then at intermittent intervals variations occur to give unsteady flow. At places still farther from the leading edge, the unsteady flow occupies larger proportions of the time, and this unsteadiness becomes more erratic. Finally, the erratic or random fluctuations are always present in all parts of the boundary layer, which is then said to be *turbulent*. The reasons for the breakdown from laminar to turbulent flow are still rather poorly understood, and are the subject for a good deal of advanced research.

The properties of the transition boundary layer are partly those of laminar and partly of turbulent flow, and fluctuate from one to another. The stresses and coefficients of friction for the boundary layer at this stage seem to be very dependent on the turbulence of the undisturbed stream. The difficulties of measurement are such that no useful values of C_f can be quoted that can be of general use. However, the point is of small importance in most engineering work, for the transition boundary layer occupies only a small part of the length of a surface exposed to a fluid flow. In fact, its length is considerably less than that of the laminar boundary layer. The drag due to this small length can therefore be neglected unless the surface is very short in the direction of the motion.

12.6 Properties of the turbulent boundary layer

The part of the boundary layer wherein the flow is entirely turbulent is by far the most important part to the engineer, because most surfaces subject to fluid flow are covered with it. As has already been described, the turbulent boundary layer extends downstream to an infinite extent on a smooth flat surface if the pressure remains uniform. The thickness δ increases also, and may eventually be many times greater than that for the laminar boundary layer. For example, the boundary layer at the stern of a 300 m long ship travelling at 30 knots (15·4 m/s) is about 1·4 m thick if the steel plates are smooth : if they are rough, the boundary layer will be still thicker. Because δ is so much greater in the turbulent than in the laminar boundary layer, it is easier to determine the velocity distribution. Experiments have shown that the velocity distribution can be represented, with minor errors only, as a power law $u/U = (y/\delta)^n$, n varying from about $1/5$ near the transition from laminar flow, to $1/7$ farther downstream. The effect of the eddies in the turbulent boundary layer may be seen by comparing a plot of the above velocity distribution curve with that of the laminar layer, equation *12.1*. Near the surface the velocity gradients of the turbulent layer are greater than those of the laminar layer, but near $y = \delta$ the reverse is found.

As in the laminar boundary layer, the force that has caused the slowing down of the fluid is

$$F = \rho \int_0^\delta (U - u)\, u \, \mathrm{d}y \qquad (6.5)$$

Substituting $u/U = (y/\delta)^{1/7}$ and integrating,

this becomes $F = \dfrac{7}{72} \rho \, U^2 \, \delta.$

As before, this force also equals the summation of the varying stresses τ_0 all along the surface from the leading edge. If the surface is long compared with the extent of the laminar layer near its leading edge, then an easy approximation to make is to ignore the laminar layer and assume that the *turbulent* layer occupies the whole surface, so that τ_0 everywhere is that applicable to a turbulent layer.

Thus $$F = \int_0^X \tau_0 \, \mathrm{d}x$$

or $$\frac{7}{72} \rho \, U^2 \, \delta = \int_0^X \tau_0 \, \mathrm{d}x.$$

To solve this equation another relationship is required to eliminate τ_0. In the laminar layer it was derived from the viscosity and velocity gradient at $y = 0$. This cannot be used for a turbulent flow where τ and $\mathrm{d}u/\mathrm{d}y$ are connected by the eddy viscosity, a coefficient that varies with the circumstances of the turbulence and with the place in question. Aid comes, however, from data found from experiments on circular pipes. As will be described in Chapter 13, a pipe, if flowing full of fluid, is wholly occupied by the boundary layer on the walls : there is no central core of constant velocity fluid, but only a single point of maximum velocity (see fig 12.5). Thus, the flow within the pipe may be regarded as a boundary layer on a flat plate which has been wrapped round an axis at a distance δ from the plate equal to the radius r of the pipe : and the axis velocity U_{max} is equivalent to the undisturbed stream velocity U of the flat surface boundary layer.

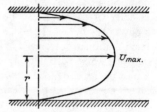

Fig 12.5 Typical velocity distribution within a circular pipe.

It is easy in the case of the pipe to measure τ_0, for this drag causes a measurable drop in pressure along the pipe. In Chapter 13 the connection will be developed between pressure drop and τ_0, but it suffices here to say that experiments show that a rather good empirical equation is

$$\tau_0 = 0\cdot023\,\rho\ U_m{}^2\,(\nu/Ur)^{1/4}$$

for smooth-bore pipes of all sizes. Since $r = \delta$ for the corresponding boundary layer on a flat surface, the expression may be used to equate with the rate of momentum equation, that is

$$\frac{7}{72}\rho\ U^2\,\delta = \int_0^X 0\cdot023\,\rho\ U^2\,(\nu/U\delta)^{1/4}\mathrm{d}x.$$

This may be integrated in the same way as was done for the laminar boundary layer and it gives

$$\delta/X = 0\cdot376\,(UX/\nu)^{-1/5}.$$

Measurements of δ are just as difficult to make in the turbulent layer as they were in the laminar layer. But the foregoing equation for δ/X can be used as before to determine the resultant coefficient of drag, C_f, giving

$$C_f = 0\cdot073\,(UX/\nu)^{-1/5}\qquad . \qquad . \qquad (12.6)$$

and this equation is plotted in fig 12.6.

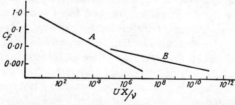

Fig 12.6 The friction coefficient C_f for a smooth plate when the boundary layer is turbulent (curve B) compared with its value for laminar flow (curve A). *Note logarithmic plotting.*

These theoretical values of C_f can be checked, as before, by experiments where the drag is directly measured. Since C_f is partly based upon an empirical relation for τ_0 it is not surprising that the agreement between the results of the drag experiments and equation *12.6* is good : the only error lies in the approximate nature of the velocity distribution curve $u/U = (y/\delta)^{1/7}$. Up to $UX/\nu = 20 \times 10^6$ the experimental values of C_f all lie within about 2 per cent of the values given by equation *12.6*. At higher values of UX/ν the errors become unacceptably large for engineering work concerned with large surfaces in the X direction exposed to high fluid velocities U, thus giving large values of UX/ν. (The 300 m ship sailing at 30 knots gives $UX/\nu = 4 \times 10^9$ for the boundary layer at the stern.) Reliable information about the drag under these conditions requires a better theory based more solidly upon rational explanations than upon experimental data. A simplified version of such a theory will therefore be given.

12.7 Transfer of momentum by turbulent eddies

To build up a rational theory for the drag caused by a turbulent boundary layer, it is necessary to consider the action of the irregular motions or eddies that are superimposed on the mean velocity. Consider a turbulent flow, such as a cross section of a boundary layer, where there is a gradient across the flow du/dy of the mean velocity u. The mean velocity in this context is the velocity at a point averaged over a long period : that is, the fluctuating velocities of turbulence are ' averaged out '. The drag force of the surface τ_0 would eventually stop the adjacent layer of fluid completely, unless this layer had exerted on it another force by the layer next above. Viscous forces given by the viscosity equation $\tau = \mu du/dy$, which act in a laminar boundary layer, are not nearly great enough, so that other ways must be found whereby the momentum of the layers nearer the surface is continually refreshed from layers farther away. One of these ways is by reason of the random and erratic motions that are superimposed on the mean velocity in turbulent flow, and are sometimes in a direction across the mean direction of flow. In this way a small quantity of faster moving fluid can be moved sideways into a layer of slower moving fluid, increasing the latter's momentum. At the same time, to avoid an accumulation of fluid in the slower layer, a corresponding motion must take place somewhere in the opposite direction, taking slower fluid into the fast layer where it is in turn accelerated. But such a system would result in an accumulation of fluid at two opposite corners of a small area of the flow (AA in fig 12.7) unless there were corresponding motions along the direction of mean flow. Thus a rotary set of complementary motions is set up as shown in the figure and these are called *eddies*. It will be seen that the complementary motions change

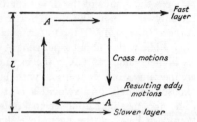

Fig 12.7 The motions comprising an eddy connecting two layers of fluid travelling at different speeds.

the speed of the upper and lower layers by the same amount. Thus, if u is the mean speed of the centre of the eddy relative to the boundaries of the flow, and $\partial u/\partial y$ the instantaneous velocity gradient of the flow, then the speed of the upper layer is $u + \frac{1}{2} l \, \partial u/\partial y$ and of the lower layer $u - \frac{1}{2} l \, \partial u/\partial y$. The eddy motions across the flow are, therefore, $\frac{1}{2} l \, \partial u/\partial y$ relative to the mean motion (see fig 12.8).

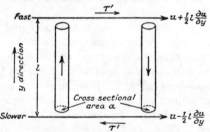

Fig 12.8 Transfers of momentum occur through each of the cylinders of fluid shown, which are the same distance $l/2$ on opposite sides of an eddy. A shear stress τ' has produced a gradient $\partial u/\partial y$ of the mean velocity u so that the upper edge of the eddy is faster than the lower edge.

This simplified diagram of the motions in an eddy can be used now to determine the momentum transferred from one layer to another. In the cylinders of cross-sectional area a shown on each side of the eddy, a velocity $\frac{1}{2} l \, \partial u/\partial y$ is occurring, transferring a mass of $a \rho \frac{1}{2} l \, \partial u/\partial y$ in unit time from the fast layer to the slow, and vice versa. Every unit mass of fluid changes its momentum by an amount $l \, \partial u/\partial y$, so that the total rate of change of momentum by both cylinders is

$$2 \left(a \rho \tfrac{1}{2} l \frac{\partial u}{\partial y} \right) \left(l \frac{\partial u}{\partial y} \right)$$

A momentum transfer of this sort across the flow would eventually mix the faster and slower layers together to form a uniform stream at the mean velocity, unless there are forces acting which preserve the velocity gradient. In a steady stream of real fluid with a velocity gradient there is a shear stress acting which is constantly forcing one layer to slide over the next. In the eddy of fig 12.8 the instantaneous value of this stress is τ' which, acting on the ends of the cylinder, just balances the tendency of the momentum transport to eliminate the velocity gradient.

Thus
$$\tau' 2a = 2 \left(a\rho \tfrac{1}{2} l \frac{\partial u}{\partial y} \right) \left(l \frac{\partial u}{\partial y} \right)$$

or
$$\tau' = \tfrac{1}{2}\rho \left(l \frac{\partial u}{\partial y} \right)^2.$$

Not all the eddies in the fluid are of course of this size l, and not all of any one eddy is necessarily giving the same momentum exchange. The stress τ' may therefore vary from place to place and from one moment to the next, depending upon the eddies that happen to be active. However, it is convenient to write l as the *mean* size of the eddy that occurs, τ as the *mean* stress and therefore du/dy as the *mean* gradient of velocity at any point. To preserve the truth of the equation it is therefore necessary to introduce a constant K so that now

$$\tau = K \tfrac{1}{2}\rho \left(l \frac{du}{dy} \right)^2$$

or
$$\left(\frac{\tau}{\rho} \right)^{1/2} = \left(\frac{K}{2} \right)^{1/2} l \frac{du}{dy}.$$

This differential equation may be solved if assumptions are made about the way τ and l change with y. A very simple one is that $\tau = \text{constant} = \tau_0$: in the laminar boundary layer it was shown that this simple assumption gives a remarkably good approximation to the results of more elaborate stress distributions. Also experiments tend to show that $(K/2)^{1/2} l$ is proportional to the distance y from the solid surface on which the boundary layer is formed. This is confirmed by simple observations of a river in flood : large eddies do not exist near the sides because of the lack of room for such large cross motions there. In fact, the experiments show that

$$\left(\frac{K}{2} \right)^{1/2} l = 0.4y.$$

Thus, substituting these assumptions into the eddy differential equation,

$$du = \left(\frac{\tau_0}{\rho} \right)^{1/2} \frac{1}{0.4y} \, dy$$

and integrating
$$u = \left(\frac{\tau_0}{\rho} \right)^{1/2} \frac{1}{0.4} \left[\log_e y \right] + \text{Constant}.$$

The constant of integration may be written as

$$C = \left(\frac{\tau_0}{\rho}\right)^{1/2} \frac{1}{0\cdot4} \log_e \frac{1}{C_1} \text{ where } C_1 \text{ is another constant,}$$

so that the velocity equation is

$$u = \left(\frac{\tau_0}{\rho}\right)^{1/2} \frac{1}{0\cdot4}\left[\log_e y + \log_e \frac{1}{C_1}\right]$$

or

$$u = 2\cdot5 \left(\frac{\tau_0}{\rho}\right)^{1/2} \log_e \frac{y}{C_1}.$$

Changing to common logarithms

$$u = 2\cdot5 \times 2\cdot303 \left(\frac{\tau_0}{\rho}\right)^{1/2} \log_{10} \frac{y}{C_1}$$

$$= 5\cdot75 \left(\frac{\tau_0}{\rho}\right)^{1/2} \log_{10} \frac{y}{C_1} \qquad . \qquad . \quad (12.7)$$

This logarithmic velocity distribution has been confirmed by experiment. Values of u are taken at a number of distances y from a plate whereon there is a turbulent boundary layer. A graph is made of u against $\log_{10} y$ and it is found that all points lie in a straight line, as in fig 12.9 : if τ_0 is measured as well, then the slope of the line is

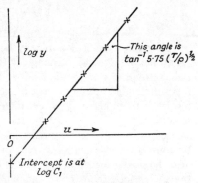

Fig 12.9 Experimental determination of velocities in a turbulent boundary layer shows $u \propto \log y$. Slope and intercept therefore give $(\tau/\rho)^{1/2}$ and C_1 respectively.

found to be $5\cdot75 \, (\tau_0/\rho)^{1/2}$. This logarithmic curve does not give a value for δ, where the velocity becomes constant : it gives a velocity increasing indefinitely with y, though at a decreasing *rate* of increase as in fig 12.10. Thus the experimental difficulty of finding δ to confirm a theoretical formula does not arise. But the place where there are large and therefore measurable changes of velocity is at small values of y, and here the very presence of the surface creates errors in the readings of Pitot tubes and other devices. Experimental verification of the logarithmic velocity formula at small values of y cannot be made. However, extrapolation to $u = 0$ of the straight line of the logarithmic velocity profile (fig 12.9) gives an intercept on the log y axis of $y = C_1$. Such a finite intercept is of course inevitable with a logarithmic equation. But it is now necessary to explain why apparently the fluid seems to be stationary at a finite distance C_1 above the surface. This seems hardly possible and in fact does not occur.

12.8. Turbulent eddy motions, as an action producing a shear (friction) stress, can also be viewed more generally as a process of mixing. Consider one point in a stream of fluid (whether in a boundary layer or in the ' main stream ') where the flow is turbulent, and so where the instantaneous velocity can be decomposed into components u and v at right-angles to each other. Each component then consists of the mean, steady velocity $\bar{u}$ (or $\bar{v}$) which does not vary, and an instantaneous velocity fluctuation u' (or v') which varies erratically from instant to instant. Thus $u = \bar{u} + u'$ and $v = \bar{v} + v'$. Notice that u' and v' can be either positive or negative. By choosing suitable axes, then if u is along the direction of total mean motion, $\bar{v} = 0$. The fluctuating components u' and v' are thus non-steady and could be measured by sufficiently sensitive and rapid-acting instruments.

Now consider the situation at an instant where $u = \bar{u} + u'$; $v = + v'$. In a unit of time the transverse velocity v' will carry sideways to the mean total motion a mass of fluid $\rho v'$ per unit area : this fluid has temporarily a surplus u' of u-momentum above the steady value $\bar{u}$ (both values per unit mass). So the amount of fluctuating u-momentum transferred sideways in the v-direction per unit of time and of area is $\rho u' v'$. This surplus mixes instantaneously with the u-momentum already in the new layer to which the transverse velocity has brought it ; the fluctuation would speed up the u-velocity in the new layer and so would lead to a non-steady situation, with gradual speeding up. However, this situation does not arise because of the existence of a shear stress which restrains the acceleration. In fact, a steady turbulent flow with a fluctuating transfer of momentum is inevitably accompanied by a shear stress $\tau = -\rho u' v'$.

Now at another subsequent instant, due to a change in the turbulence, u' might be negative so that there is a *deficit* of u-momentum available. If v' is still positive, the motion would slow down in the second layer, unless it were reversed for the instant. Similarly, if the negative u' were accompanied by a negative v', there would be a slowing of a layer on the opposite side of the original layer, with the same effect as the original positive u' and v'. Over a long period, with many separate instants in which u' and v' are measured, the mean value $\overline{\rho u' v'}$ of all the separate values of $\rho u'v'$ will be the mean stress over that period. (The bar over $\rho u'v'$ implies a simple arithmetical average of a number of values of the product $\rho u'v'$.) Of course, it is possible to have this mean value zero (i.e. no stress), even through there is turbulence present ; then, such turbulent velocities are called ' uncorrelated ' with each other. On the other hand, if positive u' are *always* accompanied by positive v' (and negative u' with negative v'), there is a *relatively* large stress since the mean value $\rho u'v'$ is large : such turbulence is called ' correlated '. The stress in a boundary layer is accompanied by correlated turbulence : the correlation falls towards the outer edge of the boundary layer ; and outside the boundary layer in the main stream the turbulence is un-correlated (so there is no stress there).

A further point can now be considered. There is always present a wide variety of frequencies at which u' and v' change. There are slow changes of both mixed with fast changes. If the instants already re-ferred to are widely spaced (in time), then the influence of the faster changes will be entirely missed by the instrument concerned. Instants close together in time sample both fast and slow changes and so take into account more turbulence than observations taken at instants further apart. So, in general, rapid and very frequent sampling of u' and v' gives a higher $\tau = \overline{\rho u'v'}$ than infrequent sampling. The type of instruments and their rapidity of following the velocities thus controls the apparent value of τ. It should be noted that this method of finding shear stress is the only one where the variation of τ with distance y across the flow can be measured. The method of § 13.3 in a pipe where the pressure gradient along it is measured by small holes in the pipe wall, gives only τ_0, the particular value at the wall. Generally, experiments show that τ increases towards a maximum at τ_0. The tacit assumption of the mixing length theory that τ is constant through a boundary layer is therefore strictly incorrect, but more refined analyses show that the error is not great, and can be tolerated for many engineer-ing purposes.

A very similar approach can be made to consider the mixing of a pollutant in a stream by the action of turbulence. Such a ' pollutant ' may be a chemical, or heat, or merely a deficiency of a gas (oxygen for example). Consider a situation where polluted fluid exists at a mean strength $\bar{s}$ (units of polluted matter per unit volume of fluid) in a particu-lar layer. In another layer there is less pollution because the pollutant is being taken away (for example clean water running over polluted water, or heat going away to the atmosphere). If a steady situation has been set up, the pollutant must be steadily transferred between the layers, by turbulent action of eddies. Thus, if a sensitive instrument is used to measure pollution, the instantaneous pollution is $\bar{s} + s'$, the

bar and the prime ' having the same meaning as for the velocity u. So
the amount of pollutant carried sideways is $s'v'$ at the one instant ; if this
is immediately accepted into the new layer, the pollution there would
rise unless the transport away just balances it. So, if many instants
are considered, the mean transport over them must be *exactly* balanced
by the mean transferred pollution $\overline{s'v'}$. This transfer of pollution is an
exact analogy of the stress caused by the transfer of u-momentum.

The method of determining a transport rate from turbulence measurements is always in principle possible, although there are sometimes
severe instrumental problems to overcome so as to find u', v' or s' precisely and rapidly. It is then often helpful to relate the rate to the
gradient of the mean value of the polluting substance across the stream—
in the same way that in the mixing length theory τ is associated with the
gradient of the mean value $d\bar{u}/dy$. Thus for a chemical pollutant

$$\overline{s'v'} = \mathrm{K}_1 \frac{d\bar{s}}{dy}.$$

For heat

$$C_p \, \overline{T'v'} = \mathrm{K}_2 \frac{d\bar{T}}{dy}$$

where T is the temperature and C_p is the specific heat at constant pressure.

For u-momentum

$$\tau = \overline{\rho u'v'} = \mathrm{K}_3 \frac{d\bar{u}}{dy}$$

The K terms, sometimes called exchange coefficients, have a direct
analogy with the coefficient of viscosity (for the situation where there is
no turbulence) for which in Chapter 1 it is shown

$$\tau = \mu \frac{du}{dy}$$

and K_3 is called the eddy viscosity.

It is relatively easy to measure gradients of mean properties such as
$d\bar{s}/dy$, $d\bar{u}/dy$, for all that is necessary is a well-damped, averaging, instrument ; but turbulence measurements need a rapid-acting instrument
that will detect small changes of a property in the presence of a large
average value of the property. Much effort has been devoted to finding
K values in different situations. Unfortunately, K varies widely, and
although in the same situation changes of K give a useful estimate of
changes of transport rates, a K found in one situation cannot be relied
upon for another. Generally, K for large-scale motions (ocean currents,
and the atmosphere) will be larger than K for small scale motions. It
would also be useful if in one particular situation $K_1 = K_2 = K_3$,

u m/s	u' m/s	v m/s	v' m/s	c mg/l	c' mg/l	$u'v'$ $\times 10^{-4}$	$c'v'$ $+10^{-4}$
1·00	+0·01	−0·02	−0·02	10·05	+0·043	−2	−8·6
1·02	+0·03	+0·03	+0·03	10·00	−0·007	+9	−2·1
1·04	+0·05	−0·01	−0·01	9·97	−0·037	−5	+3·7
0·90	−0·09	+0·05	+0·05	10·08	+0·073	−45	+36·5
0·97	−0·02	−0·01	−0·01	10·04	+0·033	+2	−3·3
1·01	+0·02	+0·01	+0·01	9·99	−0·017	+2	−1·7
1·02	+0·03	−0·05	−0·05	9·98	−0·027	−15	+13·5
0·96	−0·03	+0·02	+0·02	10·02	+0·013	−6	+2·6
1·00	+0·01	0	0	10·00	−0·007	0	0
0·98	−0·01	−0·02	−0·02	9·94	−0·067	+2	+13·4
Sum 9·90 **Mean** $\bar{u} = 0{\cdot}990$		0 $\bar{v} = 0$		100·07 $\bar{c} = 10{\cdot}007$		$\left\{ \begin{matrix} +15 \\ -73 \end{matrix} \right\}$ $= -58 \times 10^{-4}$	$\left\{ \begin{matrix} +69{\cdot}7 \\ -15{\cdot}7 \end{matrix} \right\}$ $= +54 \times 10^{-4}$

As $\bar{v} = 0$, it turns out that the axes of measurement of velocity are precisely along and normal to the mean fluid motion.

for then a simple experiment to find K_3 (by measuring pressure gradients, for example) could then be directly used to find the more difficult transports of pollution or heat. Again, rather unfortunately, $K_1 = K_2 = K_3$ only in rather special circumstances, when the pollution does *not* change the density of the fluid: usually it does so (heat changes density by thermal expansion; pollution of a solid makes fluid heavier).

Example

At a point in a boundary layer, instantaneous and simultaneous measurements are made at intervals of 1 second, of the velocity components u and v, and of the concentration c of a pollutant. The fluid is water and pollutant is measured in milligrams/litre. Also, a well-averaged reading of u and c is taken at a place 1 m above the former point, giving $u = 1·09 \text{ m/s}$; $c = 9·900 \text{ mg/l}$.

A set of ten readings is given below: estimate the shear stress there, the upward mixing of pollutant and the exchange coefficients of momentum and pollution.

u	m/s	1·00	1·02	1·04	0·90	0·97	1·01	1·02	0·96	1·00	0·98
v	m/s	−0·02	+0·03	−0·01	+0·05	−0·01	+0·01	−0·05	+0·02	0	−0·02
c	mg/l	10·05	10·00	9·97	10·08	10·04	9·99	9·98	10·02	10·00	9·94

A tabulation is necessary to find each value of u', v', c', and the products $u'v'$, $v'c'$. Care must be taken to ensure the calculations preserve the units of measurement. Work downwards in the u, v and c columns, then derive

$$u' = u \sim \bar{u}; \quad v' = v \sim \bar{v}; \quad c' \sim \bar{c}$$

Then multiply up $u'v'$ and $v'c'$ and work downwards in these columns.

Mean value $\overline{u'v'} = -\tfrac{1}{10} \times 58 \times 10^{-4} = -5·8 \times 10^{-4} \text{ m}^2/\text{s}$.

Thus stress $\tau = 1000 \times 5·8 \times 10^{-4} \text{ N/m}^2$
$= 0·58 \text{ N/m}^2$ *Ans.*

Mean value $\overline{c'v'} = \tfrac{1}{10} \times 54 \times 10^{-4} \dfrac{\text{mg}}{\text{l}} \cdot \dfrac{\text{m}}{\text{s}}$

$= 5·4 \times 10^{-4} \dfrac{10^{-3}\text{g}}{1000 \text{ cm}^3} \cdot \dfrac{100 \text{ cm}}{\text{s}}$

$= 5·4 \times 10^{-8} \text{ g cm}^{-2} \text{ s}^{-1}$
$= 5·4 \times 10^{-4} \text{ g m}^{-2} \text{ s}^{-1}$ *Ans.*

Exchange coefficient for momentum ('eddy viscosity') K_3
$= \tau/\rho \, \mathrm{d}\bar{u}/\mathrm{d}y$

Gradient of mean velocity $= \dfrac{1·09 - 0·990}{1·0} = 0·1 \text{ s}^{-1}$

So $K_3 = \dfrac{0·58}{1000 \times 0·1} = 5·8 \times 10^{-3} \text{ m}^2/\text{s}$ *Ans.*

Exchange coefficient for pollution K_1
   Gradient of mean pollution

$$\mathrm{d}c/\mathrm{d}y = \frac{10\cdot007 - 9\cdot900}{1\cdot0} = 0\cdot107 \times 10^{-3}\,\frac{\mathrm{g}}{\mathrm{lm}}$$

So

$$K_1 = \frac{5\cdot4 \times 10^{-4}\ \mathrm{g\,m^{-2}\,s^{-1}}}{0\cdot107 \times 10^{-3}\,\mathrm{g\,l^{-1}\,m^{-1}}}$$

$$= 5 \times 10^{-1}\,\mathrm{m^{-1}\,ls^{-1}} = 5 \times 10^{-1}\,\mathrm{m^{-1}}\,\frac{\mathrm{m^3}}{1000}\,\mathrm{s^{-1}}$$

$$= 5 \times 10^{-4}\,\mathrm{m^2/s} \qquad\qquad\qquad\qquad \textit{Ans.}$$

It is quite common to find K_1 much smaller than K_3, particularly if the polluted water has a different density to that of the unpolluted stream.

12.9   The laminar sub-layer

The apparent paradox of the logarithmic velocity profile giving zero velocity at a finite distance C_1 can be explained by the presence next to the surface of a thin layer of fluid where the flow is entirely laminar, even if flow in the rest of the boundary layer is turbulent. Apparently if the velocity gradient is great, as it is if y is small, the viscous forces tend to oppose the formation of eddies, and eventually prevent them from forming at all. Consequently the logarithmic profile of velocity is only valid for the part of the boundary layer outside this *laminar sub-layer* : inside it, the velocity increases approximately linearly with y (see fig 10.2). The sub-layer (which must

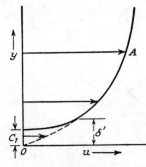

Fig 12.10   The velocity distribution curve for a turbulent boundary layer on a smooth surface. A is the logarithmic velocity curve with intercept C_1, but in the layers of fluid nearest the surface, the flow is laminar, the velocity decreasing linearly, as shown by the dotted line.

not, of course, be confused with the wholly laminar boundary layer near the leading edge of the surface) is, however, usually thin : experiments have shown that its thickness δ' is given by

$$\delta' = 11\cdot5\nu\left(\frac{\tau_0}{\rho}\right)^{-\frac{1}{2}} \qquad . \qquad . \qquad . \qquad . \quad (12.8)$$

Thus for water at a speed of 3 m/s, at a point 3·6 m from the leading edge of a smooth plane surface (i.e. $UX/\nu = 10^7$ approx), the laminar sub-layer of the turbulent boundary layer has a thickness δ' of only 0·033 cm. The turbulent layer thickness above the laminar sub-layer is $\delta = 5·6$ cm, approximately as given by the empirical formula $\delta/X = 0·376 \, (UX/\nu)^{-1/5}$ already derived.

A laminar sub-layer then exists near a smooth surface, and the stress τ is transmitted finally through the distance δ' to the surface wholly by the molecular forces of viscosity. However, smooth surfaces are rather rare in engineering work, where surfaces usually have projections on them (roughnesses) whose size may be many times greater than δ'. Under these *rough boundary* conditions, the extrapolated value of the constant C_1 has been found to depend on the shape and size of the roughness. If the roughnesses are grains of sand, all just passing through a sieve of size k, experiments have given $C_1 = k/33$: but it must be emphasized that other shapes of roughness (perhaps, say, the hemispherical heads of rivets on steel plates) may give constants other than $k/33$.

From equation *12.8* it will be seen that for a given surface and fluid, δ' decreases if τ_0 increases. The stress τ_0 is largely controlled by the velocity U, for $\tau_0 = C_f \frac{1}{2} \rho \, U^2$, so that at high speeds the laminar sub-layer becomes thinner. Consequently if the surface is a rough one, it is quite possible that at low speeds the roughnesses are submerged in the laminar sub-layer, and the surface acts as if it were smooth. The velocity distribution in the turbulent part of the boundary layer is then quite independent of k and is

$$u/u_* = 5·75 \log_{10} (u_* y/\nu) + 5·5$$

Where $u_* = (\tau_0/\rho)^{1/2}$. By contrast the same surface at higher speeds has on it a thinner sub-layer so that the roughnesses may now project through it and control the constant C_1, leading to a velocity distribution

$$u/u_* = 5·75 \log_{10} 33y/k.$$

These two conditions are reflected in the coefficient of friction found by the substitution of the above velocity profiles into the momentum integral equation 6.5. These integrations are of course more difficult than those of the laminar boundary layer and give expressions that are rather inconvenient for use in computations. However, very close approximations have been found which are more convenient. These are

$$C_f = 0·455 \, (\log_{10} UX/\nu)^{-2·58} \text{ for the smooth boundary}$$

and $\quad C_f = (1·89 + 1·62 \log_{10} X/k)^{-2·5}$ for the rough boundary.

In the smooth boundary case, it will be seen that C_f is controlled by the viscosity of the fluid, through its influence on the thickness of the laminar sub-layer. In the case of the rough boundary, the roughness size alone controls C_f, because it determines the size of the eddies thrown off in the wake of each individual roughness element (i.e. grain of sand or rivet head). There is an intermediate stage between the true smooth and the rough boundary cases, when the laminar sub-layer is about the same thickness as the height of the roughnesses : the eddies thrown off by the top of the roughnesses are now weak and are strongly affected by the proximity of the laminar flow : C_f now lies between the smooth and rough boundary values, and depends on

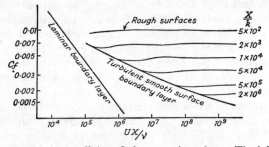

Fig 12.11   The friction coefficient C_f for a rough surface. The left-hand line is for the laminar boundary layer at low values of UX/ν, which is exactly the same as for a smooth surface. The lowest right-hand line is for the *smooth* surface equation which the rough surface also gives when there is a laminar sub-layer thicker than the size k of the roughness on the surface. The upper right-hand lines are for C_f when the roughness elements are causing eddies directly, each line being for a different value of X/k : C_f in this case is independent of UX/ν but changes only with the ratio X/k. X is the distance from the leading edge of the surface.

both UX/ν and also X/k. A graph can therefore be made of C_f against UX/ν, which gives a single line for all smooth surfaces. Coefficients for rough surfaces at low UX/ν also follow this line, but gradually diverge from it in the intermediate stage, until at the higher values of UX/ν they become independent of it, being then only dependent on X/k (see fig 12.11).

12.10   Application of flat plate friction coefficients

The curve of C_f against UX/ν for flat surfaces, both rough and smooth, may be also used, with caution, for finding the tangential friction forces on gently curved surfaces, providing that breakaway does not occur. If breakaway occurs the estimates so found will be greatly in error. A frictional drag force on a gently curved object may be expressed in the form of a Coefficient of drag so that

$$C_{\text{friction drag}} = \text{Frictional drag force} / \tfrac{1}{2}\rho\, U^2\, A,$$

where A is, as in Chapter 8, the maximum cross-sectional area of the object *across* the flow direction. A distinction must be made between this frictional force and the drag force caused by the summation of all the pressure forces around the object, the pressures having arisen because of the distortion of streamlines around the object. The integration of an experimentally or theoretically determined pressure distribution to give a lift or drag force has already been described. The drag obtained in this way is called the *form drag*, and is quite independent of the friction drag. It is also usual to express form drag as a coefficient thus,

$$C_{\text{form drag}} = \text{Form drag force} / \tfrac{1}{2}\rho\, U^2\, A.$$

The total drag, as found by direct measurement or by the wake traverse method of Chapter 6, is the sum of the Form and Friction drags, and gives a *total drag coefficient*. The relative magnitude of the coefficients of form and friction drags, as well as their absolute values, are related to the shape of the solid body. Well-streamlined shapes have the form drag and friction drag of the same order of magnitude with both small : poorly streamlined shapes with breakaway occurring near the leading edge and large wakes behind them have the friction drag only 1 per cent or 2 per cent of the form drag and the total drag coefficient is relatively large.

12.11 Effect of pressure changes on the boundary layer

The boundary layer on a solid surface has been shown to depend predominantly on the shear stress of the surface on the fluid, and to be nearly independent of the properties of the main stream. But if the pressure increases in the direction of motion, the boundary layer may affect the main stream by producing *breakaway* (sometimes called *separation*).

Consider a surface OABC along which there is a fluid flow and on which a boundary layer has formed on the leading portion OAB (the part OA will be wholly laminar flow). As has been described, the thickness δ increases downstream and at the point B the velocity distribution would be given by the dotted curve of fig 12.12 (*b*) if the pressure is constant along the surface. If, however, the pressure has been increasing in the direction of motion (i.e. $p_a < p_d$) there is a pressure force opposing the fluid motion. This opposing force, though spread uniformly over the whole cross section of the boundary layer BB_1, does not produce a uniform deceleration on all the fluid passing through BB_1. The low-speed fluid near the surface has less momentum than that farther away so that the former is more easily retarded by the opposing force. Thus the velocity distribution is modified to that shown in the full line, there being little change in velocity near the outer limit of the boundary layer but much more change near the surface.

Farther downstream however, at C, the normal development of the boundary layer would have produced a thicker layer than that at B. Consequently there is more low-speed fluid close to the surface than at B and this is more sensitive to the opposing pressure force. A greater retardation occurs and an appreciable layer of fluid is brought to rest, fig 12.12 (c). Still farther downstream, at D, the opposing force has actually reversed the flow and giving the profile of velocity shown in fig 12.12 (d). The point where the flow is first reversed is called the

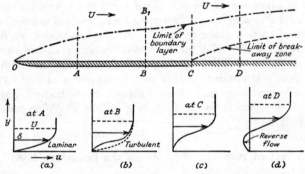

Fig 12.12   Growth of a boundary layer on a flat surface along which the pressure rises in the downstream direction. Velocity distribution at A, B, C, and D also shown, D being at a higher pressure than A. At B the distribution is also given for the velocity in a boundary layer at constant pressure. The breakaway (or separation) point is at C.

breakaway point. It will be seen from fig 12.13 that the reversed flow causes a large slow eddy which is permanently present, and which has large velocity gradients at its boundaries. A large degradation of energy into heat occurs in such an eddy. Thus breakaway is caused by a combination of the reduced velocities in a boundary layer and a pressure gradient opposing the flow (an *adverse* pressure gradient). Breakaway cannot occur unless there is an adverse pressure gradient: on the flat plate at constant pressure there is never breakaway; and breakaway can only occur with a real fluid which produces a boundary layer. Do not however confuse the permanent slow eddy due to breakaway with the smaller temporary eddies of turbulent motion.

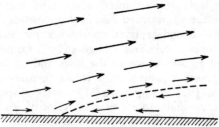

Fig 12.13   The flow in the vicinity of a breakaway point.   Arrows show fluid velocities.   The effect is to make a generally rotatory motion centred on the limit of the breakaway zone (shown dotted), which is not a streamline.

Adverse pressure gradients are produced whenever there is a tendency for the fluid to decelerate, for by Bernoulli's equation,

$$\frac{u_1{}^2}{2g} + \frac{p_1}{\rho g} = \frac{u_2{}^2}{2g} + \frac{p_2}{\rho g}$$

if the energy is constant.   Thus, if $u_1 > u_2$, $p_2 > p_1$, so that the pressure increases as velocity decreases.   Such a deceleration occurs where the streamlines of a theoretical pattern tend to diverge, say, in the rear of solid objects travelling relative to a fluid.   For instance, a cylinder, exposed to a stream of ideal fluid, causes a distortion of the streamline that can be predicted (Chapter 5), and there is no boundary layer.   The velocity at different places round the periphery can be predicted from the streamline spacing and, by Bernoulli's equation, the pressure p at any point found as

$$(p - p_0)/\tfrac{1}{2} \rho\, U^2 = 1 - 4 \sin^2 \theta.$$

This distribution is shown in fig 12.14 and it will be seen that for $90° < \theta < 180°$ the pressure gradient is opposing the flow.   In a real fluid a laminar boundary layer is formed on the leading side of the

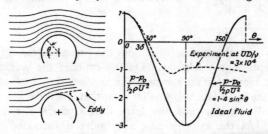

Fig 12.14   Flow round a cylinder held with axis normal to a stream of velocity U.   (*Left upper*) Theoretical ideal fluid streamlines.   (*Left lower*) Actual streamlines, showing breakaway and eddies in the wake.   (*Right*) Theoretical ideal fluid, and actual experimental curves of pressure distribution on the surface of such a cylinder.

cylinder. The layer grows thicker as the fluid progresses towards $\theta = 90°$, so that there is retarded fluid near the surface of the cylinder. As soon as this boundary layer approaches the adverse pressure gradient, breakaway occurs and a large eddy is formed. The main flow is diverted to the outside of the eddy and no longer tends to revert to the streamline pattern which it had upstream of the cylinder (compare fig 12.14 (a) and fig 12.14 (b)) : there is now no diverging flow to return the fluid to its original velocity, and consequently there is no appreciable rise of pressure in the eddy. The pressure distribution found experimentally under these conditions of breakaway is shown also in fig 12.14. Such an experimental pressure distribution can be integrated to find the form drag, and form drag coefficient, of a cylinder.

If the transition from a laminar to a turbulent boundary layer occurs before the breakaway commences, then the pressure distribution, form drag and flow pattern are all changed. The transition occurs when UX/ν reaches a critical value (5×10^5 to 2×10^6 for a flat plate, but not necessarily the same for a cylinder), X now being the circumferential distance from the leading, stagnation point. Thus an early transition occurs if U is large or ν small. The turbulent boundary layer following the transition has a velocity distribution with much higher speeds close to the surface than does a laminar boundary layer (see fig 12.15). Thus a turbulent layer has more momentum available

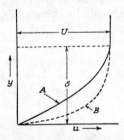

Fig 12.15 Comparison of the velocity distribution in two boundary layers of the same thickness, A being laminar and B turbulent. B always has greater velocities at a given distance y from the surface, has more momentum, and therefore is less susceptible to adverse pressure gradients.

at places near the surface to oppose the pressure gradient, and is so *less* susceptible to breakaway. On the cylinder the breakaway point therefore moves farther downstream to about $\theta = 130°$ or so. The eddy in the wake is much smaller than that when the boundary layer was wholly laminar, and the form drag coefficient is considerably reduced. As the velocity past a cylinder is increased the change between the two régimes occurs quite suddenly, as soon as the transition occurs before the breakaway. It is sometimes worth while deliberately to cause an early transition so as to have a small, low drag wake.

It will therefore be seen that the properties of the boundary layer are of the greatest importance in determining not only the frictional drag but also the wake and so the form drag of solid bodies. Although clever streamlining can delay the breakaway considerably it cannot always prevent it. Other ways of controlling the breakaway can be used if additional complications can be tolerated : for example, a narrow slot can be made in the surface across the flow and fluid drawn inwards by a suitable suction pump or fan as shown in fig 12.16 (a). The nearer, slower, fluid which is most susceptible to adverse pressure gradients is thus removed. Breakaway can be entirely inhibited by this method on poorly streamlined shapes which will then have a very low drag. It is theoretically possible to apply boundary layer suction

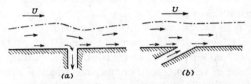

Fig 12.16   Two ways of reducing the sensitivity of a boundary layer to an adverse pressure gradient, and therefore delaying the breakaway point. (a) Drawing-off the slow fluid through a slot ; (b) speeding up the near-surface layers by a jet of fluid coming out of an inclined slot.

to aerofoils of any shape, reducing the drag, and thereby saving power, but the complications in the structure of an aircraft's wing to provide the slots and the internal passages is usually regarded as intolerable. Another method of control of breakaway is by fitting a slot as in fig 12.16 (b), through which a jet of high-speed fluid is forced in the original direction of motion. The momentum of the jet speeds up the slow fluid near the surface and therefore makes it more resistant to adverse pressure gradients. This method has been successfully used

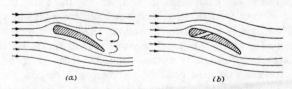

Fig 12.17   (a) An unslotted aerofoil at a large angle of incidence has breakaway on upper surface. This stalling reduces the lift force catastrophically. (b) Slotted wing at the same incidence has no breakaway and continues to give a large lift force.

on aerofoils, as shown in fig 12.17 : passages are cut through an air-craft's wing to convey the higher pressure air below the wing into the boundary layer on the upper side.   A current of air passes through the passage, which delays breakaway sufficiently to allow the aerofoil to be used at a much greater angle of incidence before stalling occurs, thus increasing the lift force at a given speed.   Such wings are termed *slotted*.

12.13 Factors controlling eddy formation

The preceding part of this chapter has shown how quite different types of flow patterns around solid objects are associated with slight changes of the properties of the boundary layer, which in turn are largely dependent upon the eddy motions therein.   In fact, the type of flow pattern round a solid boundary depends greatly upon the eddy formation both in the boundary layer and outside of it : if the right conditions exist for a particular sort and size of eddy, then a certain flow pattern will appear, unless of course there are effects also acting other than those of friction, for example, the effect of a free surface, see Chapter 14.   To determine a flow pattern it is therefore necessary to know what controls the life and death of eddies.

Eddies are greatly in evidence when one part of a fluid is accelerated relative to the rest.   For instance, the water behind the blade of an oar of a rowing-boat is accelerated somewhat by the pull on the oar, and large eddies are immediately formed at the blade-tip : the harder the pull on the oar, the more vigorous are the eddies.   It is reasonable to suppose that the forces tending to make eddies are inertia (i.e. acceleration) forces.   On the other hand, eddies are not apparent when velocities are very low or viscosities high.   An eddy produced in a highly viscous fluid, treacle for instance, is rapidly attenuated and damped out by the viscosity forces in the parts of the eddy where there is relative motion between it and surrounding fluid.   Viscosity forces, then, tend to reduce eddies.

Inertia forces are dealt with in Chapter 6 : these are the forces generated when a fluid velocity is changed and are found by applica-tion of Newton's Second Law of Motion.   They are always propor-tional to $\rho\, u^2\, a$, where u is a velocity of the fluid measured at some appropriate place, and a is a cross-sectional area.   The particular inertia force per unit area producing eddies, at a certain place in a fluid flow, can therefore be written $K \rho\, U^2$. K is a constant for the given configuration of boundaries, chosen simply so that U may be taken as the velocity at a convenient point and not necessarily at the place where the eddies are produced.   Changing the velocity at this convenient point, without changing the boundaries, will change the velocity at all places in the same proportion (including the place of the eddy). The inertia force per unit area is thus proportional to $\rho\,U^2$.

Viscosity forces are considered in Chapter 1, the definition of a viscous stress being the product of coefficient of viscosity and the velocity gradient. For one given configuration of boundaries, the velocity gradient at any one place is proportional to U/d, where d is some length measurement of the particular boundaries concerned. Increasing the size of the boundaries (without changing their shape) decreases all velocity gradients in the same proportion, whether they occur locally in eddies or over large areas of the flow. Thus the viscous force per unit area at any place is proportional to $\mu U/d$.

Now it is conventional to express the relative importance of the two sorts of force by their ratio, so that

$$\text{Inertia force/Viscous force} = \rho\,U^2/\mu\,U/d = \rho\,Ud/\mu = Ud/\nu,$$

where ν is the kinematic viscosity of the fluid $= \mu/\rho$. This ratio is termed the *Reynolds number* after O. Reynolds who first proposed it. When the number is small there will be little tendency towards eddy production, because the viscous forces are large compared with the inertia ones : when the ratio is large there will be a great tendency for eddies to occur.

It will be seen that the Reynolds number is dimensionless so that it is numerically the same no matter what are the units in which the variables U, d or ν are measured, provided of course that all are measured in units of the same system (metric or f.p.s. for example). Also it will be seen from the derivation of the expression that a Reynolds number only expresses the tendency towards eddy formation for one particular shape of the boundaries at a time : it cannot be used for comparing the eddy formation around different shapes of boundaries. For example, the sort of flow around an aerofoil will be governed by the Reynolds number $\mathbf{R} = UC/\nu$, where U is the undisturbed velocity of the air relative to the aerofoil, C is the chord (see fig 12.18), and ν

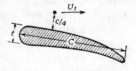

Fig 12.18 A perfectly possible (though unusual) method of defining the Reynolds number for an aerofoil would be to use the speed U_1 (as shown), the thickness t and the fluid kinematic viscosity ν to form $\mathbf{R} = U_1 t/\nu$.

the kinematic viscosity of the air. Two aerofoils, both the same shape but of different sizes and travelling at different speeds, can now be compared so far as the fluid motion is concerned : for if the number UC/ν is the same for both aerofoils then the eddy formation and the flow pattern will be the same for both. But the same process cannot be used to compare the flow round this aerofoil and, say, a circular cylinder. There would be no meaning at all to the comparison of the Reynolds numbers, as the flow pattern of each shape depends differently upon the eddy formation. It is also evident from the derivation that for comparison of Reynolds numbers it does not matter where in the system a velocity and length measurement is chosen for U and d, providing that they are always made in the same places relative to the boundaries. For the aerofoil case already mentioned, it would be just as valid for $\mathbf{R}$ to be written $U_1 t/v$, where U_1 is the velocity measured at a place a quarter of a chord above the aerofoil, and t is the thickness of the aerofoil (see fig 12.18). The numerical value of $\mathbf{R}$ will be different, of course, from UC/v, but provided that a uniform convention is always followed, the Reynolds number is still valuable for comparing flow patterns round this shape. Nevertheless, it has become usual in scientific work to refer $\mathbf{R}$ in common cases to certain conventional ways of measuring U and the length, and these are so well known that it is unnecessary to specify them.

The expression UX/v which appeared often in the boundary layer analyses is a Reynolds number which expresses the sort of eddy present in the layer. The property of these eddies to produce a momentum change, and therefore a drag force on a smooth surface, is solely dependent upon the Reynolds number at the place considered, and this is shown by the unique character of diagrams such as fig 12.6. For rough plates both the relative roughness X/k and the Reynolds number fix the coefficient of friction C_f.

It should not be thought that the flow pattern changes continuously as $\mathbf{R}$ increases : there may be ranges of $\mathbf{R}$ when the pattern does not change at all, and there may also be sudden changes of pattern. A good example is the flow pattern around a circular cylinder with its axis normal to the flow. The pattern can be seen by the experimental methods described in Chapter 5, by dust particles or other tracers. Fig 12.19 is divided into several sections, each of which shows the flow pattern for a certain range of $\mathbf{R} = Ud/v$ where U is the undisturbed velocity well upstream, d is the diameter of the cylinder, and v is the kinematic viscosity of the fluid. If $\mathbf{R} < 2$ approximately, the flow pattern is that shown in (a) and there are no eddies at all : the pattern is very similar to that given by the theoretical streamline pattern (Chapter 5). If $\mathbf{R}$ lies between about 2 and 40, there is breakaway on each side of the cylinder, with two simultaneous eddies in the wake, which do not, however, detach themselves periodically and create turbulence in the stream. If $\mathbf{R}$ lies between 40 and 10^5 a breakaway occurs alternately on each side of the cylinder, at about

$\theta = 85°$, and a wake eddy alternates on one side and the other. These eddies periodically detach themselves and create additional turbulence in the stream. And if $R > 10^5$ the breakaway is delayed to about $\theta = 130°$ and a much narrower wake is caused. Thus a succession of several different types of flow pattern exist, dependent only upon the value of $R = Ud/v$. Sometimes the change from one type to another is sudden (as is the one at $R = 10^5$ with the cylinder), and sometimes gradual (as is the case at about $R = 2$). Changes such as these occur with most flow patterns though it must not be assumed that they occur at the same values of R as occurred with the cylinder, or even that they are of the same sort.

Since the type of flow pattern affects the pressure distribution and therefore the drag, it is therefore not surprising to find a unique connection between the coefficient of drag and the Reynolds number,

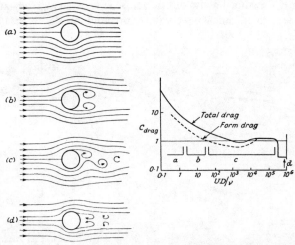

Fig 12.19 (*Left*) Four different sorts of flow pattern around a circular cylinder, each with its own range of UD/v. (*Right*) Curve of C_{drag} against UD/v for a smooth circular cylinder, showing also the ranges in which the flow patterns occur. Both Total drag and Form drag coefficients are shown the difference being the Friction drag coefficient.

a result which may also be obtained by Dimensional Analysis (Chapter 10). The curve of R against C_{drag} for smooth cylinders is given in fig 12.19, showing both the form drag coefficient and the total drag coefficient. The difference is the part of the drag due to the friction. Similar experimental curves can be drawn for any other shape. These experiments can be done with a wide variety of sizes, velocities and

viscosities of fluids, *providing the shape under test is always the same.*
The Reynolds number correlates all tests to a common basis.　Examples
of different flow conditions are illustrated in Plate 6 (facing p. 149).

The wake behind a solid ' bluff ' body, as has been described above,
is an area where fluid has been slowed down by the drag forces on the
body.　Outside the wake, the velocity is only changed by a small amount
from the original upstream value—(usually increased, particularly if
there are constricting walls each side of the body).　Thus a cross-
section of the flow just downstream of the body will show a non-uniform
velocity distribution.　This non-uniformity gradually fades out further
downstream, until the original velocity of the stream is regained.

A somewhat similar situation of a non-uniformity dying out arises in
the neighbourhood of a *diffusing jet*.　Such a jet occurs, for example,
when a duct discharges air into a large room ; or when a water flow
from a pipe enters a tank well below water surface level.　The jet of
Chapter 6 is assumed not to diffuse and so is equivalent to a heavy fluid
(water) stream in much lighter (air) surroundings as, for example, a

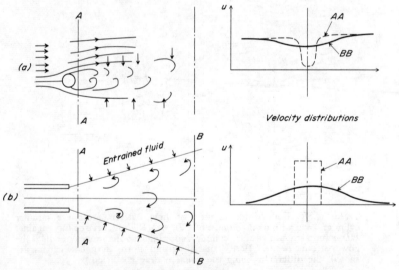

Fig 12.20　Two cases of non-uniform flow gradually becoming less non-
uniform by diffusion processes:
　(*a*) The wake behind a cylinder gradually disappearing downstream and a
　　　uniform flow re-appearing ;
　(*b*) The spreading of a jet from a pipe which gradually changes from a high
　　　speed, concentrated flow to a much more widespread one.
　In both cases cross-section AA, taken as a whole, gives pronounced non-
uniformity, and BB shows much less non-uniformity.　Entrainment
shown by small arrows at right angles to main flow.

fireman's jet. A diffusing jet presents another case of non-uniform flow at one place (the plane of the cross-section of the nozzle) which gradually becomes more uniform at places further downstream.

In both diffusion situations there are no solid boundaries affecting the flow. Clearly no shear stresses can act (see Chapter 1) for if they started to be formed, they would immediately set fluid into motion, causing a velocity gradient which in turn would destroy the stress. Thus without a force on the fluid, no change of the momentum flow can take place along the jet or wake axis ; the observed changes of speed must be accomplished by a quite different mechanism. This is done by the effect of the eddies which steadily draw in, or *entrain*, fluid across the originally sharply defined boundary between fast and slow fluid. In a jet, the quantity of fluid in motion increases at successive cross-sections downstream as fluid, originally still, is entrained into the moving fluid. In the wake, the quantity of slow moving fluid decreases at successive cross-sections as fast fluid is entrained into it. This change of mass in motion, while there is no change of momentum, is characteristic of diffusion systems. At the same time, because of the high local shear stresses inside eddies, there is a degradation of kinetic into a thermal form of energy. Any situation where high and low speeds are adjacent in a fluid gives rise to turbulent entrainment and so to energy degradation, while the momentum flow remains constant at all cross-sections.

Summary

The study of a boundary layer is essentially experimental, though certain stages of the analysis can be theoretically examined. Both empirical and also semi-rational expressions have been developed for the tangential drag of a fluid flow on solid surfaces : the choice between these is often determined by the ease of computation.

Although the frictional drag of the boundary layer gives directly a force on the underlying surface, there may be important secondary effects of the boundary layer. If the pressure of the fluid rises in the direction of motion, breakaway may occur, giving rise to large-scale changes in the flow pattern. These changes affect the drag forces considerably and may cause pressure forces to act on a solid body which are much larger than the purely frictional forces. The Reynolds number is an important grouping of variables which show what sort of eddies may occur.

PROBLEMS

1. Calculate the drag coefficient C_f for a flat plate at a Reynolds number $\mathbf{R} = UX/\nu = 2\cdot5 \times 10^5$, if the flow is (a) entirely laminar, and (b) turbulent assuming the power law $u/U = (y/\delta)^{1/7}$ and $\delta \propto \mathbf{R}^{-1/5}$. What are the practical consequences of any difference of (a) from (b)?

Ans. (a) 0·00265 . (b) 0·00616.

2. A flat plate is placed in a very turbulent stream of water at 40 °C with the flow parallel to its surface. The water speed is 3·57 m/s. Where is the transition point and how thick is the boundary layer just before this point?

Ans. 0·09 m : 0·069 cm.

3. Find the thickness δ of the boundary layer 30 cm from the leading edge of a flat plate held edgewise to a water current of 50 cm/s and viscosity 0·01 poise, assuming that the velocity distribution in a laminar layer is precisely

$$u/U = 2y/\delta - 2y^3/\delta^3 + y^4/\delta^4.$$

What is the distribution of shearing stress τ?
Calculate also the drag force per metre width.

Ans. 0·142 N.

4. Develop an expression for the coefficient of drag and δ for the laminar boundary layer on a flat plate assuming that the velocity in it increases to its maximum as the sine of the distance from the plate, i.e. $u/U = \sin \pi y/2\delta$.

Ans. $C_f = 1\cdot310\mathbf{R}^{-1/2}$.

5. Find the discharge through a boundary layer of thickness δ, in which the velocity distribution is $u/U = (y/\delta)^{1/6}$. Then find the amount δ^* through which the surface would have to be moved outwards so that if it then had ideal fluid passing over it (i.e. no boundary layer) the same quantity of fluid would be flowing. This distance δ^* is called the *displacement thickness* of the boundary layer, and it can be considered as a correction term to find the discharge in an infinite stream from experiments with a comparatively narrow stream with boundary layers at the walls.

Ans. $\delta^* = \delta/6$.

6. Following the general method of paragraph **12.11**, show that the Froude number U^2/gl is the ratio of the inertia (accelerational) forces on an element of moving fluid to the gravitational forces on it.

7. Find the ratio of the friction drags on the front and rear halves of a flat plate set parallel to a uniform stream. Assume that the boundary layer is turbulent over the whole plate and that the velocity profile can be represented by the seventh root approximation.

Ans. 1·35.

8. Find the ratio of the drag in water to the drag in air on a thin flat plate of chord 1 m at zero incidence in a stream flowing at 5 m/s. The drag coefficient is $2\cdot656/\mathbf{R}^{1/2}$ or $0\cdot148/\mathbf{R}^{1/5}$ for a laminar or a turbulent boundary layer respectively. The critical Reynolds number is $0\cdot5 \times 10^6$. Assume that the effective origin of the turbulent layer after transition is at the leading edge of the plate.

The density and kinematic viscosity are to be taken as 1000 kg/m³ and 1·11 × 10⁻⁶ m²/s for water, 1·21 kg/m³ and 1·47 × 10⁻⁵ m²/s for air.

Ans. About 1100 : 1.

9. A rectangular thin flat plate is held in a uniform airstream with its surface parallel with, and one edge perpendicular to, the direction of the stream. The boundary layer is entirely turbulent, and the drag coefficient, based on the wetted area, can be taken as $0·074/R^{1/5}$.

R is the Reynolds number based on the dimension parallel with the stream direction.

Obtain a general expression for the drag in terms of the area and aspect ratio of the plate, the density and kinematic viscosity of the air and the air speed.

Hence compare the drag of a rectangular plate which has its sides in the ratio 4 : 1 with the drag of a square plate of the same area in the same airstream, for both the possible orientations of the rectangular plate. Outline briefly the physical reasons for the difference in drag.

Ans. 1·15 : 0·87.

10. Distinguish between the *Reynolds Number* and the *Reynolds stresses* in a fluid flow.

At one point, distant 0·1 m from the wall of a channel with a water flow in it, a sensitive instrument measured two components u and v of the velocity. Eleven consecutive measurements, at constant time intervals are listed below :

| u mm/s | + 104 | − 109 | + 83 | + 88 | + 101 | + 93 | +110 | + 100 | + 86 | + 94 | + 88 |
| v mm/s | − 2 | − 15 | + 10 | + 24 | − 5 | − 19 | − 19 | + 3 | + 20 | − 2 | + 5 |

Determine the mean velocity of flow in the u-direction and find the local value of the Reynolds shearing stress.

At another point, distant only 0·05 m from the wall, the corresponding stress was 0·35 N/m². Estimate the stress at the wall.

Ans. $\bar{u} = 96$ mm/s ; Stress 0·09 N/m² ; 0·61 N/m².

13

FLOW THROUGH PIPES AND CLOSED CONDUITS

13.1 The engineer is often engaged in designing works to convey fluid from place to place by a closed conduit or pipe wholly filled with the fluid. In general, because of the relative motion, a drag force is exerted by the walls on the fluid so that a driving force is needed in order to balance the drag and to preserve the motion. The pressure intensity of the fluid is therefore higher at points upstream than at points downstream in the pipe. It is desirable to know this pressure drop accurately so that if it is desired to apply it mechanically, with a pump, the horsepower required may be calculated : alternatively, if the pressure is being applied by gravity (for example, when a high level reservoir is forcing water down a pipe to a lower level), then it may be essential to forecast the size of pipe necessary to supply the required quantity of fluid. There is a great economic importance in high accuracy for this sort of calculation, and much research effort has been put into the problem. As an example, an error of 7 kN/m^2 (i.e. about 1 lbf/in^2, or a pressure-head of only 0·715 m) in forecasting the pressure drop along a length of 1·5 m diameter water main in which the mean water speed is 3 m/s causes an error of the estimated pump power of 37 kW.

13.2 The inlet to a pipe

The conditions near the inlet of a pipe from a large container of nearly static fluid can be investigated using Bernoulli's equation. Over a short length of the pipe adjacent to the inlet, the energy degradation into heat is small and the conditions are therefore rather like those of orifice flow (see Chapter 8). Consider a reservoir of water with the surface at a height h above the centre-line of the pipe, the entry of which has a well-rounded, ' bellmouth ' shape, fig 13.1 (a). Water is being made to flow through the pipe at a speed u. In the reservoir, however, the water is all static, so that the total energy per unit weight, $H = p/\rho g + z$, is the same everywhere in it. It is convenient to take a datum level for the energy at the level of the centre-line of the pipe, so that $H = h$ everywhere. Since there is little or no degradation of energy in the initial short length of pipe, the total energy H

is preserved to the point where a vertical pressure tube (piezometer) has been arranged.   The water stands static in this tube to a height y_1

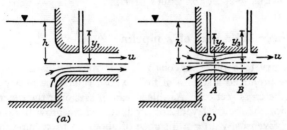

(a)   (b)

Fig 13.1 (a) Flow out of a reservoir into a well-rounded entry of a pipe. The pressure just within the pipe is measured by a vertical piezometer. (b) Flow out of a reservoir into a sharp-edged pipe. Notice how there is breakaway at the edge, causing an eddy to form, and the jet reduces in diameter, subsequently expanding to pipe diameter with an accompanying energy degradation.

above the centre-line so that the total energy in the pipe at this place is
$$H = u^2/2g + y_1 = h$$
or
$$(h - y_1) = \frac{u^2}{2g} \qquad . \qquad . \qquad . \qquad . \quad (13.1)$$

Thus at a well-designed inlet to a pipe there is a drop of pressure $h - y_1$ due solely to the acceleration of the fluid from rest to a velocity u. Such a pressure measurement is often a convenient way of finding the flow.   It must be emphasized here that this drop of pressure is quite unconnected with the drop due to friction with the walls, which will be discussed later.

If the entry to the pipe is not curved to a bellmouth, but is sharp edged as in fig 13.1 (b), then the conditions are different, being rather like those in a sharp-edged orifice.   There is a vena contracta at A and the pressure there, y_2, is given solely by Bernoulli's equation or $h - y_2 = u'^2/2g$, where u' is the velocity in the vena contracta.   Downstream, however, the flow diverges until it occupies the whole of the pipe cross section, causing considerable turbulence and eddies as it does so.   There is a consequent degradation of energy E in these eddies so that Bernoulli's equation must be modified if it is to be applied to points downstream of the vena contracta.   For example, at the second piezometer tube, where the water rises to a height y_3,
$$h = y_3 + \frac{u^2}{2g} + E$$
or
$$(h - y_3) = \frac{u^2}{2g} + E \qquad . \qquad . \qquad . \quad (13.2)$$

Thus the drop of pressure at a sharp-edged entry of a pipe is always greater than that at a rounded entry, by an amount E (see Appendix at end of this chapter for values of E).

13.3 The middle part of a pipeline

The entry to a pipe, especially if it is rounded as in fig 13.1 (a), will have produced a stream of fluid whose velocity is nearly uniform all over the cross section. As this stream passes over the inner surface of the pipe, boundary layers are produced which grow thicker downstream. Eventually after a distance of about 30 to 50 pipe diameters the layers from opposite sides meet at the centre-line : thence forward no further growth of the boundary layer can occur, and the velocity distribution in the pipe is the same at all subsequent cross sections : there is no centre core of constant mainstream velocity, and the pipe is completely full of boundary layer (see fig 13.2). In the common

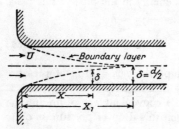

Fig 13.2 The growth of boundary layers at the inlet to a pipe. At a distance X_1 from the inlet the boundary layers have grown to a width equal to the pipe radius : thenceforwards the whole pipe is full of boundary layer and there is no central core of fluid with uniform velocity.

case of a pipe cross section which is symmetrical and which has uniform roughness everywhere on it, the maximum speed is at the centre.

The drag of the fluid on the walls which has caused the boundary layers is due to exactly the same mechanics as was the case for the flow over a flat surface, discussed in Chapter 12. In the initial stages of the development of the layers, before they have met, they grow and produce a stress in accordance with the same sort of laws which apply to the flat plate, the parameter UX/ν (where X is the distance from the end of the pipe) governing both the drag stress τ_0 and the layer thickness δ. The numerical values of the constants in the equations are somewhat different in the pipe case from the flat plate boundary layer case. In the final, fully developed, stage of the flow when the layers from each side have met, δ is constrained to be equal to the radius of the pipe r, for the thickness cannot go on increasing indefinitely as was the case on the flat surface. The drag stress τ_0 therefore remains constant at a value fixed by r, $U_{\max}$, ν, and the roughness of the walls.

There is a convenient connection between τ_0 and the pressure drop along the pipe.   Consider a short length δx of a pipe through which fluid is passing, and creating a drag stress τ_0 on the walls.   The resultant pressure drop is the difference between a pressure p downstream and a pressure $p + \delta p$ upstream, as shown in fig 13.3.   The pressure

Fig 13.3   The forces on the fluid flowing steadily in a short length δx of a pipe.   The excess of pressure intensity δp acting over the cross-sectional area a just balances the shear stress τ_0 which is spread all over the inside of the pipe (perimeter P).

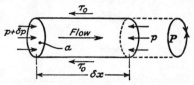

force balancing the drag is therefore $a\,\delta p$, where a is the cross-sectional area of the pipe.   The drag force is the product of τ_0 and the surface area of the walls over the length δx, that is $\tau_0 P \delta x$, where P is the perimeter of the cross-sectional area of the pipe.

Equating the drag and pressure forces

$$\tau_0 \, P \, \delta x = a \, \delta p$$

or

$$\delta p / \delta x = \tau_0 \, P / a.$$

In this expression, p and τ_0 are measured in the same units of force per unit area.   Engineers often express pressure intensity however as the head h of fluid causing the pressure p.   Thus

$$\delta p = \rho g \, \delta h$$

Substituting above,

$$\rho g \frac{\delta h}{\delta x} = \tau_0 \frac{P}{a}$$

or

$$\delta h / \delta x = \tau_0 \frac{P}{a} \frac{1}{\rho g}$$

The ratio a/P is termed the *hydraulic mean depth* and is denoted by m : for a circular pipe of diameter d, $m = d/4$.   Also the ratio $\delta h/\delta x$

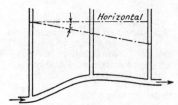

Fig 13.4   The hydraulic gradient of a pipe is the gradient of a line joining the fluid levels in vertical piezometers at intervals along the pipe.

is termed the *hydraulic gradient*, denoted by i ; it is the angle made with the horizontal by the line joining the fluid surfaces in a succession of piezometers along the pipe, fig 13.4.   From above,

$$i = \tau_0/\rho g m \quad . \qquad . \qquad . \qquad . \quad (13.3)$$

so that the hydraulic gradient is constant where τ_0 is constant, that is, where the flow is fully developed and has no central core of constant velocity.   In the entry length (about 30–50 diameters long) neither τ_0 nor i are constant.   However, this length is usually small compared with the remainder of the pipe, where i is truly constant, so that it is usually good enough to regard i as constant throughout the whole length of the pipe.

13.4 Pipe outlets

The outlet of a pipe into a large reservoir full of nearly still fluid (or a wind tunnel discharging air into a large room) presents the problem of high-speed fluid being decelerated.   If the pipe finishes abruptly as in fig 13.5 (a) a jet of high-speed fluid is projected into the still fluid.

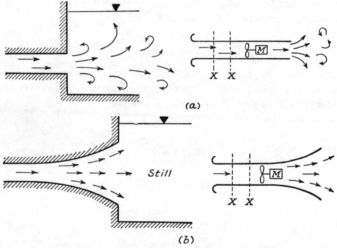

Fig 13.5   (a) Abrupt outlets from pipes cause vigorous eddy formation and consequent large energy degradation : (left) the outlet of a water pipe into a reservoir ; (right) the outlet of a wind tunnel ; the energy so dissipated must be supplied by the fan and motor.   (b) Gradual outlets (diffusers) reduce the eddy formation and energy degradation considerably, and exhaust the fluid at low speed.   XX is the working section of the tunnel.

Near the outlet pipe the boundary between moving and still fluid is well marked, and there is a pronounced velocity gradient.   Vigorous eddies are formed by this gradient, tending to mix the moving and still fluids, the mixture having an intermediate speed.   The mixing process occurs all along the jet so that the boundary becomes less distinct and the velocity gradient negligible at places far from the pipe.   The incoming momentum of the jet is preserved, the reduced speed farther from the outlet being compensated by the increased quantity of fluid in motion. For constant momentum there must be no forces acting in the direction of motion, so the pressure remains constant throughout this dissipating jet, and the surface of water in a reservoir, for instance, remains horizontal above the jet. The kinetic energy $u^2/2g$ per unit weight of the incoming fluid is, however, completely degraded into heat by the eddy motions, so that there is a drop of total energy of $u^2/2g$ as the fluid leaves the abrupt outlet.

The energy so wasted in low-grade heat must have been supplied to the fluid somewhere, in a wind tunnel by the fan and motor, in a water pipe by gravity or a pump. For a flow of Q units of volume per second, or of $Q\rho$ mass per second, the total power so wasted at an abrupt outlet is $\rho\,Qu^2/2g$. This power may be considerable and it is often desirable to reduce it and so decrease the energy required for the whole system. For example, in a 1·5 m diameter water main with a mean speed $u = 3$ m/s, the wasted power would be 24 kW. The waste of kinetic energy can be reduced by decelerating the fluid gradually in a slowly diverging pipe, so that only a low-speed jet is released into the reservoir. In this way, some of the kinetic energy in the pipe is converted into pressure energy, instead of thermal energy. Such a diverging pipe is called a *diffuser*, fig 13.5 (b). The difficulty of designing an efficient diffuser lies in avoiding breakaway of the main flow from the walls, for there is a pressure gradient opposing the flow (see Chapter 12). If breakaway does occur, then eddies are set up on each side of the central jet (see fig 13.6), and the energy

Fig 13.6 A poor diffuser allows breakaway to take place, the central jet being surrounded by eddies, and there is considerable energy degradation.

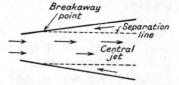

degradation is increased nearly to that which occurs with an abrupt outlet. A conical diffuser of about 6° semi-vertex angle will avoid breakaway and will convert about 80 per cent of the inlet kinetic energy into pressure energy. Only about 20 per cent is wasted, mainly by the friction against the walls. If a diffuser is used therefore on a pipe outlet, the total energy in it is nearly constant, but the pressure *rises* as the fluid passes through and is decelerated.

A great deal of research has gone to produce efficient diffusers that are not unduly narrow angled and long. As in the case of aerofoils and other surfaces, methods of boundary layer control can be used with success to delay or inhibit breakaway altogether (see Chapter 12). Suction is used to reduce the boundary layer thickness if the complications of the equipment required is tolerable.   Carefully controlled roughess can be applied to the walls in order to modify the velocity

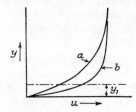

Fig 13.7   Velocity   distribution   above   smooth (curve a) and rough surfaces (curve b).   At any given place y_1 a rough surface gives higher speeds than a smooth surface and thus is less likely to cause breakaway.

distribution so that there are higher speeds near the wall (fig. 13.7); such a distribution makes the boundary layer more resistant to the adverse pressure gradient.   Care must of course be taken in applying roughness so that the increased drag does not cause an energy degradation larger than that saved by the prevention of breakaway.

13.5 Energy line diagrams

A convenient way of showing graphically the degradation of energy in the several parts of a pipe system is by using an *energy line diagram*. Examples are shown in fig 13.8 for water pipelines and a wind tunnel. On a vertical cross section of the system, the total energy of the fluid is set off at any point by a vertical ordinate, above the centre-line of the pipe.   The line joining the tops of the ordinates is called the *energy line*.   Thus at reservoirs of still fluid, the energy line is at the level of the fluid surface : at places where there is a concentrated degradation of energy there is a step down in the energy line, as occurs at abrupt inlets and outlets : at places where there is an energy input, such as at a pump or fan, there is a step up in the direction of motion of the fluid : and along pipelines where there is a uniform degradation of energy, due to fluid friction, the energy line is inclined to the horizontal at an angle equal to the hydraulic gradient i.   It is usual to assume that i is the same in the inlet length (about 50 diameters long) as in the remainder of the pipe where the flow has developed its full boundary layers to the pipe axis.   The error is small, for most pipes are much longer than 50 diameters.

As well as the energy line it is also useful to plot the *pressure line*. This is a line drawn so that the vertical distance between it and the pipe centre-line at any point is the pressure of the fluid there.   If a pressure tapping were made in the pipe walls at such a point, and a piezometer attached to it, the fluid would rise until the surface reached the pressure line. Since the total energy H is equal to the sum of kinetic, potential and pressure energy, $H = u^2/2g + p/g\rho + z$, it will be seen that the pressure line is always $u^2/2g$ vertically below the energy line. The potential energy z is the height of the pipe above an arbitrary datum and it is included in the height above datum of both energy and pressure lines. Also if the pipe is coincident

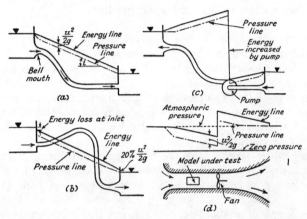

Fig 13.8 Four examples of energy line diagrams. (*a*) A pipeline between two reservoirs. Notice the vertical drop in the energy line at the abrupt outlet. (*b*) A pipeline which rises above the pressure line has a pressure in it *below* atmospheric, and the arrangement is called a *siphon*. Notice the drop in the energy line at the abrupt entry. (*c*) A pump in a pipeline gives a concentrated increase to the energy in a pipe. (*d*) An energy line diagram can be made for a wind tunnel, but an atmospheric pressure datum line must be shown. There may be an additional decrease of energy and pressure as the air flows over the model.

with the pressure line anywhere, then the pressure of the fluid is atmospheric : if the pipe is above the pressure line then the pressure is below atmospheric and it is then called a *siphon*. With an ideal fluid the pressure cannot fall more than 100 kN/m² below atmospheric, as a perfect vacuum would be caused, and the flow would stop. With water it is not possible to allow the pressure to fall more than about 80 kN/m² below atmospheric (i.e. the pressure line not more than 8 m below the pipe) or the dissolved gases of the air come out of solution and gather in the highest part of a siphon, stopping the flow. This is called an *air lock*.

The energy and pressure lines for a wind tunnel are also shown in fig 13.8. The tunnel is of the straight-through type which takes from and exhausts its air into a large room. The air velocity in the room is negligible as it returns slowly to the inlet end of the tunnel. The pressure line at each end of the tunnel is at atmospheric pressure and the step at the fan represents the energy applied to the air to overcome the degradation due to fluid friction. If the degradation is large, due to a rough-walled tunnel, for instance, then the gradient of the pressure line, and the height of the step, will be greater.

13.6 Estimation of the hydraulic gradient

The main problem in pipe flow calculations is the estimation of the hydraulic gradient i for a given pipe size and mean velocity $\bar{U}$ of the fluid passing through it. Alternatively, i may be given and it is desired to find which size pipe is required for a certain discharge Q to pass through it. The problem is of such great economic importance that few other subjects in fluid mechanics have attracted so much research effort, and so many formulae have been proposed that they may appear confusing.

The obvious way to solve the relationship between i, Q, and pipe size is entirely empirical. Experiments are made on lengths of pipes, both circular and non-circular in cross section, and both Q and i measured. Usually i is found from the drop in pressure δh for a certain length δl of the pipe. It is found that a law of the form

$$\bar{U} = K\, m^x\, i^y \qquad . \qquad . \qquad . \qquad . \quad (13.4)$$

gives a very fair approximation to the experimental data if the variables do not extend over a wide range. In this equation $\bar{U} = Q/a$ is the mean velocity in the pipe, $m = a/P$ is the hydraulic mean radius of the pipe, K is a coefficient and x, y are indices. a is the pipe cross-sectional area.

Unfortunately, there is considerable divergence of opinion as to the numerical values of K, x and y. Not only does it appear that they vary according to the roughness of the pipe walls, but they change with the pipe size and the mean velocity, even if the roughness remains constant. Also the equations seem to be accurate only in the restricted range of $\bar{U}$ in which the experiments have been conducted; at greater or smaller velocities the equations give unacceptably inaccurate predictions. However, such formulae are often used in the present state of engineering knowledge, though a good deal of experience and guess-work is required to estimate K, x and y for pipes which have not been subject to experiment and, indeed, may not have been made.

Of the formulae of the above sort, those due to Chézy and Manning are most often used. Chézy's formula is $\bar{U} = C\sqrt{(mi)}$ and the coefficient

C depends on the roughness of the walls and on m. In Manning's formula, $\bar{U} = Mm^{2/3}i^{1/2}$, the coefficient M is much more independent of m. Both equations are simple to use, and there is an ever-increasing body of experience with which to estimate C or M for a pipe of a given construction and roughness. There are several formulae (also empirical) which purport to express C and M in terms of m, and of parameters typical of the roughness. It is important to remember when using either Chézy's or Manning's equation that neither are dimensionally correct so that the numerical value of C or M is dependent on the system of measurement in use. For example, in the SI system C for a large, very smooth pipe would be of the order of 66 m$^{1/2}$/s: in the obsolescent f.p.s system it would be $66/0.304^{1/2} = 120$ ft$^{1/2}$/s.

It is in many ways far better to use an equation which is dimensionally correct. The one sometimes called Darcy's equation is one that is so. It is

$$h = f\frac{l}{m}\frac{\bar{U}^2}{2g} \qquad . \qquad . \qquad . \qquad . \quad (13.5)$$

where h is the loss in pressure in length l of the pipe (see fig 13.9).

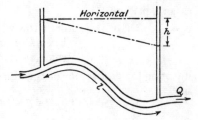

Fig 13.9 The hydraulic gradient gives a drop of pressure h in a length l of pipe. The length l may be greater than the straight line distance between pressure tapping points.

(Notice that by putting $i = h/l$ and $C = \sqrt{(2g/f)}$ this reduces to Chézy's formula above.) In this equation f is termed the *pipe friction coefficient* and its value is independent of the system of measurement used. The term $\bar{U}^2/2g$ is the kinetic energy per unit weight of fluid corresponding to the mean velocity and it is a length measurement, or head of fluid in motion. Notice that it is *not* the mean kinetic energy of the fluid in the pipe (see Chapter 4). For a circular pipe of diameter d the equation is $h = 4f\dfrac{l}{b}\dfrac{\bar{U}^2}{2g}$ because now $m = d/4$.

Some confusion is sometimes caused by the figure 4 because many text-books (notably American ones) prefer to incorporate it into the coefficient f, but still call the combined coefficient f. It should always be made clear whether the general coefficient (as f in equation *13.5*) is meant, or the particular value f' applicable to circular pipes $\left(\text{that is } f' = 4f \text{ and so } h = f' \dfrac{l}{d}\dfrac{\bar{U}^2}{2g}\right).$

It requires just as much experience and guess-work to estimate f as was required for the coefficients and indices of the other empirical equations. There is now no intention of trying to make an equation so that the coefficient f remains constant, as was attempted before, so that it is not surprising that f changes with $\bar{U}$ and d even if the same roughness is used on the pipe walls. Nevertheless, in restricted ranges of $\bar{U}$ and d, roughnesses on the pipe walls caused by certain materials give sufficiently constant values of f that tables of them can be made and used by engineers. These values have been found by experiments where $\bar{U}(= Q/a)$, m, and i are all measured, and f calculated from them. But large numbers of these values of f so found will only produce confusion unless they can be related to a common basis. One way of achieving such a basis is by the Method of Dimensions as given in Chapter 10. It is expected that the wall stress τ_0 will depend on $\bar{U}$, ρ, d, μ and k. The last variable is the size of the roughnesses that are on the walls.

Suppose then that the complete dependence of τ_0 can be written as an equation

$$\tau_0 = \bar{U}^a \rho^b d^c \mu^f k^g + \text{other terms with the same variables but different}$$
indices, every term being dimensionally the same as the first.

Equating the dimensions of τ_0 and those of the terms on the right-hand side

$$M\,L\,T^{-2}\,L^{-2} = L^a\,T^{-a}\,M^b L^{-3b}\,L^c\,M^f L^{-f} T^{-f}\,L^g.$$

Collecting indices, form three simultaneous equations

for M, $\quad 1 = b + f$
for L, $\quad -1 = a - 3b + c - f + g$
for T, $\quad -2 = -a - f$

One solution of the equations giving a final result which is generally known can be obtained by solving for a, b, and c. That is

$b = (1 - f):\qquad c = -1 - a + 3b + f - g:\qquad a = (2 - f)$
$\qquad\qquad\qquad\quad c = -1 - (2 - f) + 3(1 - f) + f - g$
$\qquad\qquad\qquad\quad c = (-f - g)$

Inserting into the original equation for τ_0

$$\tau_0 = \bar{U}^{2-f} \rho^{1-f} d^{-f-g} \mu^f k^g + \text{other terms}$$

or $\qquad\qquad \tau_0 = \bar{U}^2 \rho \left(\dfrac{\mu}{\bar{U}\rho d}\right)^f \left(\dfrac{k}{d}\right)^g + \text{other terms}$

This may be simplified to

$$\tau_0/\bar{U}^2\rho = \phi\left(\frac{\mu}{\bar{U}\rho d}\right)\left(\frac{k}{d}\right)$$

where ϕ means 'a function of'.

Now the connection between τ_0 and $i\,(= h/l)$ is $i = \tau_0/g\rho m$ (equation 13.3), so that substituting into the dimensional equation for τ_0

$$\frac{h}{l}\frac{gm\rho}{\bar{U}^2\rho} = \phi\left(\frac{v}{\bar{U}d}\right)\left(\frac{k}{d}\right) \text{ where } v = \frac{\mu}{\rho}$$

or

$$h = \frac{l}{m}\frac{\bar{U}^2}{g}\phi\left(\frac{v}{\bar{U}d}\right)\left(\frac{k}{d}\right)$$

$$= \frac{l}{m}\frac{\bar{U}^2}{2g}\phi'\left(\frac{v}{\bar{U}d}\right)\left(\frac{k}{d}\right),$$

where ϕ' is another function of $v/\bar{U}d$ and k/d.

Comparison may now be made with the Darcy formula, equation 13.5, and it is clear that f should be equivalent to the function of $(v/\bar{U}d)$ and (k/d). The function can be found by plotting the experimentally found values of f against $\bar{U}d/v$ for each; several curves will appear, each for a particular (k/d). Fig 13.10 shows the generally

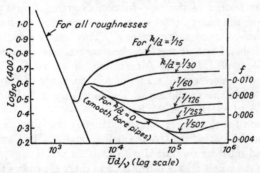

Fig 13.10   The pipe friction diagram for pipes of all diameters and roughnesses and for all velocities and kinematic viscosities. The curves have been plotted from the results of many experiments with artificial roughnesses of uniform size. Slight changes are evident for commercial pipes where roughness is non-uniform. (After Nikuradse.)

accepted curves for roughnesses that are grains of sand stuck onto the walls. Other types of roughnesses give slightly different curves but these roughnesses are more difficult to express as a single size k. Because all the values of f fall onto their correct curves of (k/d), it is seen that no important variables have been omitted from the dimensional analysis. If there had been an omission, a value of f found for a certain k/d might have fallen amongst values applicable to another k/d, if the omitted variable happened then to be operating.

The parameter $\bar{U}d/\nu$ is often called the *pipe Reynolds number* and k/d the *roughness ratio* for the pipe. When $k/d = 0$, the pipe is smooth walled and f only depends on $\bar{U}d/\nu$. The curve for this condition has been experimentally determined as far as $\bar{U}d/\nu = 1 \times 10^6$, and in this range it is closely approximated by

$$f = 0.079(\bar{U}d/\nu)^{-0.25} \qquad . \qquad . \qquad . \quad (13.6)$$

Rough-walled pipes always give higher values of f than those for a smooth pipe at the same $\bar{U}d/\nu$; but at sufficiently high values of $\bar{U}d/\nu$, f then becomes constant. At lower $\bar{U}d/\nu$ the curves converge upon the smooth pipe curve, so that in some circumstances a rough walled pipe acts as if it is smooth. Notice how f has a similarity to the coefficient of friction C_f for a flat plate (Chapter 12). Both are functions of a Reynolds number composed of a velocity, a length and the kinematic viscosity. It must be emphasized, however, that the functions are not of the same sort for the two purposes.

13.7 Pipe flow when Ud/ν is small

A striking feature of the pipe friction diagram of fig 13.10 is the way in which the many branches of the curves converge into one line at about $\bar{U}d/\nu = 2300$ approximately. This line is straight, it overlaps the left-hand end of the branched curves, and it extends to the smallest values of $\bar{U}d/\nu$ with f increasing all the while. The single line is found to represent all values of f in the range of $\bar{U}d/\nu \leqslant 2300$, no matter what the roughness of the pipe may be. The equation $f = 16(\bar{U}d/\nu)^{-1}$ exactly fits the line.

The reason for this rather sudden change is that there is no turbulence in the fluid at all if $\bar{U}d/\nu$ is small enough. The flow is wholly laminar, and must be contrasted with the flow at the higher values of $\bar{U}d/\nu$ when the whole flow is turbulent and there are eddies throughout the pipe. The differences between the 'all laminar' and 'all turbulent' flow cases can be ascribed to the conditions in the boundary layers on the pipe walls at the entry to the pipe, before they have met at the pipe axis to form the fully developed pipe flow. The initial part of these boundary layers is laminar, precisely as was the upstream part of the layers on a flat surface (see Chapter 12). If the boundary layers unite at the pipe axis before they have reached their transition points (and so before they have become turbulent), then the whole flow in the pipe is laminar and $f = 16(\bar{U}d/\nu)^{-1}$. If the transition occurs before the layers unite then the flow in the pipe is turbulent and the right-hand, branched curves of fig 13.10 apply. The turbulence in the oncoming stream largely determines where the transition occurs, as was described in Chapter 12 : with little or no turbulence in the oncoming stream entering the pipe, the transition is delayed to a high UX/ν so that there is a correspondingly high $\bar{U}d/\nu$ before the flow in the pipe is turbulent. But however vigorous the eddies are made in the oncoming stream, UX/ν never falls below a critical value (5×10^5 on a flat plate, but different in a pipe) and this corresponds to $\bar{U}d/\nu = 2300$. In other words, turbulent flow *cannot* exist in a pipe if $\bar{U}d/\nu < 2300$: laminar flow *may* exist if $\bar{U}d/\nu > 2300$, depending upon the turbulence present at the entry. With very still conditions indeed in a tank from which a bell-mouthed entry to the pipe extends, laminar flow has been known to exist in a pipe up to $\bar{U}d/\nu = 40,000$, though the slightest vibration then will start eddies which grow and create fully turbulent flow in the pipe.

For this laminar case the stress τ_0 and consequently f can be calculated precisely and does not depend on experiment. The proof is similar in many respects to that for the laminar boundary layer on a flat surface. It can be shown that the velocity distribution is then a parabola, that $\bar{U} = \frac{1}{2}U_{max}$, and that $f = 16(\bar{U}d/\nu)^{-1}$. Substituting this value of f in Darcy's formula it is found that

$$h = 32\mu l \bar{U}/\rho g d^2 . \qquad . \qquad . \qquad . \quad (13.7)$$

and this is sometimes called *Poiseuille's equation*. While it is satisfying to find a solution to a problem in fluid mechanics that does not depend on any experimental evidence, this problem of the laminar flow friction in pipes is not of great engineering importance. When air or water is passing through pipes of the usual sizes, $\bar{U}$ is very small to allow $\bar{U}d/\nu < 2300$. It is usually if viscous fluids, such as oil, are passing through the pipe that ν is high enough to ensure $\bar{U}d/\nu < 2300$ and thus to have laminar flow.

It should be noticed that the value 2300 for the *lower critical pipe Reynolds number* is applicable to flow in pipes only, and has no relevance at all to other flow phenomena also depending on a Reynolds number $\mathbf{R}$ (which is length $\times$ velocity $\div$ kinematic viscosity). For instance, the critical $\mathbf{R}$ for the change from laminar to turbulent flow in open channels is about 6000 : the critical $\mathbf{R}$ for the boundary layer to become turbulent before breakaway on a cylinder (and therefore cause a narrow wake with low drag) is about 1×10^5. The existence of a phenomenon at a certain numerical value of a Reynolds number in one particular arrangement of boundaries applies only to that arrangement.

Laminar motion in a pipe can be demonstrated by injecting a thin stream of dye or of smoke. The stream remains a thin thread throughout the length of the pipe, not diffusing and becoming faint as it would do if there were eddies in the flow mixing the stream with the remainder of the fluid. If the velocity is carefully increased so that $\bar{U}d/\nu > 2300$ then the slightest disturbance at the entry causes turbulent flow to replace laminar flow, and the dye stream is immediately diffused.

13.8 The universal pipe friction law

The pipe friction diagram of fig 13.10 was presented as having been experimentally determined throughout. Parts of the diagram may, however, be determined theoretically and then checked by experiment. In laminar flow, the coefficient f may be determined as described in the previous paragraphs; in the turbulent range, the logarithmic velocity profile derived for turbulent flow in Chapter 12 may be used, together with the properties of a laminar sub-layer near the walls to find f for a smooth-bore pipe as

$$1/\sqrt{f} = 4 \cdot 0 \log_{10} (\mathbf{R}.2\sqrt{f}) - 1 \cdot 6 \qquad . \qquad . \quad (13.8)$$

where $\mathbf{R} = \bar{U}d/\nu$. The proof will not be given here. This equation fits the experimental data better than the empirical law $f = 0 \cdot 079 \, \mathbf{R}^{-\frac{1}{4}}$ at high $\mathbf{R}$ (equation 13.6), but is not sufficiently superior at lower $\mathbf{R}$ to make it worth while using for engineering purposes since it is more difficult to use (see fig 13.11).

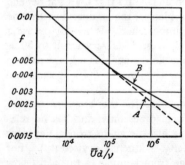

Fig 13.11 A comparison between the values of f obtained by the Blasius empirical equation $f = 0 \cdot 079 \, \mathbf{R}^{-\frac{1}{4}}$ (curve A) and those found by experiment and the exact law (curve B) $1/\sqrt{f} = 4 \cdot 0 \log_{10} (\mathbf{R}.2\sqrt{f}) - 1 \cdot 6$.

In a similar manner the exact solution can be made for f due to the logarithmic velocity distribution in a rough-walled pipe on the assumption that the roughnesses themselves project so far through the laminar sub-layer that their wakes throw off eddies into the main stream. The solution is

$$1/\sqrt{f} = 4 \cdot 0 \log_{10} r/k + 3 \cdot 48 . \qquad . \qquad . \quad (13.9)$$

showing that f is now solely dependent upon the roughness ratio r/k.

To compare effectively the friction equations for smooth- and rough-bore pipes it is necessary to find how f in the smooth-wall case depends on the thickness of the laminar sub-layer δ'. Now experiments show that approximately $\delta' = 10\nu/\sqrt{(\tau_0/\rho)}$ (p. 194).

But since $\qquad\qquad \tau_0 = g\,\rho\,i\,d/4$ for a circular pipe

So $\qquad\qquad\qquad \sqrt{(\tau_0/\rho)} = \tfrac{1}{2}\sqrt{(i\,d\,g)}$

or $\qquad\qquad\qquad\qquad \delta' = 20\nu/\sqrt{(i\,d\,g)}.$

By definition $f = i\,\dfrac{d}{4}\,\dfrac{2g}{\bar{U}^2}$ (equation 13.5), and substituting for $(i\,d\,g)$

$$\sqrt{f} = \frac{\nu}{\bar{U}\,\delta'}\,10\sqrt{2}$$

Consider first the rough-wall friction formula equation 13.9. This may be rewritten

$$1/\sqrt{f} - 4\log_{10} r/k = 3.48,$$

that is to say, the left-hand side of the equation is completely invariable.

Now consider the smooth-wall friction formula of equation 13.8; subtract from both sides $4\log_{10} r/k$, thus giving

$$1/\sqrt{f} - 4\log_{10} r/k = 4.0\log_{10} 2\mathbf{R}\sqrt{f} - 1.6 - 4\log_{10} r/k.$$

The first term on the right-hand side may be simplified by substitution for $f = 10\sqrt{2}\,\nu/\bar{U}\delta'$ above, that is

$$4.0\log_{10}\mathbf{R}\sqrt{f} = 4.0\log_{10}\frac{2\,\bar{U}\,2r}{\nu}\,10\sqrt{2}\,\frac{\nu}{\bar{U}\delta'}$$

$$= 4.0\log_{10} 40\sqrt{2}\,r/\delta'$$

$$= 4.0\log_{10}\frac{r}{k}\,\frac{k}{\delta'}\,40\sqrt{2}$$

$$= 4.0\,(\log_{10} r/k + \log_{10} k/\delta' + \log_{10} 40\sqrt{2}).$$

Insert this term into the modified equation 13.8 above, and

$$1/\sqrt{f} - 4\log_{10} r/k = 4.0(\log_{10} r/k + \log_{10} k/\delta' + \log_{10} 40\sqrt{2})$$
$$- 1.6 - 4\log_{10} r/k$$

$$= 4.0\log_{10} k/\delta' + 5.4.$$

Thus for a smooth-walled pipe, or a rough pipe having a laminar sub-layer submerging the roughness elements, the expression

$$1/\sqrt{f} - 4\log_{10} r/k$$

is not constant but depends on k/δ'.

Both the 'smooth wall' and 'rough wall' equations can now be shown on the same graph (fig 13.12), where $1/\sqrt{f} - 4 \log r/k$ is plotted against $\log k/\delta'$. The smooth-wall law shows a straight inclined line, and the rough-wall law a straight horizontal line. The experimental data always fit one or the other lines at high or low values of k/δ', but in a middle range of k/δ' the points form a transition curve from one line to the other. The shape of the transition depends on the sort of roughness but does not depend on its size which has already been taken into account by the variable k. Roughnesses consisting of a single layer of sand grains all of the same size give one transition which diverges from the smooth-wall line when k/δ' is a

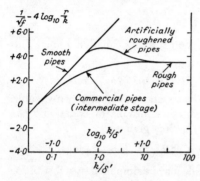

Fig 13.12 The universal pipe friction curve for turbulent flow. The ratio k/δ' is the parameter showing if the boundary roughnesses project through the laminar sub-layer or not. The shape of the middle part of the curve depends on the type of roughness and its uniformity of size.

little less than 1·0, that is when the crests of the grains are just emerging from the laminar sub-layer. Commercial pipes have roughnesses which are a mixture of large and small grains, and these give another transition starting at a lower k/δ'. This can be explained if k is the mean size of the roughnesses which will be used to correlate the high k/δ' data to the rough pipe line of fig 13.12. But while the laminar sub-layer is still thicker than k, some of the larger roughnesses are projecting through it, producing eddies from what is now a partially rough surface. It will not be until δ' is a good deal smaller than k that all the roughnesses are exposed and creating the completely rough surface.

The success of the boundary layer analysis (much of which is too advanced and lengthy to give here) in correlating all the pipe-friction data onto one curve (fig 13.12) may well be regarded as one of the triumphs of fluid mechanics. But great problems remain : how to find k by direct measurement without performing a hydraulic experiment in the high k/δ' or rough-surface law zone of fig 13.12 ? How to express the size of non-uniform roughnesses in terms of a single parameter k ? How to select the appropriate transition curve for a particular roughness shape ? It is not always possible, for instance, in large hydro-electric turbine supply pipes, to carry out experiments at a high enough $\bar{U}d/\nu$ for the roughnesses to protrude completely through the laminar sub-layer and thus to give k. Yet the accurate estimation of f is often critically important, and improved methods along the foregoing lines will no doubt be attempted.

13.9 Effect of the pipe shape on the friction

The whole derivation of the friction formulae rests on the assumption that the radial distribution of velocity is the same as that over a flat plate ; that in fact the pipe flow is the boundary layer of a plane surface wrapped around the pipe axis. It is therefore assumed that the flow is symmetrical about the axis and the drag forces per unit area is the same at all places round the perimeter. This is undoubtedly true for a circular pipe, but not so for pipes of other sections. In fig 13.13 the contour lines of equal velocities are shown for three

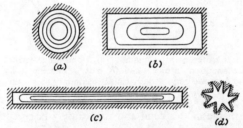

Fig 13.13 Cross sections of four different pipes, showing typical contours of equal velocity.

shapes of pipes. For a circular pipe they are symmetrical ; those for a rectangular pipe are more crowded near the midpoints of the walls than they are near the corners. There is accordingly a greater velocity gradient at the midpoints than elsewhere, giving a greater τ_0 there. For a somewhat square section, fig 13.13 (b), the corner effects form an appreciable part of the whole flow : but for a long narrow section, fig 13.13 (c), the corner effects occupy less of the total cross-sectional area. On the other hand, the velocity gradients at the short sides of pipe (c) are more different from those at the long sides, compared with the squarer pipe (b). The two effects are to some extent compensating so that it is found experimentally that f for non-circular pipes is not greatly different from that for a circular pipe, and is certainly near enough for most engineering purposes. The concept of the hydraulic mean depth (cross-sectional area divided by wetted perimeter) enables a close correlation to be obtained between friction data for many shaped pipes.   If the pipe cross-section is very irregular, however, with many reversals of curvature (fig 13.13 (*d*) shows an extreme example), the concept may break down and there may be larger errors in using the circular pipe values of *f*.   Experiment will be necessary for every separate case of this sort.

13.10 Effect of pipe bends and other non-uniformities

Pipelines are not always straight from end to end ; they have bends in them, which may be abrupt or gentle, and they may have valves and changes of cross section in them.   The effect of these non-uniformities is usually to increase the degradation of energy locally.

If the bend is sufficiently abrupt as in fig 13.14 (*a*), breakaway may

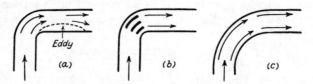

Fig 13.14   Three different pipe bends.   (*a*) A sharp elbow may create break-away and consequent eddies which (*b*) may be eliminated by using turning vanes.   (*c*) A gentle bend usually causes secondary spiral flows downstream of it (Chapter 11).

occur at the inside of the bend and will cause a large eddy formation downstream.   These eddies degrade a good deal of energy in a short length of pipe, so that such bends cause a sudden downward step in the energy gradient line, in addition to the gradient caused by the normal pipe friction.   The breakaway can be prevented, and the energy degradation reduced, by placing curved guide vanes across the corner, fig 13.14 (*b*).   These constrain the fluid to turn at the appropriate radius.   If the bend is gentle, as in fig 13.14 (*c*), no breakaway occurs, but secondary flow is caused by the interaction of boundary layer and radial pressure gradient due to the bending of the streamlines. The double spiral flow so resulting (see Chapter 11) acts across the centre of the pipe, giving a constant cross velocity which brings slow fluid to the centre and fast fluid to the inner sides.   This current therefore assists the irregular eddy motions (the turbulence) to transport momentum across the flow, and so increases the force opposing the motion.   An increased energy degradation is thus experienced around even gentle bends.

All other non-uniformities in pipes cause additional and concentrated degradation of energy. Expansions from one size pipe to another give eddy formations similar to those already described for the inlet and outlet of pipelines. Valves always cause some eddies even when they are fully open, the designs having a more intricate fluid passage giving a greater degradation than those of the straight-through flow variety. For any particular type of non-uniformity, experiments must be carried out to find the reduction of energy through it. It is found that if the flow in the pipes is turbulent (the common engineering case), then the energy degradation in the fittings is always proportional to the kinetic energy $\bar{U}^2/2g$. In laminar flow a different relation may hold. Comparison with the usual pipe friction equation $h = 4f\dfrac{l}{d}\dfrac{\bar{U}^2}{2g}$ shows that the friction of every pipe bend or fitting can be expressed as an additional length of the pipe concerned. The sum of the real length and the additional length gives the effective length, which may then be used in the pipe friction equation to obtain the relation between i, d and Q.

Example

A smooth-walled pipeline 3500 m long is to connect two reservoirs 7 m different in elevation. Entry is abrupt, outlet is a conical diffuser. There are two globe valves, and five 60° bends are inevitable. If gravity is to cause a flow of water, what should be the diameter so that the discharge is 0·03 cumec? Water temperature 15 °C.

First approximation—ignore valves, inlet, bends, etc. Flow is turbulent, most probably, so guess $\bar{U}d/\nu = 10^4$. Thus estimate f from fig 13.10 as $f = 0·0079$.

So
$$h = 4f\frac{l}{d}\frac{U^2}{2g} = 4f\frac{l}{d}\frac{Q^2 16}{\pi^2 d^4 2g}$$

or
$$d^5 = \frac{32}{\pi^2}\frac{flQ^2}{gh}$$

with $f = 0·0079$, $l = 3500$ m, $g = 9·81$ m sec^{-2}, $h = 7$ m.

$$d^5 = 117 \times 10^{-5} \quad \text{or} \quad d = 0·259 \text{ m provisionally.}$$

Use this provisional value of d to check that the guessed value of $\bar{U}d/\nu$ was correct ($\nu = 1·45 \times 10^{-2}$ cm^2/s).

$$\bar{U} = \frac{0·03}{\pi/4 \times 0·259^2} = 0·568 \text{ m/s provisionally.}$$

So
$$\frac{\bar{U}d}{\nu} = \frac{0·568 \times 100 \times 0·259 \times 100}{1·45 \times 10^{-2}} = 1·01 \times 10^5$$

Thus the first approximation of $\bar{U}d/\nu$ was seriously underestimated.

Second approximation—try $\bar{U}d/\nu = 1\cdot2 \times 10^5$. Thus $f = 0\cdot0044$
from fig 13.10.

So $d^5 = 65\cdot3 \times 10^{-5}$ or $d = 0\cdot230$ m

and $\bar{U} = 0\cdot717$ m/s

Check for $\dfrac{\bar{U}d}{\nu} = \dfrac{71\cdot7 \times 23\cdot0}{1\cdot45 \times 10^{-2}} = 1\cdot14 \times 10^5.$

This estimation is therefore much better than the first. Since d is
changed so little by the change of $\dfrac{\bar{U}d}{\nu}$ from 1×10^4 to 12×10^4, no
further approximation will be made. It is probably good enough for
most engineering purposes.

Third approximation takes bends, valves, etc., into account.
From the appendix (p. 240)

an abrupt entry is equivalent to 25 diameters of pipe
a diffuser outlet   „   6   „   „
a globe valve   „   75   „   „
a 60° bend   „   22   „   „

Thus the total additional length of plain pipe equivalent to the fittings is

$$25 + 6 + (2 \times 75) + (5 \times 22) = 291 \text{ diameters}$$

or a length of $291 \times 0\cdot230 = 67$ m
Thus the effective length is   3567 m
Amending the second approximation

$$d^5 = 65\cdot3 \times 10^{-5} \times \frac{3567}{3500} = 66\cdot7 \times 10^{-5}$$

and d is barely affected.
Thus $d = 0\cdot23$ m is the diameter necessary.
The conclusion above that the fittings in a *long* pipeline are of little
importance in the determination of the diameter demonstrates the usual
engineering convention of ignoring them.

13.11 Changes of pipe friction with time

It is commonly found that in the course of time the friction coefficient
of pipes carrying water increases, so that the flow decreases for a given
pressure difference. This is due to the growth of rust and of lime
nodules, especially if the water is hard. It has been found that to
a first approximation the nodules grow always at the same rate, so
that the roughness size k increases linearly with time. That is,
$k = k_0 + \alpha t$, where k_0 is the initial roughness of the pipe. The
constant α can be found from data previously obtained from other
pipes in the same neighbourhood. Since for rough pipe

$$1/\sqrt{f} = 4 \log_{10} r/k + 3\cdot48,$$

the original roughness k_0 can be found by a hydraulic experiment with the new pipe : substitution of the future roughness k will give the future value of f which is then used in the friction formula $h = 4f\dfrac{l}{d}\dfrac{U^2}{2g}$ to give the future flow.

13.12 Pipe networks

The engineer is often concerned with the properties of a system of interconnected pipes being supplied with, or supplying, fluid at different points. A city water supply network is such a system, and it may be necessary to calculate the pressure at all points in the network for a given flow. The calculations also may be made for a particular network if it is desired to know how much the pressure is changed if a large flow (say for fire-fighting purposes) is taken from one point. One sort of network, fig 13.15 (a), is essentially a group of pipes all

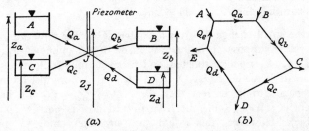

(a)   (b)

Fig 13.15 Two sorts of pipe networks. (a) Several reservoirs feeding a junction point. (b) A ring main.

meeting in a common junction point J. Different pressures are applied to the outer ends of the pipes (by connecting to reservoirs or pumps) so that a flow occurs from the higher pressure ends towards the lower pressure ends. The problem is to find what the flow will be in each pipe. It is clear that the total fluid arriving at J must equal the total flow away from J ; that is, if flow towards J is reckoned as positive then the total flow towards J is zero, or

$$Q_a + Q_b + Q_c + Q_d = 0,$$

where Q_a is the flow through pipe A, etc. Now imagine an open-ended pipe erected vertically from J, wherein the fluid stands hydrostatically with its surface at z_J above some arbitrary datum level. If the surface of the reservoir connected to pipe A is at a height z_a, then

$$(z_A - z_J) = 4f_a\frac{l_a}{d_a}\frac{\bar{U}_a^2}{2g} = 4f_a\left(\frac{l_a}{d_a}\right)\frac{16Q_a^2}{\pi^2 d_a^4 2g}$$

or $$h_a = K_a \, Q_a{}^2,$$

where $h_a = z_a - z_J$ and $K_a = 4 f_a \dfrac{l_a}{d_a{}^5} \dfrac{16}{\pi^2 2g}.$

Similarly for all the other pipes,

$$h_b = K_b \, Q_b \,; \quad h_c = K_c \, Q_c{}^2 \,; \quad h_d = K_d \, Q_d{}^2.$$

It will be seen that z_J appears in all these friction equations so that if it changes all the flows will change. There are therefore 5 unknowns (z_J, Q_a, Q_b, Q_c and Q_d) and, using $Q_a + Q_b + Q_c + Q_d = 0$, there are 5 equations with which to solve them. The quickest and neatest way to do so is as follows.

Consider the effect of a small change dh of the friction head h between the ends of a pipe.

Since $$h = K Q^2,$$
then, differentiating, $$dh = 2 K Q \, dQ,$$
or substituting for K $$dh = 2 dQ \, h/Q.$$

Thus the small change dh gives a change dQ in the flow through the pipe. Now suppose an estimate is made of the unknown z_J: then h_a, h_b, h_c, h_d are all estimated, and from the four friction equations an estimate is made of Q_a, Q_b, Q_c, Q_d. If the original estimate of z_J happened to be correct then $Q_a + Q_b + Q_c + Q_d = 0$ and the problem is solved (Remember that inward flow is positive, outward negative). However, this would be pure luck and, in general, $Q_a + Q_b + Q_c + Q_d = \Delta Q$, the total error in Q, made up of errors dQ in the respective pipes. But ΔQ is caused by an error dh in the estimated pressure at J; and to put this error right involves changing the flow in each pipe, according to the equation $dh = 2 dQ \, h/Q$ already derived.
So that

$$\Delta Q = dQ_a + dQ_b + dQ_c + dQ_d$$
$$= \tfrac{1}{2} Q_a/h_a \, dh + \tfrac{1}{2} Q_b/h_b \, dh + \tfrac{1}{2} Q_c/h_c \, dh + \tfrac{1}{2} Q_d/h_d \, dh$$
$$= \tfrac{1}{2} \, dh \, \Sigma Q/h$$

or $$dh = 2 \frac{\Delta Q}{\Sigma Q/h}$$

Thus from an initial estimate of z_J, ΔQ and $\Sigma Q/h$ may be found and the correction dh determined by the equation. The calculation is best done in tabular form, as in the following example, which may be extended by further approximations until the desired degree of accuracy is obtained.

Example

Four pipes from reservoirs meet at a point J, viz. :

Pipe	Reservoir level m above datum	Pipe length m	Diameter m	f
a	100	3000	1·5	0·004
b	110	6000	1·0	0·007
c	80	3000	1·0	0·006
d	40	10,000	2·0	0·004

Determine the flow in each pipe, and the pressure at J.

Clearly, z_J must lie between 40 and 110 m above datum, so for first approximation let a and b discharge to c and d. Therefore estimate $z_J = 90$ m above datum.

Pipe	$4f \dfrac{l}{d^5} \dfrac{16}{\pi^2} \dfrac{1}{2g} = K$	Estimated h m	$Q = \sqrt{(h/K)}$ cumecs	Q/h
a	0·52	100 − 90 = 10	4·4	0·44
b	13·9	110 − 90 = 20	1·19	0·06
c	5·95	80 − 90 = − 10	− 1·3	0·13
d	0·41	40 − 90 = − 50	− 11·0	0·22

$$\Delta Q = -6 \cdot 7 \text{ cusecs} \qquad \Sigma \frac{Q}{h} = 0 \cdot 85$$

Thus
$$dh = 2 \frac{\Delta Q}{\Sigma \dfrac{Q}{h}} = - 2 \times \frac{6 \cdot 7}{0 \cdot 85} = - 15 \cdot 8 \text{ m}$$

Clearly the first estimate of z_J was badly in error, so make a second approximation of

$$z_J = 90 - 15 \cdot 8 = 74 \cdot 2 \text{ m}$$

Pipe	h new estimate	Q	Q/h
a	25·8	7·04	0·27
b	35·8	1·61	0·05
c	5·8	0·99	0·17
d	−34·2	− 9·08	0·27

$$\Delta Q = + 0 \cdot 56 \qquad \Sigma \frac{Q}{h} = 0 \cdot 76$$

New correction $dh = + 2 \times \dfrac{0 \cdot 56}{0 \cdot 76} = + 1 \cdot 47$ m

Thus the third estimate of $z_J = 74 \cdot 2 + 1 \cdot 47 = 75 \cdot 7$ m.
Check this estimate by a third tabulation.

Pipe	h	Q
a	24·3	6·83
b	34·3	1·57
c	4·3	0·85
d	− 35·7	− 9·30

$$\Delta Q = - 0 \cdot 05 \text{ cumec}$$

This is small enough for most purposes, though further corrections could be made if necessary.

Thus
$$z_J = 75 \cdot 7 \text{ m}$$
$$Q_a = 6 \cdot 83 \; ; \quad Q_b = 1 \cdot 57 \; ; \quad Q_c = 0 \cdot 85 \; ; \quad Q_d = 9 \cdot 30 \text{ cumecs}$$

13.13 Doubling pipes

A special case of the pipe network just described is when a pipeline between two reservoirs is doubled by a parallel pipe for a part or the whole of its length. This situation occurs in water supply systems when a city outgrows the capacity of its supply mains, and it is desired to increase the flow.

The network is shown in fig 13.16, and, as before, it is convenient

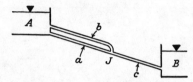

Fig 13.16 A doubling pipe part way between two reservoirs increases the flow. Pipes a and c are usually the same size, being the original pipe. Pipe b is the new pipe.

to use the junction pressure z_J as a variable.

So for pipe a,
$$4f_a \frac{l_a}{d_a{}^5} \frac{16 \, Q_a{}^2}{\pi^2 \, 2g} = z_A - z_J$$

for pipe b,
$$4f_b \frac{l_b}{d_b{}^5} \frac{16 \, Q_b{}^2}{\pi^2 \, 2g} = z_A - z_J$$

for pipe c,
$$4f_c \frac{l_c}{d_c{}^5} \frac{16 \, Q_c{}^2}{\pi^2 \, 2g} = z_J - z_B$$

at the junction
$$Q_a + Q_b = Q_c$$

and
$$l_a = l_b.$$

These equations, together with the additional information that the left-hand sides of the first two are equal, may be solved directly by the usual methods of subtraction for simultaneous equations. Sometimes the increased flow $(Q_a + Q_b)$ and d_b is known and the correct length l_b for the doubling pipe calculated : sometimes $(Q_a + Q_b)$ and l_b are fixed and d_b is calculated : sometimes l_b and d_b are fixed and it is desired to know by how much the flow is increased. Usually the diameter of pipe c is the same as that of pipe a, the original pipe.

Doubling pipes are often laid in portions at intervals of time, as the water demand grows, until they are the same length as the original pipe. By the time this full development is required, the first pipe has usually become corroded, the roughness has increased, and f is larger than that for the newer pipe.

13.14 Ring mains

The other sort of pipe network is shown in fig 13.15 (b), and is essentially a ring of pipes supplied with fluid at some points and supplying fluid to outgoing pipes at others. The arrangement is a common one in town water supply systems, water being supplied at a few points and being taken off at many. The problem is to determine the pressures at every junction point, and the flow in every part of the ring, if the supply quantity and the several outlet quantities are given.

The method of solution of the problem is very similar to that for the junction network. A first guess is made of the discharge in each pipe, the guesses being made so that at each junction the flow arriving is the same as the flow leaving. The pressure drop along each pipe, h, is then calculated by the usual pipe friction formula $h = 4f \dfrac{l}{d} \dfrac{\bar{U}^2}{2g}$.

In the ring one direction, say clockwise, is taken as the positive direction. A pressure fall in this direction would be regarded as a positive h, and a rise in this direction a negative h. Under this convention, the sum of all the values of h for the successive pipes of the ring should be zero if correct guesses have been made of the discharges. Usually, of course, an error Δh is found which is made up of the sum of the errors in the several pipes. This error is caused by the wrong estimation of the discharges. However, the only correction that can be made to the discharge is one that is applied to all the pipes in the ring so that the algebraic sum of the flows at every junction remains zero. For example, fig 13.17 shows one junction where a flow Q_x has been

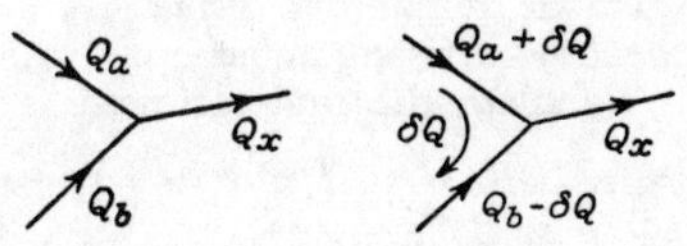

Fig 13.17 One junction of a ring main showing how the balance of quantity can only be preserved if the same correction is made to both of the flows in the limbs of the ring. Pipes a and b belong to the ring. Pipe x is the outflow from the ring at the junction point.

specified to be removed. The original guesses Q_a and Q_b have been found to be wrong, giving together with the other ring pipe flows an error Δh around the ring. If a correction δQ is applied as shown in the clockwise direction to *all* pipes, then the condition of flow into the junction equalling the flow out of junction is preserved at each junction.

The error in h due to an error in Q has already been established as

$$dh_a = 2dQ_a\,h_a/Q_a \text{ for pipe a}$$

and similar expressions for the other pipes.

The total error round the ring is therefore

$$\Delta h = dh_a + dh_b + dh_c + \ldots \text{ etc.}$$

$$= \left(2\,\frac{h_a}{Q_a} + 2\,\frac{h_b}{Q_b} + 2\,\frac{h_c}{Q_c} + \ldots\right)dQ$$

That is

$$dQ = \frac{\Delta h}{2\,\Sigma h/Q}.$$

The error dQ so found can now be corrected by applying a balancing discharge of the same magnitude but opposite in sign. The error in h should now be small, but the estimation may be repeated until the required accuracy is obtained, as shown in the following example.

Example

A four-sided ring main ABCD has a supply of 16·4 cusecs of water at A and delivers to other pipes at B, C and D to the extent of 11·7, 2·9 and 1·8 cusecs respectively. What are the flows in the ring, and the pressures at B, C and D if the pressure at A is 100 ft? The pipe characteristics are given below.

Pipe	Length ft	Diameter ft	f
AB	3000	1·5	0·004
BC	6000	1·0	0·007
CD	10,000	2·0	0·004
DA	3000	1·0	0·006

Original estimates of discharges are made as shown in the following table. It was noticed that AB is a low resistance pipe (K low) so that the discharge through it must be higher than AD. Having thus fixed Q_{AB} the remaining discharges are also fixed because at each junction the flow arriving must equal the flow leaving.

Tabulate the first estimate as follows :

Pipe	$K = 32fl/\pi^2 d^5 g$	Q estimated	$h = KQ^2$	h/Q
AB	0·160	+ 13·0	+ 27·0	2·1
BC	4·24	+ 1·3	+ 7·1	5·5
CD	0·126	− 1·6	− 21·0	0·2
DA	1·81	− 3·4	− 21·0	6·2

$$\Delta h = + 12\text{·}8 \qquad \Sigma\frac{h}{Q} = 14\text{·}0$$

Thus error in flow $\quad dQ = \dfrac{\Delta h}{2\Sigma h/Q} = \dfrac{+\,12\text{·}8}{2 \times 14\text{·}0} = +\,0\text{·}46$ cusec.

The second estimate may then be made by applying a correction of − 0·46 cusec to all discharges, which should then reduce the above error.

Pipe	K	Q revised	h ft	h/Q
AB	0·160	13·0 −0·46 = 12·54	+25·2	2·01
BC	4·24	1·3 −0·46 = 0·84	+ 3·0	3·57
CD	0·126	− 1·6 −0·46 =−2·06	− 0·5	0·25
DA	1·81	− 3·4 −0·46 =−3·86	−27·0	6·73

$$\Delta h = +\ 0·7 \qquad \Sigma\frac{h}{Q}=12·56$$

The error in h ($+ 0·7$ ft) is probably near enough for most engineering purposes, but a still nearer approximation can be made by applying a correction of

$$\frac{-\ 0·7}{2\ \times\ 12·56} = -\ 0·028\ \text{cusec.}$$

Thus
$$Q_{AB} = \quad 12·54\ -\ 0·03 = \quad 12·51\ \text{cusecs}$$
$$Q_{BC} = \qquad 0·84\ -\ 0·03 = \quad 0·81\ \text{cusec}$$
$$Q_{CD} = -\quad 2·06\ -\ 0·03 = -\ 2·09\ \text{cusecs}$$
$$Q_{DA} = -\quad 3·86\ -\ 0·03 = -\ 3·89\ \text{cusecs}$$

And pressures are
$$p_A = 100\ \text{ft}$$
$$p_B = 100\ -\ 25·2 = 74·8\ \text{ft}$$
$$p_C = 74·8\ -\ 3·0 = 71·8\ \text{ft}$$
$$p_D = 71·8\ +\ 0·5 = 72·3\ \text{ft}$$
$$\text{or}\quad 100\ -\ 27·0 = 73·0\ \text{ft}$$

The first estimate of the discharge was good (and it was not known beforehand !) so that the corrections were small.

13.15 More elaborate networks

Networks on water supply systems are usually more complicated than the foregoing examples, though they can often be broken up

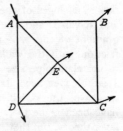

Fig 13.18   A more elaborate pipe network which would involve lengthy approximations.

into a number of rings and junctions as, for example, fig 13.18.   In this case the ring main method is used, first on ABC, say ; then using the value of the flow in EC which has just been calculated, the flows in the ring DEC are then guessed and corrected : then using the flows in DE and AE, ring AED is guessed and corrected. But by now, the newly corrected flows for AE and EC have made ring ABC in error, so a further correction procedure must be made in ABC. Finally, the outer ring ABCD is tested for errors in h, using the computed flows given by the analyses for the inner rings, and if necessary a correction applied. This in turn puts errors into the inner rings so the whole computation is then repeated, when it will be found that the errors in the rings slowly decrease until an acceptably correct result is given.

The complete procedure is tedious and slow for complicated networks so that other mathematical methods have been evolved. These are usually more easily adapted for use with computing machines than the above method (e.g. the ' relaxation ' method of Southwell). However, very high precision is not needed because of the uncertainty in practice of finding f. For many purposes an electrical network can be used to simulate a pipe network, a circuit being used which contains resistances that vary with the square of the current. The voltage drop across the resistance corresponds to the pressure drop in a pipe, and the current to the flow. Such electrical models are a practical way of solving difficult pipe flow problems experimentally, but they do not help at all to solve the difficult problem of finding f.

Conclusion

The flow of fluids in pipes is a most important branch of engineering fluid mechanics. Essentially the engineer wishes to know the energy degradation in the several parts of a pipe system. This degradation results in a decrease of pressure in a downstream direction, which must be made good by pumps or by gravity in order to preserve the flow. Changes of energy and of pressure occur at the inlets, outlets and at valves and other fittings in the pipe, but the major cause of a gradient of energy is the turbulence in the pipe caused by the fluid friction with the walls. There have been many empirical attempts to correlate pipe size and roughness, hydraulic gradient and flow in a simple yet accurate manner. These are successful within small ranges of the variables concerned. Much more successful attempts have been made to rationalize friction measurements using boundary layer theory, but they are only truly valid for uniform sand roughnesses on the walls of the pipe. There are still great difficulties in expressing the usual sort of roughnesses found in commercial pipes by one simple parameter. Systems comprising a network of pipes supplied by and

supplying fluid at a number of points can be analysed to find the flow
in each pipe, but the accuracy is no better than that of finding the
friction coefficient for the pipes.

Appendix : Values of coefficients in the pipe friction formula

Straight uniform pipes. If the roughness to diameter ratio k/d is
known then the curves of fig 13.10 may be used to determine f for a
given $\bar{U}d/\nu$. This always involves a successive approximation method
of calculation if h, l and Q are known and it is desired to find $\bar{U}$ and
d (see example in text). The following values of k are sometimes
used.

Asbestos cement	0·0012 cm
New steel pipes	0·005–0·012 cm
New cast iron	0·025 cm
Smooth concrete	0·025–0·05 cm
Rock—depending on smoothness of finishing	

In general it is rare to find f smaller than about 0·0035, or much higher
than 0·01 unless artificial roughnesses have been deliberately added to
the pipe walls.

Chézy's formula, $\bar{U} = C\sqrt{(mi)}$. One fairly adequate empirical
formula for C is that due to Bazin

$$C = 87 \left/ \left(1 + \frac{\gamma}{\sqrt{m}} \right) \right. \mathrm{m^{1/2}\,s^{-1}}$$

where γ is a constant depending on the roughness of the pipe (or of an
open channel).

Planed timber, smooth plaster	$\gamma = 0·06$
Brick	$\gamma = 0·16$
Rubble masonry	$\gamma = 0·46$

If a friction experiment can be done on smaller pipes than the full-size
ones, with the same roughness, then the method outlined in Chapter 14
should be used to find k, which can then be applied to the larger pipe.

Manning's formula $\bar{U} = Mm^{2/3}i^{1/2}$

Cast iron	$M = 94 \ \mathrm{m^{1/3}\,s^{-1}}$
Riveted pipes	$M = 80$
Asphalted cast iron	$M = 114$
Concrete	$M = 91$

For historical reasons, M is often written $1/n$ ($1·49/n$ in f.p.s. units),
where n is called Kutter's n. There is a slight advantage since n increases
as roughness increases. The Manning formula is attributed to Strickler
in European countries outside Britain.

Fittings in pipes. Nearly all fittings and irregularities in pipes cause an energy degradation. A selection of fittings is shown in fig 13.19, with the degradation shown as a proportion, α, of $\bar{U}^2/2g$. As well as the constant α, another way of presenting the data is to give the equivalent length of uniform pipe that would cause the same degradation. The constant β is given so that the equivalent length is βd, where d is the diameter of the pipe. It is assumed that f for this pipe is 0·005. Note that if $\alpha = 1·0$, then $\beta = 50$, so that in this case the equivalent length is 50 diameters.

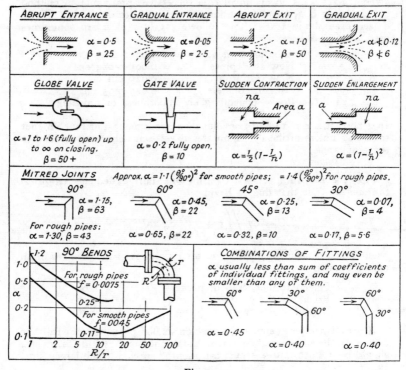

Fig 13.19

PROBLEMS

1. A flow of 420 l/min of oil is pumped through a 7·5 cm pipe, 62 m, whose outlet is 3 m higher than the inlet. The oil density is 0·91 g cm^{-3} and viscosity 1·24 poise. Estimate the power required.

Hint. Compute the pipe Reynolds number first.

Ans. 675 W.

2. A 75 cm bore water pipe carries 0·66 m^3/s. At point B the pressure is 175 kN/m^2 gauge and the elevation is 36 m. At point C, 1500 m

from B, the pressure is 310 kN/m² absolute and the elevation is 30 m.
Determine the pipe friction coefficient f.

Ans. $f = 0.0072$.

3. Calculate the diameter of a pipe 800 m long to convey coal gas
at 600 m³/h from a gasholder to a power station. Delivery is 15 m
above the entrance to the pipe ; pressure at holder is 10 cm water gauge
and at station is 5 cm.

Density of gas 0.7 kg/m³ ; of air 1.25 kg/m³
Friction coefficient $f = 0.005$

What would be the diameter of the pipe if the delivery was 15 m
below the inlet, all other conditions remaining the same ?
Hint. Variation of atmospheric pressure is important.

Ans. 20.6 cm : 24.2 cm.

4. In a hydro-electric scheme the power house is to be 5 km from
the dam and the available head between impounding level and tail race
is 75 m. It is desired to generate 12,000 kW and the turbine and electrical efficiencies are 82 per cent and 96 per cent respectively. The
water is to be conveyed by a double pipeline with the conservative
value of $f = 0.006$.

Calculate the diameter of the pipes (*a*) if the energy degradation by
friction is not to exceed 1 per cent of the available energy and (*b*) if
this degradation is 5 per cent.

Ans. (*a*) 4.29 m : (*b*) 3.16 m.

5. If in question 4 the amount of degraded energy is not important,
what are the maximum powers that can be developed by the scheme
using the pipe diameters calculated above ? Discuss the factors which
would affect the final choice of diameter, including cost of pipeline, of
water, of power-house and the future development of the plant.
Hint. Establish that differentiation shows $h = \frac{1}{3}H$ for max power.

Ans. (*a*) 56,800 kW : (*b*) 26,600 kW.

6. Discuss cavitation and its effect on design of structures. A spillway pressure tunnel 6 m in diameter has a gate in it 10 m below the
free surface of the lake supplying the tunnel. In a model study, the
speed at the corners of the gate was found to be twice the mean speed
in the tunnel. At what discharge will cavitation begin in the full-size
tunnel ? Assume that the water commences to boil at $-$ 10 m gauge
pressure.

Ans. 280 cumecs.

7. Given that the friction factor f in a pipe which is roughened to an
effective roughness size k is

$$1/\sqrt{f} = 4 \log r/k + 3.48,$$

show that Chézy's coefficient is $C = 18 \log_{10} 3.7d/k$ where d is the
pipe diameter.

C for a certain 30 cm water pipe has been observed to deteriorate from
65 m$^{1/2}$/s to 47 between the years 1920 and 1950, due to the growth of
roughnesses by corrosion on the bore. Estimate C for a 75 cm main at
the beginning and end of a 20 years' service in the same district.
Assume the roughnesses grow linearly with time.

Ans. 72 m$^{1/2}$/s ; 56 m$^{1/2}$/s.

8. Four reservoirs, A, B, C, and D, in which the water-levels are respectively 50, 30, 10 and 20 m above datum, are connected by pipe to a common junction point J.

Pipe	Length m	Diameter cm
AJ	500	60
BJ	1000	30
CJ	1500	30
DJ	3000	45

Assuming $f = 0.005$, calculate the head at J and the flow in each pipe.
Ans. Head at J 45·6 m : AJ 0·63, JB 0·15, JC 0·19, JD 0·29 cumec.

9. A quadrilateral network of pipes ABCD is joined across AC by another pipe. There is an inflow of 0·1 m³/s at A and outflows of 0·03 and 0·07 m³/s respectively at B and C.

Pipe	Length m	Diameter cm
AB	1000	30
BC	1000	30
CD	1000	30
DA	1000	30
AC	2000	45

Assuming $f = 0.005$, calculate the flow in each pipe.
Ans. AB 0·275 : CB 0·025 : AC 0·532 : ADC 0·193 cumec.

10. Water is led from a reservoir through a pipe to a nozzle H m below. Show that the maximum power available in the jet from the nozzle occurs when the degradation of energy by friction in the pipe is $H/3$, so that the total energy in the pipe just upstream of the nozzle is $\frac{2}{3} H$. Discuss the factors, including the capital cost of the civil engineering works that must be considered in deciding if a pipeline is to be used in this way.

11. Draw the total energy and pressure diagrams for a closed-circuit wind tunnel. You are recommended to develop the centre-line of the tunnel and to cut it at the working section.

12. At what radius should a Pitot tube be placed in a pipe in order to give a direct measure of the average velocity? Give two answers, one for turbulent and one for laminar flow. Assume the 1/7th root approximation for the velocity distribution in turbulent flow.
Ans. 70·7 and 76 per cent of the pipe radius.

13. A town is supplied with water through a pipe 2 m in diameter, $k = 0.2$ mm, of length 5×10^4 m. If the difference of levels between entry and exit reservoirs is 150 m, estimate the flow.
For many years, only half the flow will be required. Explain how the flow could be so limited, estimate the power to be dissipated, and show with diagrams how the position of the dissipator will affect total head and piezometric lines along the pipe. Indicate regions of low pressure.
Kinematic viscosity of water 0·01 cm²/s.
Ans. $\delta' \gg k_s$, so rough pipe ; 9·9 m³/s ; 5·5 MW.

14

FLOW IN OPEN CHANNELS—RIVERS AND CANALS

14.1 The flow of water with a free surface exposed to atmospheric pressure presents perhaps the most common problem of fluid mechanics to a civil engineer. The designs of drainage and flood discharge channels, of waterways under bridges and of irrigation canals often call for an exact knowledge of the water-level so that retaining walls and other structures may be made to an appropriate height. By applying the principles of Fluid Mechanics as given in preceding chapters, the changes of velocity, pressure, force and energy may be found, as indeed with flows of all kinds; the special feature of open surface flow being that along one boundary of the flow (i.e. the free surface) the pressure is the same irrespective of changes of velocity. In this respect open channels are strikingly different from pipe-flows, where every change of velocity must be accompanied by a change of pressure. However, in channels just as in pipes, there are two distinct families of problems: the first where differences of depth (pressure in pipes) and velocity occur within short distances downstream (the Bernoulli type problem); and the second where appreciable differences of energy occur only over long distances downstream (the friction-dominated problem).

A useful and simple approximation to many change-of-depth problems in channels can be made by invoking the following four simplifications.

(i) The fluid is incompressible and homogeneous—this excludes problems where air is entrained into water making a froth, as occurs in high speed flows.

(ii) At all relevant cross-sections of the stream, where information is needed, the streamlines are straight, when viewed in elevation from the side of the flow. This includes cases where they diverge or converge, but excludes cases where the water surface has a curvature. The importance of this simplification is that hydrostatic pressure is therefore assured at all points in the vertical. Curvature would have presumed centrifugal accelerations and consequent complicated pressure distributions.

(iii) At all relevant cross-sections the flow is two-dimensional. This implies that although cross-sections may be of different widths, each one has a horizontal floor, has a water surface that is a horizontal straight line, and that the velocity found down *any* vertical line in the cross-section is the same as that for any other line in the same cross-section.   Places where the flow having turned a corner in plan has a ' super-elevation ' of the surface are thus excluded from the analysis.

(iv) At any cross-section, the velocity is uniform throughout, despite the presence of shear forces on the walls and bottom.   This is clearly not possible in practice, since the shear creates a boundary layer.   In problems where boundary layers are well developed some error is introduced by this simplification.

14.2   General analysis of an element of channel

The simplification of **14.1** will be applied to the material cross-sections AA and BB of the general element of open channel shown in fig 14.1.   Between A and B, the conditions are not in general known, and may indeed be quite different from those at AA and BB.   The discharge Q is the same at all points, but since the width is w_1 at A and w_2 at B, the discharge per unit width is q_1 and q_2.   The horizontal distance between A and B is finite, and τ is the average shear stress between A and B acting on the fluid by reason of bottom friction.

The changes u_1 to u_2, d_1 to d_2 in this element may now be analysed by momentum and energy principles.   At some place between A and B (shown conventionally as a dotted box in fig 14.1) a suitable device exerts a force F' backwards on the water, and causes energy E' to be degraded to heat and so made non-available.   Both E' and F' may be either positive or negative ;   the former when there is a solid object on which the water exerts a drag force (the most common case) ;   the latter when there is a force assisting the motion, so giving it energy (as occurs if there was a pump assisting the flow).   The weight force W of the water between A and B has a mean component $W \sin \theta$ down the gradient from A to B ; and so the water may also be regarded as having gained potential energy by falling from A to B.   Since the depths at A and B are different, there will have been a difference of hydrostatic force on the ends of the element ;   or alternatively, the ' pressure energy ' term in Bernoulli's equation can be regarded as having changed.   Thus every force on the system can be regarded also as having a counterpart in an energy change, so that two quite separate analyses can be made by the Force-Momentum Theorem, and by Bernoulli's Energy equation.

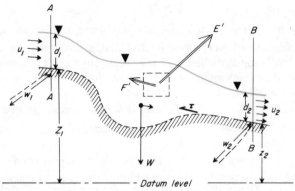

Fig 14.1 Longitudinal section of a length of an open channel, with its bed generally inclined downstream from A to B. The weight force on the water between A and B is W, and the shear stress due to friction is τ. The dotted square indicates that in a narrowly defined place, there is a concentrated force F' acting against the flow, and that an energy E' is converted to a thermal form, and therefore is no longer available in the flow. The widths w_1 and w_2 are not necessarily the same.

14.2 (a) Momentum Balance.

By Momentum Theorem, total forces in direction of motion just balance the increase in flow of momentum in direction of motion

$$H - F' + W \sin \theta - \tau AB = - \rho q_1 u_1 w_1 + \rho q_2 u_2 w_2$$
$$= - \rho \frac{u_1^2}{d_1} w_1 + \rho \frac{u_2^2}{d_2} w_2. \quad (14.1)$$

H is the resultant hydrostatic force on the element, and is the difference between these forces on the end section AA and BB, plus the downstream component of hydrostatic pressures on the walls where the mean depth is d.

i.e. $\qquad H = \tfrac{1}{2}\rho g d_1^2 w_1 - \tfrac{1}{2}\rho g d_2^2 w_2 + (w_2 - w_1)\tfrac{1}{2}\rho g d \, AB$

Eqn. (14.1) is conveniently rearranged to bring terms in d_1 together, and d_2 together

$$\left(\tfrac{1}{2}\rho g d_1^2 w_1 + \rho \frac{q_1}{d_1} w_1\right) - \left(\tfrac{1}{2}\rho g d_2^2 w_2 + \rho \frac{q_2}{d_2} w_2\right)$$
$$= - (w_2 - w_1) . \tfrac{1}{2}\rho g d AB + \tau AB \bar{w} - W \sin \theta + F'$$

It is further convenient to (i) refer to the right-hand terms as ' side forces ', ' friction forces ', ' weight forces ' and ' concentrated forces ' respectively, and (ii) refer to $(\tfrac{1}{2}\rho g d^2 + \rho(q^2/d))$ as

$$F, \text{ the ' flow-force '}$$

(Note each of these two terms has the dimension MLT^{-2}/L, a force per unit length.)

So $F_1 w_1 - F_2 w_2$

$\qquad$ = $-$ side $+$ friction $-$ weight $+$ concentrated forces   ($14.2a$)

This equation is of the most general kind, and it permits of any *one* of the terms being evaluated if all the others are known.   However, it is simplified in many engineering cases as follows.

If the channel width is constant, then

$$F_1 - F_2 = -\text{o} + \text{friction} - \text{weight} + \text{concentrated}   (14.2b)$$

If width is constant, and bed always horizontal (i.e. no longitudinal slope)

$$F_1 - F_2 = -\text{o} + \text{friction} - \text{o} + \text{concentrated} .   (14.2c)$$

If width is constant, bed horizontal and there is no friction (or if the frictional force just equals the gravity, weight force)

$$F_1 - F_2 = -\text{o} + \text{o} - \text{o} + \text{concentrated forces} .   (14.2d)$$

All these equations can be summarised by the definition

‘ the change of flow-force is the imposed force on the stream ’.

Thus the function $F = \frac{1}{2}\rho g d^2 + (\rho q^2/d)$ and its changes is the heart of any open channel problem for which forces are either known as part of the data, or desired as an answer.

The flow-force function F may be easily shown graphically, either as a series of F–d curves, each curve for a different q, or a series of d–q curves, each for a different F.   These curves are shown in fig. 14.2; notice that at higher values of d the F–d curves tend towards parabolae. The following features should be observed :

(a) The minimum point in each of the F–d curves :

(b) The tendency in the F–d curves towards a parabola at the higher values of d :

(c) The maximum point in each of the d–q curves.

Further development and the use of these curves will be made in §14.3.

14.2 (b) Energy Balance.   In this form of analysis, energy in all its relevant forms is assessed at both of the sections AA and BB, and equated.   This process is, of course, precisely the same as using Bernoulli's equation.

Taking one section only for the time being and considering the point X in it, the components of the total energy there are easily written e.g.

Kinetic, $\dfrac{u^2}{2g}$ because velocity $= u$ everywhere ;

‘ Pressure ’, $\dfrac{\rho g x}{\rho g}$ because there is hydrostatic pressure everywhere ;

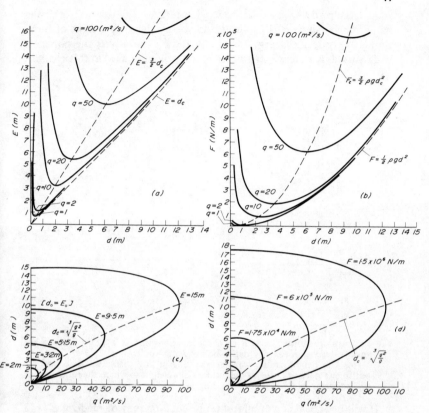

Fig 14.2 The open-channel functions E and F. The upper two graphs, (a) and (b), show how both E and F have *minimum* values at a critical depth, for each value of q. The lower two graphs (c) and (d) show that q has a maximum at a critical depth for each value of E or F.

and Potential, $z + (d - x)$ above the reference or datum level as shown in fig 14.3.

So the total energy, *relative to the datum*, is

$$H = \frac{u^2}{2g} + \frac{\rho g x}{\rho g} + z + (d - x), \qquad . \qquad . \qquad . \quad (14.3)$$

simplifying to $H = (u^2/2g) + d + z$.

It is convenient to call $(u^2/2g) + d$ the Specific Energy E

so that $\qquad H = E + z \qquad . \qquad . \qquad . \qquad . \qquad . \quad (14.4)$

As has already been explained in §7.1, total energy is strictly a wrong name for H, since it is a ' head ' or energy per unit weight of fluid. Similarly, ' specific energy ' is wrong for E. However, the phrase is widely used by practical engineers and it will be so used in this chapter.

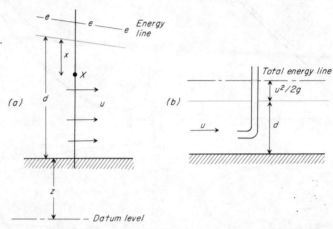

Fig 14.3   (a) Definition sketch to show relationships at a point X between specific energy E and the depth below water surface x.
(b) The height of the total energy line at any place can be found by putting a total head tube in the fluid.   The height to which the fluid rises in a piezometer is the height of the line.

It will be seen that a graphical representation may be made of E (and so of H) along a channel by plotting at every cross-section a point $u^2/2g$ above the surface there.   The resultant graph is that of the ' energy-line '.   Heights of this line above a fixed datum give the total energy ; heights above the bed (or ' invert ') give the specific energy there.   It is always advisable in a problem to draw the energy line.   Since a degradation of energy into a thermal form involves a decrease of total energy, the energy line slopes downward (relative to the horizontal) whenever friction operates.   An increase of total energy, for instance by means of a pump, gives an upward step in the energy line.   Notice that H can always be measured by putting a total head tube into the flow (fig 14.3) ; the fluid rises in the stem of the piezometer of the tube only as far as the energy line.

Referring again to fig 14.1, the total energy at both cross-sections can be evaluated, the difference being the energy degraded by friction or by any localized abstraction E' at a particular point.

Thus $\dfrac{u_1{}^2}{2g} + d_1 + z_1 = \dfrac{u_2{}^2}{2g} + d_2 + z_2 + E' +$ friction degradation

$$(14.5)$$

or $\qquad E_1 - E_2 = (z_2 - z_1) + E' +$ friction $\quad . \quad . \quad (14.6a)$

This equation is again of the most general kind and allows any term to be found if all the others are known. If E_1 or E_2 is unknown, then this equation can be used to determine u and d at this place. The following simplifications can be made:

If the bed is horizontal, $z_1 = z_2$ and

$$E_1 - E_2 = E' + \text{friction} \quad . \quad . \quad . \quad (14.6b)$$

If no friction forces (or localized changes of total energy) are present

$$E_1 - E_2 = (z_2 - z_1) \quad . \quad . \quad . \quad (14.6c)$$

All these equations can be summarized by the definition:

' The change of specific energy is the degradation of total energy into heat plus or minus the increase of potential energy downstream.'

So E can be changed *either* by the Total energy being altered *or* by the bed level changing.

The specific energy E may be easily presented graphically, either as a series of E–d curves each curve for a different q, or a series of d–q curves, each for a different E. These curves are shown in fig 14.2. Notice the following features.

(*a*) The minimum point in each E–d curve:

(*b*) The tendency of the E–d curves towards a straight line at the higher values of d:

(*c*) The maximum point in each d–q curve.

14.3 Further development of the F and E functions

It proves useful to determine the maximum or minimum points in the curves of fig 14.2. To emphasize the similarity of treatment, the algebra will be done in parallel columns for F and for E.

$$\text{Flow-Force } F \qquad\qquad \text{Specific Energy } E$$

$$F = \rho q u + \tfrac{1}{2}\rho g d^2 \qquad\qquad E = \dfrac{u^2}{2g} + d$$

With the uniform velocity assumption (iv), at any cross-section, $u = q/d$.

So $\qquad F = \dfrac{\rho q^2}{d} + \tfrac{1}{2}\rho g d^2 ; \quad E = \dfrac{q^2}{2gd^2} + d \quad . \quad . \quad (14.7)$

These are cubics in d, treating q as constant. For the minimum points,

$$\frac{\mathrm{d}F}{\mathrm{d}d} = -\rho q^2 d^{-2} + \rho g d = 0; \qquad \frac{\mathrm{d}E}{\mathrm{d}d} = \frac{-2q^2}{2gd^3} + 1 = 0$$

$$\rho q^2 d^{-2} = \rho g d; \qquad\qquad \frac{q^2}{gd^3} = 1$$

$$d^3 = \frac{q^2}{g} \qquad\qquad\qquad d^3 = \frac{q^2}{g} \qquad . \qquad . \quad (14.8)$$

This value of d (at the minimum point of the function) is the *critical depth* and is denoted d_c. Notice that both E and F have the same minimum point, and that if u is the velocity there (called the critical velocity u_c)

$$q = u_c d_c$$

and substituting in $d_c = \sqrt[3]{(q^2/g)}$,

$$u_c = \sqrt{(gd_c)} \qquad . \qquad . \qquad . \qquad . \quad (14.9)$$

In a similar way, the equations for F and E may be differentiated keeping E and F constant, varying d and q. The maximum of d in the curves of fig 14.2 (*c*) and (*d*) is shown to be at $d_c = \sqrt[3]{(q^2/g)}$. Thus if a flow q is a maximum possible with the particular boundaries concerned, then somewhere along it the depth must be d_c and velocity u_c. If the *position* of d_c is known, then a single measurement of the depth there will give the velocity (for $u_c{}^2 = gd_c$), and also the discharge (for $d_c = \sqrt[3]{(q^2/g)}$).

14.4 The general force and energy equations

Every term in the equation for F has the dimensions of a force per unit width; every term in the equation for E has the dimensions of a length (or energy ' head '). It is often convenient to reduce all terms of an equation to a general form so that each term is non-dimensional and will not change its numerical value if the system of units is changed. This is done as follows :

$$F = \frac{\rho q^2}{d} + \tfrac{1}{2}\rho g d^2 \qquad\qquad E = \frac{q^2}{2gd^2} + d$$

Divide throughout by $\rho g d_c{}^2$ (which is a force per unit width)

Divide throughout by d_c (which is a 'head ' of energy)

$$\frac{F}{\rho g d_c{}^2} = \frac{\rho q^2}{\rho g d_c{}^2 d} + \frac{1}{2}\frac{\rho g d^2}{\rho g d_c{}^2} \qquad\qquad \frac{E}{d_c} = \frac{q^2}{2gd^2 d_c} + \frac{d}{d_c}$$

$$= \frac{d_c{}^3}{d_c{}^2 . d} + \frac{1}{2}\left(\frac{d}{d_c}\right)^2 \qquad\qquad = \frac{d_c{}^3}{2d_c d^2} + \left(\frac{d}{d_c}\right)$$

$$= \left(\frac{d_c}{d}\right) + \frac{1}{2}\left(\frac{d}{d_c}\right)^2 \;(14.10) \qquad = \frac{1}{2}\left(\frac{d_c}{d}\right)^2 + \left(\frac{d}{d_c}\right) \;(14.11)$$

Notice that both equations have the form

$$\xi = \eta + \frac{1}{2\eta^2} \cdot \qquad \cdot \qquad \cdot \qquad \cdot \qquad (14.12)$$

if for the energy equation, $\xi = E/d_c$ and $\eta = d/d_c$ and for the force equation, $\xi = F/\rho g d_c^2$ and $\eta = d_c/d$. Also, both equations can be plotted on the same axes and give the same curve if d/d_c is used for one and d_c/d used for the other, as is done on fig 14.4. All values of q are now represented on the one curve, replacing the families of curves on fig 14.2.

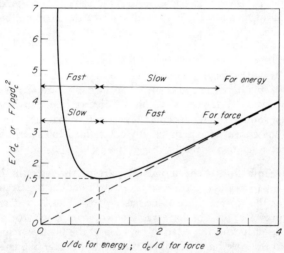

Fig 14.4   Graph of the general flow-function for steady flows in open channels. Notice that the portions marked SLOW and FAST are reversed for E as compared with F.

14.5 The Critical depth and its significance

The special value $d_c = \sqrt[3]{(q^2/g)}$ is of importance because it separates two zones of quite different behaviours of an open channel flow. In a zone where $d < d_c$ a reduction of F (done by imposing a retarding force to the stream) gives an increase of d; and a reduction of E (done *either* by taking total energy away by say friction, *or* by raising the bed) also increases d. In the other zone, where $d > d_c$, the opposite occurs, and decreases of F and E actually increase d. The opposing nature of the d-changes in the two zones has led in the past to many errors, when it was not first determined whether $d < d_c$ or $d > d_c$. In general, if a given flow has a definite E or F, it can occur at two possible depths d_1 and d_2, one above and one below d_c. If the flow is at d_2, the velocity $u = q/d_2$ is smaller than u_c ($= \sqrt{gd_c}$), and the condition is called *slow* or *tranquil* flow : when the flow is at the smaller d_1, then $u > u_c$ and the condition is called *fast* or *shooting* flow.*

Another contrasting property of the two zones is the relative importance of the two components on the right-hand sides of equations *14.10* and *14.11*. In critical depth flows $E = E_c = \frac{3}{2} d_c$, and $F = F_c = \frac{3}{2} \rho g d_c^2$. In fast flows, E and F are both larger than E_c and F_c, and the terms involving q both increase as d decrease. Thus the proportion of E and F due to kinetic energy and to momentum flow respectively increases compared to the proportion due to potential energy and to hydrostatic pressure. In slow flows, the reverse occurs and the proportion of potential energy and hydrostatic pressure begins to predominate.

14.6 Applications of the general theory

When using the above general theory for a particular set of boundary conditions, it is important to ensure that the simplifications of **14.1** are closely followed. If the actual conditions diverge from these simplifications, then some error will occur. These errors may be corrected by inserting some form of experimentally determined coefficient, obtained from a test at another scale.

14.6 (a) Slow flow over a raised part of the stream bed.

A raised part of the bed exerts a backward force on the stream by the pressure on the upstream face of the raised part. This force decreases F. If this pressure distribution was known, the flow-force equation could be used to find the relation between q, the upstream speed and depth, and the speed and depth on the top of the rise (i.e. using Eqn. *14.2d*). Usually, however, this is not known and an alternative method must be used.

Use of the energy equation is, however, possible and is justified because the streamlines of the approaching flow converge over the raised bed. Consequently, there is little or no degradation of total energy by fluid turbulence, the energy line is horizontal, and E changes only by the amount z of the rise of the bed.

Thus $\qquad u_1^2/2g + d_1 = u_2^2/2g + d_2 + z$ on fig 14.5 (b)

On the curve of the generalized flow-function equation,

$$E/d_c = \tfrac{1}{2}(d_c/d)^2 + d/d_c, \text{ fig 14.5 } (a)$$

* Slow flow is sometimes termed *streaming* flow. Because the meaning and sound of the word is so close to the word *shooting* neither will be used henceforward. ' Fast ' and ' slow ' are regarded as more expressive terms, and less likely to error. The use of the terms ' sub-critical flow ' and ' super-critical flow ' is also to be avoided, as it is not specified whether velocity or depth is indicated. The same criticism may be made of ' subundal ' and ' superundal ' (from the Latin *unda*, a wave) (but see Appendix).

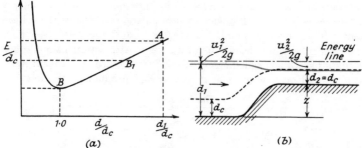

(a)   (b)

Fig 14.5   The conditions of flow over a broad-crested weir shown on the energy equation curve of fig 14.5. (a) The rise z of the weir decreases E so that the point A on the curve representing the upstream conditions must be at a greater E/d_c than the downstream points B, B_1. If z is large enough, then B lies at the critical point (E_c, d_c) as at (b), but if z is smaller, then B_1 is still on the slow part of the curve and the depth over the weir is greater than d_c. Blue line is the water surface.

and the upstream conditions may be represented by the point A on the slow side of the curve. An increase of z decreases E and therefore E/d_c (for d_c is constant if the width is the same throughout) and the point on the energy curve referring to the cross section of the higher bed level will be lower and nearer to the critical point. If z were made large enough, E/d_c would be brought down as far as E_c/d_c and therefore the depth would be d_c. But E/d_c cannot be reduced any further so that the critical depth is the smallest possible under these conditions. If z were increased still further the weir depth would remain constant at d_c while the upstream depth (and head E) increases so as to account for the larger difference between E/d_c and E_c/d_c caused by z (see fig 14.6).

Having become critical on a part of a weir, the flow undergoes other changes at the downstream end, where the weir top starts to fall again. The weir height z decreases now so that E increases.

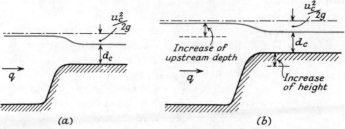

(a)   (b)

Fig 14.6   Effect of an increase in height of a weir. (a) The weir has been made just high enough to create critical flow over it as in fig 14.8. (b) Any further increase of height preserves critical flow over the weir but increases the upstream depth.

The flow accelerates and becomes fast, and the point on the energy curve representing the flow now comes on the fast side of the critical point. The lower the bed, the greater E and the faster the flow. The depth therefore steadily becomes less. A downward sloping bed or chute like this is called a *spillway*, if it is used to spill excess water from a canal or reservoir ; it is one way of producing fast flow. If

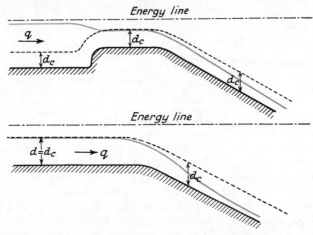

Fig 14.7   Fast flow produced on a spillway. (*Top*) Slow flow in the approach channel becomes critical at the crest of the weir. As the bed of the downstream slope becomes lower, E increases so that the flow becomes faster and faster. (*Bottom*) If there is no weir crest, there has been no obstruction to the flow which is then maximum for the given E in the whole approach channel, that is, the flow is at critical depth.

there is no rise of the bed preceding the spillway, then the flow in the whole upstream approach channel will be a maximum for the given energy, and will therefore flow at a depth $d_c = \frac{2}{3}E$. Farther down the spillway the flow is fast, in the same way as has just been described (fig 14.7).

The discharge over a weir such as this may also be derived as follows. Consider the longitudinal section of a channel shown in fig 14.8. A flow of q per unit width approaches the raised portion XX. Downstream of XX the bed falls away again so that the jet of fluid has no further obstruction. With XX long and high enough, it is found that the surface is drawn down to a new depth d_2 and remains there, parallel to the raised bed. Since there are no restraining forces on the fluid, the discharge over XX will be the maximum possible with the particular energy content of the fluid. In fact, conditions will be critical on XX, with $d_2 = d_c$. If, for example, the surface were drawn down below d_c, then the conditions would not be critical and the flow would be less than the maximum possible.

Since $\qquad\qquad d_2 = d_c = \sqrt[3]{(q^2/g)}$

therefore $\qquad\qquad q = g^{1/2} d_2^{3/2}.$

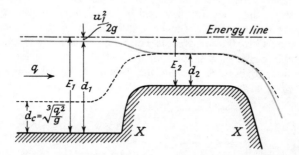

Fig 14.8 Longitudinal section of a slow flow ($d > d_c$) in an open channel approaching and passing over a raised part of the bed (a weir). The depth decreases over the weir. Critical depth shown by dotted line.

A single measurement of d_2 will enable q to be found. This method of measurement is not used much in practice for the surface of the fast-flowing water over XX is difficult to determine accurately; there is a tendency for ripples and waves to appear which obscure the mean surface.

It is more common to express q in terms of the total specific energy E_2 of the fluid, which at the place where the flow is critical, is $1·5$ times the depth there. So

$$E_2 = 1·5d_2 = 1·5\sqrt[3]{(q^2/g)}.$$

That is $\qquad\qquad q^2 = (\tfrac{2}{3})^3 g\, E_2^3$

or $\qquad\qquad q = 0·544\, g^{1/2}\, E_2^{3/2}.$

Now E_2 can be measured by putting a total head tube and piezometer into the flow (fig 14.3), but this is not always necessary. If the upstream depth d_1 above the channel bed is large compared with $d_2(= d_c)$, then u_1 is small and $u_1^2/2g$ is quite negligible compared to d_2. Consequently, the energy line at a height E_2 above the raised bed is for all practical purposes coincident with the upstream surface. A single measurement of the height of the upstream surface above the weir crest is therefore adequate. This measurement of E_2 is sometimes called the *head over the weir*. Using metre units ($g = 9\cdot81$ m/s^2), the discharge equation becomes

$$q = 1\cdot70\,E_2^{3/2} \quad . \qquad . \qquad . \qquad . \quad (14.13)$$

or $Q = 1\cdot70\,b\,E_2^{3/2}$, where b is the width of the channel.   Such a raised floor is called a *broad-crested weir*, and so long as the flow is critical and parallel somewhere along its length, the above equation holds good.

In practice, when water is the fluid concerned, the effect of non-uniformity in the oncoming flow and frictional forces of the water on the weir top cause the flow to be a little lower than the theoretical value, and a coefficient $1\cdot68$ is commonly used.   At large heads ($E > \frac{1}{4}$ the length of XX approx.) the weir may not be long enough for the flow to become parallel and therefore critical, see fig 14.9.

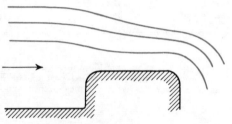

Fig 14.9   Three successive profiles of the fluid surface over a weir, at increasing discharges.   At the high discharges the weir is not long enough to allow the stream to become parallel to the weir surface.

In this case the coefficient is larger than $1\cdot68$.   At low heads, the frictional forces predominate and the coefficient is slightly less.

Broad-crested weirs are commonly used for measuring the flow in open channels, and will do so accurately, providing that the flow is a maximum (i.e. is not otherwise impeded).   This may not always be so. Another obstruction farther downstream may increase so much the depth between it and the weir that the flow does not become critical at the weir.   The flow will be critical somewhere else, usually at the crest of the downstream obstacle (see fig 14.10).   In this case, the simple discharge equation for the weir is no longer valid.   The water surface is lowered over the weir only to the depth d_2, so that

$$E_1 = E_2 + z \quad \text{as before}$$

where z is the height of the weir above the upstream bed.

That is $u_1^2/2g + d_1 = u_2^2/2g + d_2 + z.$

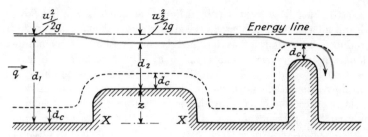

Fig 14.10 A broad-crested weir XX 'drowned' by another obstacle downstream over which there is critical flow. Note how the critical depth $d_c = \sqrt[3]{(q^2/g)}$ is *always* the same height above the bed at places where the flow is parallel, no matter how the bed rises or falls (provided the channel is always the same width).

For a high weir u_1 and $u_1^2/2g$ are negligible, so that

$$u_2 = \sqrt{(2g(d_1 - d_2 - z))}$$

and $$q = u_2 d_2 = d_2\sqrt{(2g(d_1 - d_2 - z))} \quad . \qquad .(14.14)$$

This equation is greatly different from that applicable to the critical conditions of flow over the weir (equation *14.13*). It will be seen that $(d_1 - d_2 - z)$ is the difference in water-levels in the approach channel and over the weir. Thus two measurements of water-level are required to find the flow when a weir is so *drowned*. Since a difference is required, both d_1 and d_2 must be measured more accurately than was the case for the single measurement of d_1 in the critical flow case, if the same accuracy is required. The practical difficulties of doing so are such that drowned weirs are rarely used for flow measurement. Notice, however, that if the weir were raised sufficiently, the flow would then become critical there, and equation *14.13* would become valid.

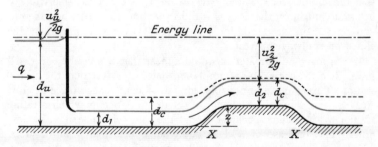

Fig 14.11 Fast flow (caused by the sluice) passing over a sufficiently low weir XX. The flow becomes deeper over the weir, and providing that the depth does not exceed d_c there, the flow becomes faster again downstream. (Compare fig 14.6 for slow flow.)

14.6 (b) Fast flow over a raised bed. Consider now a fast flow of ideal fluid approaching a rise in the stream bed. Such a flow could be produced by a spillway, as has just been described, or by a sluice as shown in fig 14.11. The opening d_1 of this rounded sluice has been so adjusted that it is smaller than the critical depth d_c for the flow q in the channel, where $d_c = \sqrt[3]{(q^2/g)}$. The stream depth d_u is fixed for the given q by the ordinary orifice formula, using the difference of pressure $d_u - d_1$ between the two sides of the sluice. Thus $q = C_d d_1 \sqrt{(2g(d_u - d_1))}$ where C_d is the coefficient of discharge (approx. 1·0 for a well-rounded opening).

The fast flow issuing from under the sluice can be represented by a point such as A on the fast side of the energy diagram of fig 14.12. On reaching the raised bed XX of fig 14.11, the rise z decreases the specific energy E by that amount, so that the flow must occur at a larger d/d_c. The point B on the energy diagram is one such point, so

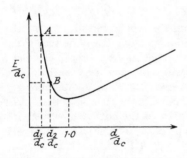

Fig 14.12 Fast flow over a weir shown on the energy equation curve of fig 14.4. The raising of the bed decreases E so that the conditions change from A to B (an increase of depth) on the energy diagram. To be used in conjunction with fig 14.11.

that the flow remains fast but at a depth nearer d_c than before. If z is great enough B may be depressed to the critical value of E, so that the depth over the weir will rise to d_c. However, this will not act as a control on the flow as it did in section **14.5 (a)** when the on-coming stream was slow, for q has already been determined by the sluice or spillway upstream.

If z is made still greater, it would appear that B must be depressed lower than the critical point, implying that E/d_c is less than the critical value. This is quite impossible, for a flow cannot take place at all if $E/d_c < 1.50$. Instead, a change of the depth d_1 occurs which is rather similar to that which occurred under the same circumstances in slow flow. The increase of z does not change the depth on the weir, which remains d_c, and so B is still at the critical point of the energy diagram. But to accommodate the increased change in E due to the increased z, d_1 is increased and changes to slow flow, right back to the sluice (fig 14.13). This is called *drowning* a sluice. The control

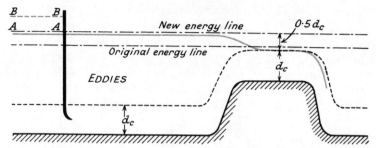

Fig 14.13 If the weir of fig 14.11 is raised more than that just necessary to make the depth critical there, then the flow between sluice and weir becomes slow, and the energy line rises so that it is $1\cdot5d_c$ above the crest of the weir. AA is the energy line above the sluice if the fluid is ideal; BB is that if the fluid is real and so degrades energy in the eddies where there is diverging flow.

of the system has changed from the sluice to the weir, where there is now critical flow, and where the total head is $E = 1\cdot5d_c$ above the crest. With an ideal fluid the total energy line is horizontal and at the same level both upstream and downstream of the sluice : but with a real fluid there will be eddying between the weir and the sluice, as the high speed fluid diverges to the greater depth. There is a considerable degradation of energy so that the energy line must be higher upstream of the sluice than downstream. The energy line remains horizontal over the weir where there is converging flow and consequently little eddy production.

14.6 (c) Flow passing a drag-force producing object. A wide variety of obstacles in a stream produce a drag force. The piers of a bridge, concrete blocks on the bed, and the bars of a grid to catch refuse (a ' trash-rack ') are all examples. Very often it is possible to estimate the drag force of such an arrangement, by measuring the cross-sectional area, finding an appropriate coefficient of drag, and using the oncoming stream velocity (for method see Chapter 8). When the drag is known,* the resultant change of depth (and velocity) of the stream can then be calculated using the flow-force F. If the drag is F' then F is reduced by that amount as the water passes the obstacle. Thus $F_1 = F_2 + F'$ where suffixes 1 and 2 refer to upstream and downstream conditions. Notice, however, that if F' arises because of a single object in a much wider stream (a single pier of a bridge for example), its effect on depths only gradually spreads to include the whole stream, so that the predicted changes apply to a cross-section well downstream.

* A useful reference book from which coefficients of drag of many different shapes can be found is S. F. Hoerner, *Fluid Dynamic Drag*.

Taking $F_1 = F_2 + F'$, dividing throughout by $\rho g d_c{}^2$,

$$F_1/\rho g d_c{}^2 = F_2/\rho g d_c{}^2 + F'/\rho g d_c{}^2$$

or $\qquad \frac{1}{2}(d_1/d_c)^2 + d_c/d_1 - F'/\rho g d_c{}^2 = F_2/\rho g d_c{}^2$

Knowing d_1, F', and $d_c(= \sqrt[3]{(q^2/g)}\,)$, $F_2/\rho g d_c{}^2$ may be found and the corresponding value of d_c/d_2 obtained from the curve of fig 14.4, or by solution of the cubic equation *14.10*. The former method is demonstrated in fig 14.14. It will be seen that if $F/\rho g d_c{}^2$ is reduced from

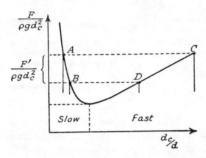

Fig 14.14   The effect of putting a force of $F'/\rho g d_c{}^2$ opposing the motion of a stream is to reduce $F/\rho g d_c{}^2$ by AB or CD. In fast flow the result is a much larger change of d_c/d than in slow flow. Notice that in slow flow d *decreases* if there is an opposing force, but in fast flow d increases.

A to B (i.e. in *slow* flow) a smaller change of d_c/d is caused than if the same reduction is made from C to D in fast flow. Furthermore, the changes of d_c/d are reversed so that d is decreased in slow flow, and vice versa in fast flow. The effect of an applied force opposing the flow is to lower the surface if slow flow approaches but to raise it if fast flow approaches (see fig 14.15).

Having found the new depth and velocity, E may be calculated upstream and downstream, and the energy degraded to heat by this drag system $E_1 - E_2$ can be found. The energy line at a place where there is a concentrated drag force always has a sudden downward step in it.

A force may also be exerted on a stream by a sluice gate, which being slightly opened allows a jet of water to issue under it. Now, both d_1 and d_2 are known for a given q since the streamlines converge under it. Thus $E_1 = E_2$ and on the energy diagram the flow is represented by a horizontal line joining slow and fast limits of the curve.

However, the water exerts a force F' on the gate (and its reaction F' is therefore a backward acting force on the water). So the flow-force falls by F' and $F_1 = F_2 + F'$. On the flow-force diagram the flow is represented by a sloping line joining slow and fast limbs.

14.6 (d) A concentrated decrease of energy—the hydraulic jump. As well as the decrease of total energy caused by frictional forces, which are distributed all along a channel, more concentrated

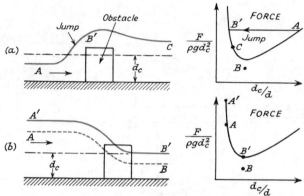

Fig 14.15 The effect of attempting to impose on a stream a larger force than the upstream conditions can support. The force is applied by the drag of a line of obstacles with gaps between. (*a*) In fast flow a jump occurs upstream of the obstacles so that the speed past them, and the hydrodynamic force they produce, is decreased, giving a point C on the force diagram. (*b*) In slow flow the upstream depth is increased to produce a larger flow-force there, so that the imposed force now just produces critical flow at the obstacles.

decreases can exist at certain places. A notable case occurs when a fast stream (produced by a flow under a sluice or down a spillway) changes to a slow stream and thereby causes a *hydraulic jump*. The height of the slow stream will have been determined by the resistance of a weir or other obstruction downstream as in fig 14.16, or by the frictional resistance of a long, slightly inclined, channel. The fast stream flows into the slow one, and the water is decelerated. The flow is therefore a diverging one from a depth d_1 to d_2. As described in Chapters 4 and 12, a divergence promotes eddy formation so that there is a concentrated degradation of kinetic into thermal energy. The eddies are very obvious in a hydraulic jump, where the irregular motions are so violent that much air is often entrained with the water. There is accordingly an abrupt downward step in the energy line at a jump.

To determine the relation between d_1 and d_2, and the flow q, the force system on the water can be written

$$F_1 = F_2 + F'$$

for a horizontal bed where F' is the frictional drag force along the bed.

Also
$$E_1 = E_2 + E'$$

where E' is the sudden drop in the energy line. Clearly E' is unknown and there is no direct way of estimating it. However, F' (on fairly

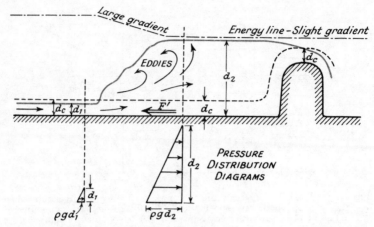

Fig 14.16   The production of a hydraulic jump when fast flow meets slow
flow.   The weir has been made so high that slow flow is caused upstream
of it (see fig 14.13).   Since the fluid is not now ideal the diverging flow
causes eddies and a degradation of energy, with a consequent drop in the
energy line.   The pressure distribution diagrams (see Chapter 2) are
shown for places upstream and downstream of the jump.

smooth surfaces) is likely to be small and *much* smaller than the hydrostatic forces acting at d_1 and d_2.   So a useful approximation is made by
putting $F' = 0$ and so $F_1 = F_2$.   Thus a hydraulic jump is to be
represented on the generalized flow force diagram as a horizontal line
joining 2 points, one on the fast limb and one on the slow limb of the
curve (fig 14.17).   On the energy diagram the line slopes downward
from the fast limb to the slow limb.

Thus $\qquad \rho g u_1 + \tfrac{1}{2}\rho g d_1{}^2 = \rho q u_2 + \tfrac{1}{2}\rho g d_2{}^2$
or $\qquad \tfrac{1}{2}\rho g(d_1{}^2 - d_2{}^2) = \rho q(u_2 - u_1)$

$$d_1{}^2 - d_2{}^2 = 2q(u_2 - u_1)/g.$$

Now $\qquad\qquad u_1 = q/d \quad \text{and} \quad u_2 = q/d_2$

so that $\qquad (d_1 + d_2)\,(d_1 - d_2) = \dfrac{2q^2}{g}\left(\dfrac{1}{d_2} - \dfrac{1}{d_1}\right)$

or $\qquad d_1 + d_2 - 2q^2/gd_1d_2 = 0$
or $\qquad d_2{}^2\,d_1 + d_1{}^2\,d_2 - 2q^2/g = 0$

This equation is a quadratic in d_1 and d_2 and may therefore be solved
for either d_1 or d_2.   It is usual to do so for d_2 it being assumed that
d_1 and q have been fixed by an upstream control (a sluice or spillway).
Thus $\qquad\qquad d_2 = -\,d_1/2 \ \pm \sqrt{(d_1{}^2/4 + 2q^2/gd_1)}$

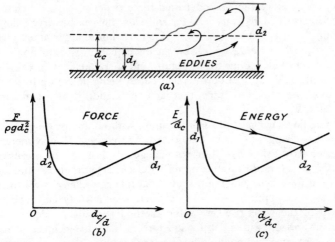

Fig 14.17 Representation of a hydraulic jump on the flow-force and energy diagrams.

The negative root is discarded as meaningless so that

$$d_2 = - d_1/2 + \sqrt{(d_1^2/4 + 2q^2/gd_1)} \quad . \quad .(14.15)$$

Experiments show that d_2 is indeed closely approximated by this equation so that the assumption of $F' = 0$ is a good one.

With d_1 and d_2 known, E_1 ($= u_1^2/2g + d_1$) and E_2 ($= u_2^2/2g + d_2$) can be found and the change of energy $E_1 - E_2$ can be computed. This change is often large so that a hydraulic jump is a relatively efficient means of reducing unwanted kinetic energy to thermal energy. It is desirable to arrange for a hydraulic jump to occur at the foot of a long spillway where a sheet of fast water is coming from the weir above : if the water is allowed to continue in fast flow over the natural bed of a river, severe scour would occur and perhaps the weir would be undermined. A hydraulic jump decelerates the flow and reduces its energy so that it may safely be discharged into the river.

A jump may be caused when a unduly large imposed force F' is put on a stream as in **14.6 (c)**. If $F'/\rho gd_c^2$ is so large that

$$\frac{F_1}{\rho gd_c^2} - \frac{F'}{\rho gd_c^2} < 1\cdot5.$$

Then there are no values of d_c/d which satisfy the equation *14.10* ; the point B or D in fig 14.14 would appear to lie below the critical point. The case arises if the obstacle is large or poorly streamlined. If the oncoming flow is fast, then this large force F' causes a hydraulic jump to occur just upstream of the obstacle, past which there is now slow flow. Since the hydrodynamic force depends on the square of the velocity, F' falls considerably, and slow flow is preserved downstream (fig 14.15 (a)). In slow flow, an attempt to apply an excessive force F', AB in fig 14.15 (b), on an inadequate upstream flow-force merely results in the upstream depth (and therefore flow-force) being increased to A' say, the downstream depth being kept to provide the minimum possible flow-force, that is at the critical depth represented by point B'.

A fast flow changes to slow by a jump, without any guiding surface, but a slow changes to fast by a sluice gate or spillway. It may therefore be asked why a slow flow does not change into fast flow by means of a negative or reversed hydraulic jump. Reference to the energy and force diagrams for a hydraulic jump shows that if such a change were to take place with no applied force ($F' = 0$) then there must be an increase of energy of the water. There is no method available of doing so at constant pressure without applying a force. The change must be made at constant energy applying a force to the water.

14.6 (e) Flow in a narrowing channel. Another way of making changes of water-level in an open channel is by changing the width. As with the case of a weir, the force opposing the stream due to pressures on the forward facing edges of the contractions reduce F; but since the amount of the reduction is not readily calculable, the flow-force equation cannot be used. For a total discharge Q in the channel, the effect of a narrowing is to increase q, the discharge per unit width. Since $d_c = \sqrt[3]{(q^2/g)}$ the critical depth is increased so that if no energy is added to or taken from the flow, E/d_c is reduced. This effect is precisely the same as that of a rise in the bed, when, as has been described for a weir, the water-level drops for slow flow, or rises for fast flow. If the decrease in width is sufficiently marked, then E/d_c may be decreased as far as $E/d_c = 1·50$; the flow in the narrow part (or *throat*) is then critical, in exactly the same way as occurs over a weir if it is high enough. If the throat is made narrower than the width just necessary for critical flow to take place, then the depth remains at d_c but the upstream depth increases so that the reduction of E/d_c prescribed by the change in q can take place. This again is similar to the effect of an unnecessarily high weir. Fig 14.18 shows the energy diagram for a throat in a channel, and the appropriate water-levels, when the oncoming flow is slow.

If it is certain that a throat in a channel has been made narrow enough to cause the flow there to be critical, then a single observation of the upstream head E, above the level of the bed, can be used to find Q.

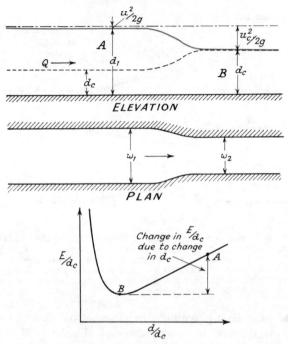

Fig 14.18 Slow flow approaching a narrowing in the channel so that the discharge per unit width increases from Q/w_1 to Q/w_2. If the narrowing is sufficient the surface is drawn down to the critical depth. On the energy curve the two points A and B represent the upstream and downstream depths.

By exactly the same reasoning as for a broad-crested weir, the discharge is given by

$$Q = 1 \cdot 70\, w_2 E^{3/2} \qquad . \qquad . \qquad . \qquad (14.16)$$

where w_2 is the width of the throat.

Downstream of the throat, if the channel is widened again to the original width, the flow should regain the original depth. Since this involves a diverging flow, a real fluid (such as water) undergoes a degradation of energy in the eddies so formed, so that the energy line is lower downstream than it is upstream. An arrangement such as this is used to measure the flow in irrigation and sewage channels, and is termed a *Venturi flume*. Providing that there is no downstream obstruction damming up the water-level so that the depth in the throat does not become critical, a water-level observation gives Q. If there is no assurance that the flow is critical at the throat (because of a high downstream level, or because the narrowing is insufficient), then an

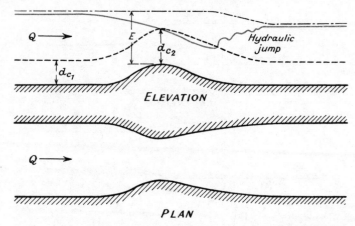

Fig 14.19 A Venturi flume. The effect of narrowing the channel is the same
as the effect of raising the bed. Thus if both occur at the same place the
depth is more quickly reduced to critical depth. Downstream of the weir
a hydraulic jump occurs with a degradation of energy. Notice that the
critical depth on the hump is greater than that upstream because q has
been increased by the narrowing.

additional water-level gauge must be placed at the throat to measure
d_2 there. In this case, the more elaborate flow equation of a drowned
weir is used

$$Q = C_d \, w_2 \, d_2 \, \sqrt{(2g \, (d_1 - d_2))} \qquad . \qquad . \quad (14.17)$$

where both d_1 and d_2 are measured above the channel bed.

One way of ensuring critical depth at the throat is by putting a rise
in the channel bed at the throat, thus combining a weir and a Venturi
flume. Since both the rise and the narrowing have the effect of
decreasing E/d_c, the combination produces faster flow than either
alone. Furthermore, as has already been described, the downstream
slope of such a rise (a spillway) produces fast flow ($d < d_c$). If the
flow upstream is slow and downstream is fast, then somewhere the
flow must be critical, and the simple equation $Q = 1 \cdot 70 \, b \, E^{3/2}$ can
certainly be used. Farther downstream, where the original bed level
is regained, the flow may be restrained by downstream obstructions
to be slow flow again ; the junction between fast spillway flow and
slow channel flow is again a diverging flow, and there is a considerable
energy degradation (fig 14.19). The change from fast to slow is by
a hydraulic jump. The presence of such a jump is a proof that the flow
is fast immediately upstream of it, and so must have passed through d_c
in getting from the slow flow which was approaching the contraction.
A Venturi flume *with a jump* is a flume acting under critical conditions.

14.6 (f) Froude Number and Models.   All the above examples have a common feature—that the way in which the water surface is distorted depends on whether the oncoming flow is fast or slow.   Even within one of these two zones of flow, the water surface changes at a different rate depending on how near the flow is to critical; a stream close to $d = d_c$ (i.e. close to $u = u_c$) tends to change its water level much more rapidly than one which has d much further from d_c.   Thus, in general, it may be expected that the ratios d/d_c and u/u_c settle the longitudinal profile of the water surface when the stream passes any particular shape of boundary change or has imposed on it a flow force or specific energy change.

If a small linear-scale model is made of an open channel situation, and it is desired to predict the water surface shape, then it is therefore always necessary to have u/u_c in the model at every point equal to the same ratio at the corresponding points in the full-scale prototype.   Since u_c for a particular point of depth d is determined by the equation $u_c = (gd)^{1/2}$, it follows that

$$[u/(gd)^{1/2}]_{\text{model}} = [u/(gd)^{1/2}]_{\text{prototype}}$$

The ratio $u/(gd)^{1/2}$ is called the Froude Number (although, rather confusingly, its square is also sometimes given the same name—see Chapter 11).   By making the Froude Number the same in a model of a full-size prototype situation, it is certain that gravity and momentum forces (with their associated potential and kinetic energies) are in the same proportion in the model as in the prototype.   If the water surface slopes are governed only by these two forces, then the surface shape is the same in both situations.

Notice that
$$\begin{aligned} d/d_c &= dq^{-2/3}\,g^{-1/3} \\ &= d(ud)^{-2/3}\,g^{-1/3} \\ &= (u/\sqrt{gd})^{2/3} \\ &= \text{Froude Number}^{2/3} \end{aligned}$$

so that the d/d_c axis on fig 14.4 could equally have a scale (non-linear) of Froude Number on it as well.

14.7 Flow of a real fluid in an open channel

The whole of the foregoing part of this chapter has described the changes in level of the surface of a stream of ideal fluid (in which of course there are no frictional forces).   These changes are sometimes called the 'Bernoulli' changes of level.   Real fluids, such as water, behave slightly differently in that frictional forces act on the fluid by reason of the boundary layers formed on the bed or sides, or by other obstacles in the stream. These shear forces cause a degradation of energy so that the total (kinetic + potential) energy suffers a continual decrease in a downstream direction. The energy line drawn for a real fluid flow therefore slopes downward, the gradient depending on the depth and the speed of flow. However, in many engineering problems the gradient is so small that it can be ignored for short lengths of the channel: the weir equation $q = 1\cdot70 \, E^{3/2}$ is a good example of how the constant energy assumption gives results close to experimental data because the energy line gradient is small.

The changes of water surface in a channel of uniform width due to this decrease of E downstream can be inferred from the general energy curve as shown again in fig 14.20 (a). If the flow is slow as in fig 14.20 (b), then a decrease of E from A to B is accompanied by a decrease of depth d. The water surface is inclined downstream though it is not necessarily parallel with the energy line. This is the usual case of a river flowing downhill. For long distances between A and B neither the energy line nor the water surface is straight: any alteration to the depth and therefore the velocity affects the rate of degradation of energy and so the gradient of the energy line;

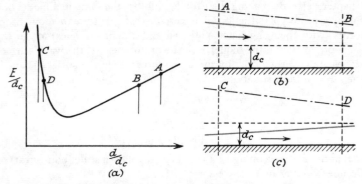

Fig 14.20 The effect of friction on the free surface of a stream. In slow flow (b), the fall in the energy line AB gives a decrease of depth as shown in the energy diagram (a), but in fast flow (c) the reverse is true, the depth *increasing* for the fall CD in the energy line.

in general, the profile of the energy line and the water surface are gentle curves.

If the flow is fast, fig 14.20 (c), then a decrease of H from C to D is accompanied by an *increase* of d. The water surface is inclined upwards, the depth becoming more nearly d_c. As before, neither energy line nor water surface is straight. Since the velocities in fast flow are greater than those in slow flow, both the energy degradation and the gradient of the energy line are greater. In fast flow surface slopes are therefore usually greater, and the depths change more rapidly than in slow flow.

14.8 Normal depth of a stream

As has already been explained, the effect of the frictional forces exerted by the sides and bottom of a channel on the fluid is to reduce both the flow-force F and total energy E of the stream. The decrease of the latter is shown by the slope of the energy line to the horizontal. This slope, denoted by the symbol i, is comparable to the hydraulic gradient in pipe flow and is similarly correlated to the mean velocity $\bar{U}$ and the hydraulic mean radius m ($=$ cross-sectional area/wetted perimeter). In fact, the same empirical formulae can be used as have been developed for pipe flow. The Chézy equation, $\bar{U} = C\,m^{1/2}\,i^{1/2}$ and the Manning equation $\bar{U} = M\,m^{2/3}\,i^{1/2}$ are commonly used by engineers. There is, however, an important difference when applying these friction equations to open channels : in the pipe beyond the first 50 diameters or so the velocity distribution, the drag τ_0, and the gradient i do not change whatever the changes may be in the pipe level ; but in an open channel a change of the level of the bed is accompanied by a change in the depth and velocity due to the Bernoulli effects that have been described in the first part of this chapter. If the bed slope s tends to accelerate the water, then the increased speeds also make i larger (by the friction square law) to produce, fairly quickly, the energy line becoming parallel to the bed. With s causing deceleration, $\bar{U}$ decreases and so does i, again tending to produce $i = s$. When this is so, the bed, the water surface, and the energy line are all parallel and inclined at the same slope, giving a uniform depth termed the *normal* depth d_0. Providing flow is at this depth all along a channel, then i is equal to the bed slope s, and only a simple surveying operation is needed to find i. If the depth changes at all then the connection between i and s is much more complicated, as will be shown later.

Thus in general the friction formulae (of which Manning and Chézy are simple examples of a large family) give the local energy line slope i at one particular cross-section ; only under the very special case of normal depth flow do they give the bed slope s. This is of importance if a test is carried out to determine (for example) Chézy's coefficient C; it is essential to ensure that the depth is quite constant all along the selected length of channel. It is fortunate that if s is constant over a great enough length, then however the depth is constrained at the ends by sluices, weirs and the like, the stream always tends towards normal depth in the middle part of the channel. Values of C or M are always quoted for uniform, normal depth.

14.9   Open channel flow with friction—the general case

The first part of this chapter dealt with the way in which a stream of ideal fluid changes its depth in an open channel according to Bernoulli's equation.   Because the fluid is ideal, there is no energy degradation, and the energy line is horizontal.   A corresponding analysis will now be made for the case of a real fluid, where the energy line slopes downstream.

Consider the short length δl of rectangular cross section channel in fig 14.21.   The bed has a slope s and the frictional forces on the bed have resulted in the energy line EE being sloped at a gradient i.   The slope i is connected to the velocity and depth by a suitable friction formula.   The velocity and depth of the stream have both changed as the fluid traverses this length of channel, the former from u to $u + \delta u$, the latter from d to $d + \delta d$.   The specific energy changes from E to $E + \delta E$, since all variables are assumed to increase in the direction of motion.   Now equating the heights AA_1 and BB_1 which are both enclosed within horizontal parallels,

$$E + s\,\delta l = (E + \delta E) + i\,\delta l$$

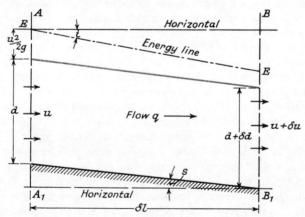

Fig 14.21   Longitudinal section of a small portion of an open channel with a real fluid flowing down the bed slope s.   The friction with the bed causes a degradation of energy to heat so that the energy gradient is i.   The energy line EE is still $u^2/2g$ above the surface where u is the velocity at any point.

But $\quad E = \dfrac{u^2}{2g} + d \quad$ and $\quad E + \delta E = \dfrac{(u + \delta u)^2}{2g} + (d + \delta d).$

So substitution gives

$$\frac{u^2}{2g} + d + s\,\delta l = \frac{(u + \delta u)^2}{2g} + (d + \delta d) + i\,\delta l$$

or $\qquad (s - i)\delta l = \delta d + \dfrac{u\,\delta u}{g} \quad$ (ignoring 2nd order terms)

or $\qquad (s - i)\dfrac{\delta l}{\delta d} = 1 + \dfrac{u\,\delta u}{g\,\delta d}.$

Now the discharge per unit width, q, is constant at both the cross sections AA_1 and BB_1.

So $\qquad\qquad q = u\,d = (u + \delta u)\,(d + \delta d).$

That is $\dfrac{\delta u}{\delta d} = -\dfrac{u}{d}$ on multiplying out and ignoring 2nd order terms.

Substituting into the slope equation gives

$$(s - i)\frac{\delta l}{\delta d} = 1 - u^2/gd$$

or $\qquad\qquad\qquad \delta d/\delta l = \dfrac{s - i}{1 - u^2/gd}$

and in the limit $\qquad\qquad \dfrac{\mathrm{d}d}{\mathrm{d}l} = \dfrac{(s - i)}{1 - (u^2/gd)}$

This differential equation for the rate of change of depth in a channel due both to friction and to inertia (Bernoulli) effects has only one major assumption: that the velocity is uniform over all of one cross section so that the discharge per unit width is constant. This assumption is tantamount to disregarding the friction of the sides of the channel, or considering a very wide channel only.*

Further simplification may be made by writing

$$u^2 = q^2/d^2.$$

Then $\qquad\qquad \dfrac{u^2}{gd} = \dfrac{q^2}{gd^3} = \left(\dfrac{d_c}{d}\right)^3$

and so $\qquad\qquad \dfrac{\mathrm{d}d}{\mathrm{d}l} = \dfrac{s - i}{1 - (d_c/d)^3} \qquad \cdot \qquad \cdot \qquad \cdot \qquad (14.18)$

If the channel is not of rectangular cross section, then q is not the same for every part of the channel, which is now not the same

* As shown in Chapter 4, the effect of the usual non-uniformity of velocity in a cross section in a uniform channel is to increase the total kinetic energy from $\bar{U}^2/2g$ to $\alpha(\bar{U}^2/2g)$ where α is a coefficient of the order of 1·10 at most. It is usually disregarded.

depth at all points on one cross section. The simple substitution $\delta u/\delta d = -u/d$ cannot now be made: instead, proceed by differentiating Q/a where Q is the *total* discharge of the channel, and a the cross-sectional area

or
$$\mathrm{d}u/\mathrm{d}d = \frac{d}{\mathrm{d}d}(Q/a) = -\frac{Q}{a^2}\frac{\mathrm{d}a}{\mathrm{d}d}.$$

But
$$b \,\mathrm{d}d = \mathrm{d}a$$

where b is the width of the channel at water-level,

so
$$\frac{\mathrm{d}u}{\mathrm{d}d} = -\frac{Q}{a}\cdot\frac{b}{a} = -\frac{ub}{a}$$

and therefore
$$(s - i)\frac{\mathrm{d}l}{\mathrm{d}d} = 1 + \frac{u}{g}\left(-\frac{ub}{a}\right) = 1 - \frac{u^2 b}{ga}$$

or
$$\frac{\mathrm{d}d}{\mathrm{d}l} = \frac{(s - i)}{1 - (u^2 b/ga)}$$

Now consider the term $(s - i)$. The connection between s and i is often expressed by the Manning friction formula (although the Chézy formula can also be used giving a slightly different final result). At normal depth this gives for a very wide channel

$$q = d_0 M d_0{}^{2/3} s^{1/2} \text{ for } s = i$$

and at any other depth $\qquad q = d M d^{2/3} i^{1/2}.$

Equating the right-hand sides of these two equations,

$$d_0{}^{5/3} s^{1/2} = d^{5/3} i^{1/2}$$

or
$$i/s = (d_0/d)^{10/3}$$

and
$$(s - i) = s\left(1 - \frac{i}{s}\right) = s\left(1 - \left(\frac{d_0}{d}\right)^{10/3}\right).$$

The differential equation for increment of depth therefore becomes

$$\frac{\mathrm{d}d}{\mathrm{d}l} = \frac{s(1 - (d_0/d)^{10/3})}{1 - (d_c/d)^3} \qquad . \qquad . \qquad . \quad (14.19)$$

with slightly changed versions if the Chézy formula is preferred, or if the channel is not of rectangular cross section or not very wide.

The engineer usually wishes to know the depths d at a number of places at distances l_1, l_2 . . . etc., from a datum point, and is not particularly concerned with the slope $\mathrm{d}d/\mathrm{d}l$. The above equation must be integrated thus

$$d = \int_0^{l_1} \frac{s(1 - (d_0/d)^{10/3})}{1 - (d_c/d)^3} \,\mathrm{d}l,$$

and this cannot be done algebraically. It must be integrated by an approximate, arithmetical, method. The possible range of d is divided into a number of increments Δd, the greater the number producing, of course, the better accuracy. The mean gradient dd/dl for each increment is then calculated assuming that d is constant over the whole increment. The gradient divided into Δd then gives the length Δl over which that change of depth has occurred. An example will make this clearer.

Example

The depth of water in a wide irrigation canal is increased to 3 m at one place by a weir. Without this obstruction, the same discharge would produce a stream of uniform depth of only 1·5 m. Bed slope is 1 : 1000 ; Chézy $C = 50$ m$^{1/2}$/s. How far upstream of the weir will the depth be 1·8m?

Using Chézy's formula for the normal depth, $d_0 = 1·5$ m

$$q = 1·5 \times 50(1·5 \times \tfrac{1}{1000})^{1/2} = 2·9 \text{ cumecs/m}$$

Critical depth $\qquad d_c = (\sqrt[3]{q^2/g}) = 0·95$ m

Divide the range of $d = 3$ m to $d = 1·5$ m into 6 increments each of 0·2 m and carry out a tabular integration working upstream from the weir.

Increment m	Mean d m	$(d_0/d)^{10/3}$	$(d_c/d)^3$	For $s = 0·001$ dd/dl	Δd m	Δl m
3–2·8	2·9	0·1115	0·0353	0·922 $\times$ 10^{-3}	0·2	217
2·8–2·6	2·7	0·1415	0·0438	0·898	0·2	222
2·6–2·4	2·5	0·182	0·0547	0·866	0·2	230
2·4–2·2	2·3	0·240	0·0705	0·818	0·2	244
2·2–2·0	2·1	0·326	0·0924	0·743	0·2	269
2·0–1·8	1·9	0·453	0·125	0·625	0·2	319

Sum = 1501 m
Say 1500 m

Note (a) dd/dl is positive so depth increases downstream
    (b) $dd/dl \rightarrow 0$ as $d \rightarrow d_0$
    (c) If $dd/dl = 1·0 \times 10^{-3}$, the water surface would be plane and horizontal, and the 1·8 m depth would be computed to occur at $l = 1000 \times (3 - 1·8) = 1200$ m.

It will be seen from the slope equations *14.18* and *14.19* that if flow is slow ($d > d_c$) and a control structure (a weir) increases the depth above the normal somewhere, then the depth decreases upstream with a varying surface slope. The curve of the water surface is called the *backwater curve*, and it is asymptotic to the normal depth. It is nowhere horizontal, and this contrasts with a usual conception of a backwater, fig 14.22. The true backwater curve is always above a horizontal surface passing through the water surface at the control. If the true nature of a backwater is not realized, unexpectedly great depths will be experienced a long distance upstream of a newly-built weir or obstruction. However, too much reliance should not be placed on backwater calculations for real rivers, in which flow may not be steady or the discharge constant, if tributaries increase the flow downstream ;

Fig 14.22 A common sort of non-uniform flow in channels : the *backwater curve* of the surface which occurs when the depth of a slow flow has been increased above normal depth by a weir. The curve is nowhere horizontal, and is asymptotic to the normal depth line.

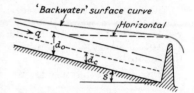

in which the roughness may vary from place to place ; and in which the Manning equation is not strictly applicable to the non-uniform flow conditions (see section **14.8**). The calculations are only a guide to the expected depths in such a case.

The backwater curve is not the only one which is calculable using the general equation *14.19* for non uniform flow in channels. There are in fact twelve distinctly different curves, the shape of each depending on the relative values of the ratios d/d_0 and d/d_c and whether the flow is constrained somewhere to be greater than d_0, less than d_c

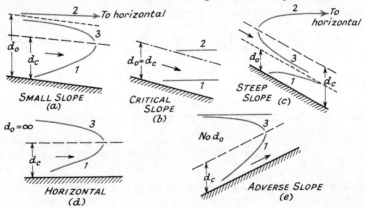

Fig 14.23 The shapes of the surface curves given by the non-uniform flow equation, *14.19*. The diagrams are all drawn with an exaggerated vertical scale compared to the horizontal. The definition of small, critical and steep bed slopes is according to whether $d_0 > d_c$, $d_0 = d_c$, or $d_0 < d_c$ respectively.

or between d_0 and d_c. The general shape of these curves is shown in fig 14.23 where the vertical scale is much exaggerated compared to the horizontal. Usually the water surface curves have a large radius of curvature. The curves for fast flow, all marked numeral 1, are produced *downstream* of the control structure which must be a sluice or spillway giving fast flow : those curves marked 2 are for slow flow, $d > d_c$, and are always produced *upstream* of the control structure, which must be a weir or obstruction or the still waters of a lake : and those marked 3 are for flow (sometimes fast and sometimes slow) between critical and normal depths. The application of the curves of fig 14.23 is shown by some examples in fig 14.24. Sometimes the curves follow directly one on the other, and sometimes the curves

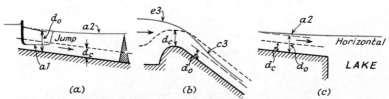

Fig 14.24   Three examples of application of the curves of fig. 14.23.   (a) Fast flow under a sluice meets slow flow which has been ponded up by a weir. (b) Slow flow meets a weir and then falls down a steep spillway.   (c) A slow stream flows into a deep lake where the surface is horizontal.   The curve numbers refer to those in fig 14.23.

are separated by a hydraulic jump. In the latter case it must be remembered that if the upstream curve is fixed in fast flow, and the downstream curve is fixed in slow flow there can only be one place where the depths are such that they satisfy the flow-force equation *14.15* and this is where the jump occurs.

The solution of the differential equations (*14.18* and *14.19*) in gradually varied flows provides a good example of the way in which the electronic computer can assist by doing repetitive work quickly. Several investigators have published the results of programmes to enable rapid determination of depths, taking them direct from graphs or tables. Two recent and useful references are given below.*

It must be emphasized that these methods are merely short-cuts to the solution of the equations. Their accuracy depends, as with any human problem, on the accuracy of the data and the appropriate nature of the assumptions built into their derivation.

* H. R. Vallentine; 'Generalised Profiles of Gradually Varied Flow'; *Journal of Hydraulic Division A.S.C.E.*, volume 93, March 1967.
P. Minton and R. J. Sobey; 'Unified Non-dimensional Formulation for Open Channel Flow'; *Journal of Hydraulic Division, A.S.C.E.*, volume 99, January 1973.

14.10 Rough-walled open channels

Laminar flow in open channels is a very rare occurrence indeed, requiring exceptionally low speeds and small depths.* Engineering problems invariably concern turbulent flow over a rough surface of the bed and sides of a channel, and these roughnesses are nearly always larger than the thickness of the laminar sub-layer. An analysis for the energy gradient i can therefore be based upon the turbulent boundary layer theory of Chapter 12. It is there shown that the transfer of momentum by eddies results in the velocity distribution of a flow over a flat rough surface

$$u = 5{\cdot}75 \left(\frac{\tau_0}{\rho}\right)^{1/2} \log_{10} 33y/k$$

where u is the velocity at a distance y above the bed on which there are roughness elements of effective size k, see fig 14.25. The stress τ_0

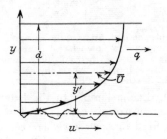

Fig 14.25　Logarithmic velocity distribution in a rough bedded stream of depth d. The mean velocity $\bar{U}$ occurs at a height y' above the bed where $y' = 0{\cdot}4\,d$.

of the stream on the bottom is connected to the energy slope i in the same way as for a pipe by the equation

$$\tau_0 = \rho\, g\, m\, i \qquad . \qquad . \qquad . \qquad . \quad (13.3)$$

or

$$\tau_0/\rho = g\, m\, i$$

---

* The criterion for laminar flow in channels is similar to that for pipes, namely, that the Reynolds number must be less than a certain critical value. For a channel the relevant Reynolds number is $\bar{U}m/\nu$ and this must be less than about 1500 for laminar flow to occur.

Substituting into the velocity distribution above,

$$u = 5 \cdot 75 \, (g \, m \, i)^{1/2} \log_{10} 33 y/k.$$

A further simplification is possible if the stream is wide compared with its depth, for then the hydraulic mean depth m is nearly the actual depth d (exactly for an infinitely wide stream).

Then $$u = 5 \cdot 75 \, (g \, d \, i)^{1/2} \log_{10} 33 y/k.$$

The requirement for any practical friction formula is to correlate $\bar{U}$, the mean velocity, with d and i. Now experimentally, it has been found that a single observation of velocity u, if taken at a height $y' = 0 \cdot 4 d$ gives a value which is the same as $\bar{U} = q/d$.[*]

It is therefore permissible to put $\bar{U}$ in the velocity distribution equation with $y = y' = 0 \cdot 4 \, d$.

Thus $$\bar{U} = 5 \cdot 75 \, (d \, g \, i)^{1/2} \log_{10} 33 \times 0 \cdot 4 d/k$$
$$= 5 \cdot 75 \, g^{1/2} \left(\log_{10} \frac{13 \cdot 2 \, d}{k} \right) (d \, i)^{1/2}.$$

Compare this result with Chézy's empirical equation for the same wide stream, namely,

$$\bar{U} = C \, (di)^{1/2}$$

and it will be seen that

$$C = 5 \cdot 75 \, g^{1/2} \log_{10} 13 \cdot 2 d/k$$

or $$C = 18 \log_{10} 13 \cdot 2 d/k \; \mathrm{m}^{1/2} \, \mathrm{s}^{-1} \qquad . \qquad (14.20)$$

Though the difficulty of assessing k without experiment remains, this link between the empirical Chézy equation and the more rational boundary layer equations is of value to the engineer. If friction experiments have been made by measuring $i = s$ on a length of a stream at normal depth d_0, then C can be found from

$$\bar{U} = q/d_0 = C \, (d_0 s)^{1/2},$$

if the stream is wide enough for $d_0 = m_0$, and then k for the bed of the stream can be found from equation *14.18*. This roughness of the bed will not alter with d so that the value of k may now be used to determine C for any other depth. It may, for example, be practicable to carry out friction experiments at small depths when it is quite impracticable to do so at larger depths because of difficulties of measuring large discharges. It will be seen that for the same roughness, C increases somewhat with d : this increase was, of course, observed experimentally in the very early days of empirical energy slope

[*] See Appendix II to this chapter for proof that $y' = 0 \cdot 4 \, d$.

formulae, but the simple form of the logarithmic formula above was not realized until boundary layer theory was applied to open channels.

While the analogy (*above*) of the two-dimensional turbulent boundary layer throws some light on experimentally determined coefficients such as C, there are other motions in open channels which also affect the friction. These motions arise because the shear stresses are not the same at every point on the perimeter of a channel, even though the roughness may be the same. The differences of τ are most noticeable near the corners of a rectangular or trapezoidal channel, although they also exist near the junction of water surface and the side walls. As shown in fig 14.26 the presence of two friction-producing surfaces near the corner A causes the contour lines of equal velocity to curve, so that the velocity gradient is less on the diagonal than elsewhere. With less friction near A than near (for example) B, less energy is taken from water which travels downstream near the corner than from water which travels near the centreline of the channel. Thus the longitudinal gradient of energy is rather smaller at A than at B. Two cross sections can now be compared, one upstream of the other, but both having the same arrangement of velocity contours. The upstream section has

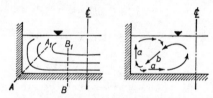

Fig 14.26 Slow, stirring actions in a straight channel, due to less friction near the corners. (*Left*) Isovels show smaller velocity gradients at AA_1 than BB_1. (*Right*) Resultant pressures give flows into A down the diagonal, but away from A to B and from A to the surface.

only flow at right angles to it. The downstream section will have water near A which has not lost as much energy as that near B ; consequently the pressure will not have fallen quite as much at A as at B : the pressure at A will therefore be a little higher than at B.

This pressure difference starts motions across the bed away from the corners, and to preserve continuity water must flow into A along a diagonal (fig 14.26). Another motion exists up the walls. In this way sets of spiral motions are set up which have the effect of giving a slow, 'stirring' action to the whole flow, assisting the mixing action of turbulent eddies. The additional mixing is in effect an increase in the momentum transfer so that the average shear stresses are increased. The values of C found from open channel experiments have a tendency to be higher than those found from pipe experiments of the same relative roughness. Much depends on the precise cross-sectional shape, and on differences of roughness across the bed. Any discontinuity of the bed starts these spirals, which are in addition to those caused by bends (see section **10.6**). All spirals cause increases of friction, and they are the principal reason why the energy gradient in a meandering river is greater than that in a straight river. Experiments to determine the spirals are difficult to arrange, because these relatively slow, steady motions are masked by the turbulence also present.

These complications in river flows give uncertainties in the values of C to be used in calculations, and it is probably not realistic to rely upon an accuracy better than $\pm 15\%$ in C unless some experimental evidence is available from the river itself. Estimates of C from the appearance of the bed are often made, but quite small variations in roughness and straightness may give surprising results. A useful collection of photographs of river beds, with the accompanying hydraulic data, is shown in *U.S. Geological Service, Water Supply Paper*, No. 1849.

14.11 Frictional forces

The effects of friction in channels can be shown in another way by consideration of the frictional forces acting on the fluid in the length dl. As in the case of pipes, section **13.3**, the shear stress on the sides and the bottom of the channel, τ_0, is connected to the energy line slope i by

$$\tau_0 = \rho g d i$$

Substituting for i in equation *14.19*, a different form of the gradually varied depth equation is obtained, thus

$$\frac{\mathrm{d}d}{\mathrm{d}l} = s\left(1 - \frac{\tau_0}{s\rho g d}\right) \bigg/ \left(1 - \left(d_c/d\right)^3\right) \qquad . \quad (14.21)$$

The term $\tau_0/s\rho g d$ is the ratio between the shear stress and the down-stream component of the hydrostatic pressure on the floor of the channel. If this ratio exceeds $1\cdot 0$ (i.e. $\tau_0 > s\rho g d$) the frictional force is relatively high, and the numerator is negative; so that for $d > d_c$ (a slow stream), $\mathrm{d}d/\mathrm{d}l$ is negative and therefore the stream becomes shallower downstream. In other words, at any one cross-section the downstream driving force, $(s\rho g d - \tau_0)$, is negative so the flow would tend to decelerate there, and become non-steady unless the depth decreases downstream to make the net hydrostatic force on the ends of a length dl exactly balance this deficit of downstream driving force. If $\tau_0 = s\rho g d$ then there is neither deficit nor surplus of the downstream driving force, so that $dd/dl = 0$ and the stream remains at its normal depth d_0. If a deficit occurs in a fast stream (for which $d < d_c$) then it must be balanced by a decrease of the momentum of the stream to preserve steady flow; thus the velocity of the stream must fall, d rise, and so dd/dl is positive. Other possible combinations of τ_0, d and d_c give slope signs according to the following table.

Signs for dd/dl

	For $d < d_c$ FAST	For $d > d_c$ SLOW
$\tau_0 > s\rho g d$ $\tau_0 < s\rho g d$	$+$ve $-$ve	$-$ve $+$ve

14.12 River models

The examples of different kinds of open channel flow given in this chapter are all for idealized conditions. The channels are generally assumed to have plane floors and vertical walls and the velocity at any one cross section is assumed uniform. Real rivers, and the modifications to them caused by engineering works, are rarely so simple and because of the possible expense of errors in design it is always desirable to predict, in advance, the effect of such modifications. Experiment on small-scale models is the only practical way of making these predictions and it is therefore necessary to know scaling laws for converting the observed discharges, velocities and water-levels in the model to those in the full-size river. Dimensional analysis (Chapter 10) can be used to determine the necessary grouping of variables for model experiments.

The magnitude of the forces F exerted on the water in the river may depend in some way on the mean velocity U, on the size of the river characterized by a length or depth measurement l, on the fluid viscosity μ and density ρ and on the gravitational acceleration g. The last must be included because any changes in water-level involve a gravity force tending to cause an acceleration or deceleration. The length measurement must be taken in the same place in the model as in the prototype so that the ratio l_m/l_p gives the scale of the model (suffix m for model, p for prototype). These variables U, l, μ, ρ and g are precisely the same as those applicable to the case of the drag force of a ship, as was explained in Chapter 10. The analysis therefore gives the same answers, that one way of grouping the variables is

$$F = U^2 l^2 \rho \; \phi \, (Ul\rho/\mu), \; (U^2/lg)$$
$$F = U^2 l^2 \rho \; \phi_1 \, (\mathbf{R}, \, U/lg)^{1/2}).$$

The term $F/U^2 l^2 \rho$ is therefore a function of the Reynolds number and also the Froude number $U/(lg)^{1/2}$. Experiments with a particular-shaped model might show that one or the other of these non-dimensional groups are unimportant for that shape, but in general both frictional and gravitational forces are present, so that both $\mathbf{R}$ and $U/(lg)^{1/2}$ must be used.

As has already been shown for the case of the drag of a ship it is impossible to ensure that $\mathbf{R}_m = \mathbf{R}_p$ and $U_m/(gl_m)^{1/2} = U_p/(gl_p)^{1/2}$ at the same time; the frictional forces cannot be reproduced to the same scale as the gravitational forces unless quite impossible viscosity scales are used. The same difficulty arises with models of open channels. The compromise usually made is to scale the model so that the gravitational forces are correct but to ignore the frictional forces. By this method the local changes of surface level due to changes in bed level and in width (the Bernoulli changes) are modelled correctly, but the gentle slopes due to frictional forces are modelled incorrectly. For this compromise it is only necessary to have

$$U_m/(l_m g)^{1/2} = U_p/(l_p g)^{1/2}$$

in order that $\phi_1 \, (U_m/(l_m g)^{1/2}) = \phi_1 \, (U_m/(l_m g)^{1/2})$

and therefore $F_m/U^2{}_m \, l^2{}_m \, \rho_m = F_p/U^2{}_p \, l^2{}_p \, \rho_p$

The scaling law for velocities is therefore

$$U_m/U_p = (l_m/l_p)^{1/2} \text{ as } g \text{ is a constant.}$$

All velocities in the model are less than those in the prototype by the ratio of the square root of the model scale. The ratio of the discharges in model and prototype may then be found: a discharge Q is the product of U and the cross-sectional area, and since l characterizes every length, horizontal and vertical, in the arrangement, then l^2 characterizes an area, so that $Q \propto Ul^2$

or
$$Q_m/Q_p = \frac{l_m{}^2}{l_p{}^2} \cdot \left(\frac{l_m}{l_p}\right)^{1/2} = (l_m/l_p)^{5/2}.$$

It is the large discharge ratio obtainable with the usual model scales that makes possible the modelling of large rivers in the laboratory. Thus if a river whose discharge is 10^5 cumecs is to be reproduced by a 1 : 100-scale model, a discharge of 1 cumec only will be required in the model.

Having ignored the part played by frictional forces (by not attempting to make the Reynolds number the same in the model as in the prototype) it is not surprising that there is good agreement between model and prototype if the portion of the stream chosen for study is short, and the changes of water-level great (so that the gravitational forces are large). Models of flow over weirs and spillways, through contractions and expansions, and past obstructions of various shapes give excellent representations of the prototype conditions, and changes in the flow caused by modifications to the boundaries may be confidently extrapolated to the prototype size. It is otherwise, however, if the stream is long with only minor changes of level : now the frictional forces on the sides and bed are important, and the gravitational forces are small. If the scaling law $Q_m/Q_p = (l_m/l_p)^{5/2}$ is used, there is poor agreement between corresponding measurements of velocity and discharge on model and prototype because the important scaling of frictional forces is ignored. Alternatively if the discharges are scaled according to the Froude law, then the water levels will not be found to correspond. It is usually found that the gradients in the model are too small, indicating that the friction forces are not large enough if the gravitational forces are to scale.

Fortunately for the engineer there is a way around this difficulty, using the hydrodynamic roughness k of the solid boundaries. If k is regarded as a variable in the dimensional analysis, it is found that

$$F/U^2l^2\rho = \phi\,(\mathbf{R})(U/(lg)^{1/2})(l/k).$$

The group l/k, called the *relative roughness*, is introduced in the same way as it occurred in the analysis for flow in pipes. It is well known that making a surface more rough increases the frictional force. The frictional forces in the model can therefore be increased by making k/l larger than in the prototype.

One way of calibrating a Froude scaled river model is to pass a given discharge through it and to measure the water levels at a number of cross sections. These levels are then compared with those of the prototype river at the discharge given by the Froude law, that is

$$Q_p = Q_m(l_p/l_m)^{5/2}$$

If these levels agree tolerably well, using the scale (l_p/l_m), the frictional forces are negligible, and the modifications desired by the engineer may be placed in the model. The new water-levels may now be measured and scaled up to the prototype by the same law. If the levels in the model do not agree well with those in the prototype, then roughness elements are placed on the bed and sides of the model until by a process of trial and error the correct water surface profile is obtained. The modifications can now be inserted as before. Models where roughness adjustment is required can never be relied upon to such an extent as those where only the Froude law is required for scaling, because it cannot be definitely assured that the modifications themselves (walls, jetties, bridge piers, etc.) do not change the frictional forces in a different manner with the roughness present from the way in which the full-size modifications affect the prototype friction (which does not rely on such roughnesses).

It is good practice to make two models of a river, if time and money permit, each being at a different scale. One should be as large as the laboratory space permits, the other smaller. If the water-levels and discharges of the smaller model scale up satisfactorily to those in the larger model, according to the Froude law, then it is fairly certain that frictional forces are unimportant, and that the same Froude law scaling will be satisfactory for the extrapolation to the prototype. The smaller model must be large enough so that surface tension forces do not become important.

A difficulty sometimes found with river models is that at the scale prescribed by restrictions in laboratory space the depths and changes of water-level are so small that they are difficult to measure accurately. Further, the combination of small depth and low speed may give laminar flow in the model so that the turbulent flow in the prototype is unrealistically modelled. Both difficulties can be overcome by exaggerating all vertical measurements compared with the horizontal, so that all depths, gradients and water surface heights are made to a larger scale than the horizontal measurements. The model is thus not geometrically similar to the prototype. However, if U and d are made so that the ratio $U/(gd)^{1/2}$ is the same in the distorted model as in the prototype it will be certain that the same type of flow (fast or slow) exists in both at the corresponding places. In this expression d is a typical *depth* measurement and is not a length measurement in the horizontal plane. If this is done then

$$U_m/(gd_m)^{1/2} = U_p/(gd_p)^{1/2}$$

or

$$U_m/U_p = (d_m/d_p)^{1/2}.$$

The scaling law for velocity in a distorted model depends therefore on the square root of the vertical scale, and is independent of the horizontal scale.

The discharge ratio must involve both vertical and horizontal scales because a typical cross-section area of a river depends on the product of a vertical depth and a horizontal length. Thus

$$Q \propto Uld$$

and so

$$Q_m/Q_p = (d_m/d_p)^{1/2} (l_m/l_p) (d_m/d_p)$$
$$= l_m/l_p (d_m/d_p)^{3/2}$$

where l_m/l_p is the horizontal scale and d_m/d_p is the vertical scale. If the discharge as given by the above scaling law flows through a distorted scale model, then the changes of depth due to gravitational forces will be reproduced truly to the vertical scale : the changes due to frictional forces can be approximated if necessary by adjustment of the roughness as before.

Distorted scale models are often used successfully to predict changes in water levels due to projected structures in the channels of rivers. They are less successful if at the same time they are used to predict changes in the sandy bed. Because of the distortion, all the slopes of the sides and of sandbanks are far greater than in the prototype. Thus sand may fall down a slope in such a model where it would not fall in the river. Also the pattern of secondary currents (**14.10**) may be different from that in the river : since the direction of the flow of the water near the bed controls the direction of the sand flow, the model may give quite misleading information about sand movements. In general, a distorted scale model is never regarded as quite so conclusive in its predictions as a natural (undistorted) scale model, if the latter can be made large enough.

14.13 Sand movements in a model

Though a time scale for water movements may be derived from the Froude relation, it should not be thought that the same scale can be used for sand movements in a model with a non-rigid bed. So little is in fact known about the action of water on silt and sand that no certain scaling law for time is yet possible, and the rate of growth of sandbanks or potholes cannot be inferred from models.

However, certain broad principles of sand bed models seem to be established. First, it is not necessary to scale down the size of the sand particles in the same proportion as the gross features of the river have been scaled down ; over a wide range of sand sizes and densities the erosion or deposition patterns are nearly the same, so long as the experiments are allowed to continue until a steady state is reached. Second, the effect of the sand on the water movements is largely controlled by the large-scale features of the sandbanks, and not by the properties of the individual grains; thus it is possible to conduct experiments with a fixed bed moulded to the shape of the present sandbanks, and to observe the motion of a small number of grains thereon, and so to infer the stability of the bank in this form. The difficulty arises here that in some parts of the model the water speeds may be too small to give sand movement, whereas there may be movement in those places in the prototype.

Third, the final erosion and deposition patterns found locally around solid structures are well and truly scaled according to the linear scale of the structure ; but large-scale sandbanks in a long length of alluvial river or estuary are far less certainly scaled. An example of this uncertainty is the bed movement of a small stream over an extensive uniform sand bed, producing a model meandering river ; it would be a matter of complete chance if the model resembled at any stage any real alluvial river (the Mississippi, for instance) for the meanders may well be started by adventitious collapses of the river bank or by unexpected inhomogeneities of the river walls.

Thus models to predict sand movements prove to be difficult and uncertain in extrapolation. Replicate experiments are necessary, and several different sands may be tested until one proves to give movements on the unmodified river in accordance with experience. Sands of reduced specific gravity, e.g. perspex or pumice, instead of quartz, may also be used so as to increase bed movements and to hasten experiments.

14.14 Density Currents

A stream of water, with its upper boundary always at atmospheric pressure, is a particular case of a heavier fluid (water) flowing beneath a lighter one (air). There are many important phenomena which are more general cases of the same sort, the density difference being much less than that between water and air. For example, in estuaries the heavier salt water often moves (due to tidal action) in the opposite direction to the lighter fresh water above, there being a sharp interface between the two fluids. A lock of a dock system filled with fresh water gives a strong surface outflow when the sea gates are opened, as salt water flows in to displace fresh water above ; and in low-lying country (like the Netherlands) the locks bringing ships from the sea to the inland waterway discharge an undercurrent of salt water which may cause biological damage or interfere with water supplies. In these cases the underflow may well carry silt which can be deposited in inconvenient and unexpected places. Air streams in ventilating systems, for example, are also prone to this *density stratification*, hot air moving differently from the colder air beneath. In general, the phenomena of open channels are reproduced in these 'density' flows, but at much lower speeds. If the depths of the layers concerned are large enough, then the analogy is close, the effective gravitational acceleration now being $g\dfrac{\Delta\rho}{\rho}$, where $\Delta\rho$ is the finite difference of density between the layers and ρ the mean density ; thus the critical velocity and the speed of small solitary (long) waves is now $\left(gd\dfrac{\Delta\rho}{\rho}\right)^{1/2}$. If the layers are thinner, then the speed of these waves is affected by two horizontal boundaries, the one at the interface, the other at the free surface with the atmosphere. More complicated expressions are needed for analysis of these situations.

In most cases, the two different-density fluids have a tendency to mix (e.g. brine with fresh water). This is caused only to a trivial extent by molecular diffusion and mixing, and is predominantly caused by turbulent eddies at the interface. Density layers therefore become less pronounced, if there is relative motion, as the difference of gravitational pull on the two layers gradually decreases. Thus non-uniform flows are usual. The tendency for mixing to occur is expressed by the value of another non-dimensional quantity, the Richardson number, which is the ratio of the inertia forces that tend to cause eddies (see section 12.11 for a discussion of this effect in the Reynolds number) and the gravitational forces that tend to keep heavier fluid in lower positions and to stop it from being carried away in eddies into the lighter fluid (where it mixes). While the eddy-producing forces on a parcel of fluid in a particular situation can be expressed as $\rho u^2 l^2$ (where l is a representative distance measurement), the gravitational force which resists the parcel of heavy fluid from moving out of its layer into the lighter one (and vice versa), and then mixing, is $g\Delta\rho l^3$. The ratio of these forces, $\dfrac{\rho u^2 l^2}{g\Delta\rho l^3} = \dfrac{u^2}{g\dfrac{\Delta\rho}{\rho}l}$, is called the Richardson number, **Ri**.

If the Richardson numbers are the same for two flows, each within boundaries which are geometrically similar to each other but of different size (one being the model of the other), then the mixing will be the same in the two cases, and similar interfaces and density and velocity profiles will be observed. Thus equality of **Ri** is another criterion for satisfactory modelling of density-layered flows.

Since $\left(gl\dfrac{\Delta\rho}{\rho}\right)^{1/2}$ is the proportional to the speed of small, long waves in a two-layer system, it can be seen that the square root of **Ri** is equivalent to a Froude number, with the addition of the fraction $\Delta\rho/\rho$. It therefore should have a significance with regard to waves. This can be explained by analogy to the production of waves on the sea by wind blowing over it. The lighter upper fluid, moving relatively to the lower fluid, causes waves to form: with high enough relative speed, the waves 'break', detaching parcels of heavy fluid which are thrown up into the lighter one. As these parcels move up they gradually acquire the speed of the lighter fluid (and so act as a mixing agent for momentum), but their outer surfaces mix more slowly, heavy with light fluid, to form a mixture of intermediate density. High values of **Ri** (**Ri**$^{1/2}$ is sometimes called the densimetric Froude Number) give large waves, which break furiously and mix momentum and density rather well ; low values of **Ri** give better mixing of momentum than density, with neither very powerful.

A more detailed review of these phenomena is given in Section 26 of *Handbook of Fluid Dynamics* (McGraw-Hill 1961), entitled 'Stratified Flow', by D. R. F. Harleman.

Conclusion

The study of flow in open channels is of great importance as so much engineering work is concerned with canals and rivers. Bernoulli's equation may be used in some circumstances when changes of depth occur within short distances and when there is little degradation of energy by eddies. A critical depth of flow is found to exist and the stream behaves differently for depths below and above it. Frictional forces and concentrated drag forces cause changes of depth by decreasing the 'force' of the stream, as well as its energy. If there is to be a change from fast, low depth flow to a slow, greater depth flow the divergence produces eddies and a degradation of energy results. The change of depth can be found because the 'force' is not diminished. This is called a hydraulic jump.

The gradual degradation of energy in a channel flowing at a uniform slope and depth can be estimated by using empirical formulae. If the depth is somewhere constrained to be other than the uniform depth, the shape of the water surface can be calculated as it regains the uniform depth, assuming that the frictional forces in such a non-uniform flow are the same as those for a uniform flow of the same depth and velocity. The complicated boundaries of real rivers give changes of level which cannot be accurately calculated, and experiments with small-scale models must be made if better accuracy is desired.

Appendix I : Surface waves in open channels

The critical depth has an important connection with the distortion of the water surface into waves. Consider a channel of uniform depth d with still water in it. If a disturbance is made in the water, perhaps by a paddle moving slightly as in fig 14.27 (*a*), a single smooth-sided wave will immediately move off, travelling at a nearly constant speed but gradually decreasing in height. The movements of the water can be seen experimentally by observing small solid particles or oil bubbles suspended in the water. It is found that the water under the wave moves in the same direction as the wave, though the water before and after the wave is stationary. The wave can be divided into two parts as in fig 14.27 (*b*), the leading part where acceleration takes place, and the trailing part where there is deceleration. Because only one wave need appear at any one time, due to a single movement of the paddle, it is called a *solitary* wave.

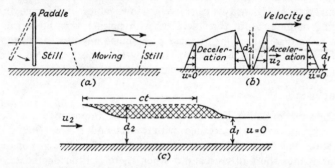

Fig 14.27 Solitary waves in an open channel. (*a*) Wave is produced by the movement of a paddle but then travels without other forces. (*b*) Wave may be divided into two symmetrical halves, with force systems given only by the hydrostatic forces. (*c*) Travel of the leading half of the wave involves a supply of water to fill the shaded space, which must be caused by the induced velocity of the water under the crest.

Now the forces causing the accelerations and decelerations are entirely the hydrostatic forces caused by the depth at the crest, d_2, being greater than the still water depth d_1. Fig 14.30 (*b*) shows the force diagram for both these depths, and the resultant force accelerating (or decelerating) the water is $\rho g(d_2^2/2 - d_1^2/2)$ in the direction of motion. It is further observed that the whole of the water in the depth d_2 is put into motion and not just the upper portion above the still water depth. The velocity of the water u_2 so induced produces a discharge of $u_2 d_2$ which is required to provide the volume of water necessary to raise the water surface from d_1 to d_2 over a length ct in a time t.

Thus
$$u_2 d_2 t = c (d_2 - d_1) t$$

where c is the velocity of the *wave*. But the total mass of water put into motion in the time t to a speed u_2 is $\rho c t d_2$ so that the *rate* of change of momentum is

$$\frac{1}{t} \, \rho c t d_2 \; u_2$$

or substituting for u_2 above, $\rho c^2 (d_2 - d_1)$.

This rate of change of momentum must be equated to the force producing it so that

$$\rho g (d_2^2 - d_1^2)/2 = c^2 (d_2 - d_1)\rho$$

or
$$c^2 = g(d_2 + d_1)/2.$$

If the height of the wave is small compared to the depth of water
$d_2 \rightarrow d_1 \rightarrow d$

or
$$c = \sqrt{(gd)}.$$

The speed of propagation of a small solitary wave is therefore proportional to the square root of the depth. Solitary waves can occur in rivers as a result of sudden floods, or of accidents to sluices or weirs, or indeed of any disturbance of the steady flow.

Now consider the critical flow in the same channel flowing at the same depth. Under these conditions, it has been shown that H is a minimum and that

$$u_c^2/2g = d_c/2$$
or
$$u_c = \sqrt{(gd_c)}.$$

Comparison of this equation with the wave-speed equation shows that they are identical in form and that the critical velocity of a stream at a certain depth is the same as the speed of propagation of a small wave in still water of the same depth.

The speed of a wave in a moving stream of velocity u can now be found. If the stream is in slow flow $c > u$ and a wave can travel upstream at a speed $(c - u)$ and downstream at a speed $(c + u)$: if there is fast flow the wave cannot be propagated upstream at all because $c < u$, and waves are washed away downstream only. But if the flow is critical $c = u_c$, and a wave attempting to travel upstream remains stationary relative to the bed. A wave travelling downstream does so at a speed $c + u_c = 2\,u_c$ and so is rapidly lost. The surface of a slow flow can therefore have waves travelling on it in both directions and these may be detected as they pass a sensitive water-level gauge. Waves may only travel downstream in fast flow, and in general the surface appears less wavy mainly because disturbances are so quickly swept away. In critical flow, any disturbance caused by inequalities of the bed or sides creates waves which are stationary and are called *standing waves*. The striking appearance of the permanently waved surface makes critical flow easy to detect. A hydraulic jump is sometimes called a standing wave, although it is really an entirely different phenomenon ; a standing wave only occurs when $d = d_c$, whereas a hydraulic jump occurs from a depth smaller than d_c to one larger than d_c.

Appendix II : The mean velocity in a wide stream

In section 14.10 the experimental fact was given that the mean velocity $U(= q/d)$ is observed in a wide stream at a height above the bed $y' = 0.4\,d$, where d is the total depth of the stream. The result may also be inferred by integration, assuming a logarithmic velocity profile.

Thus, putting $q = U d = \int_0^d u\,dy$ and inserting
$$u = 5.75(\tau_0/\rho)^{1/2} \log_{10} 33y/k$$
and integrating, it is found that
$$U = 5.75\,(\tau_0/\rho)^{1/2}\{\log_{10} 33/k + \log_{10} d - 1/2.303\}.$$

Now suppose $\bar{U}$ occurs at a height y' above the bed. Then
$$\bar{U} = 5 \cdot 75 \, (\tau_0/\rho)^{1/2} \log_{10} 33y'/k,$$
and comparison with the former equation for $\bar{U}$ shows that
$$\log_{10} 33/k + \log_{10} d - 1/2 \cdot 303 = \log_{10} 33y'/k.$$
But since $1/2 \cdot 303 = \log_{10} e.$

Then $\log_{10} 33d/ke = \log_{10} 33y'/k$

or $y' = d/e = 0 \cdot 37 \, d.$

PROBLEMS

1. Assuming that shearing forces in a turbulent stream are caused solely by the eddies, show that Chézy's C in a wide river which has rough walls and bottom is

$$C = 18 \log_{10} \frac{13 \times \text{depth}}{\text{sand size}} \; \text{m}^{1/2}/\text{s}$$

Plot this curve in the form $\log C$ against $\log d/k$ and find the equations to tangents of this curve at $C = 33, 44,$ and 67. Compare the equations of the tangents with the empirical formulae of Lacey ($\bar{u} = Lm^{3/4}i^{1/2}$), Manning ($\bar{u} = M \, m^{2/3} \, i^{1/2}$) and Blasius $\left(h = A(\mathbf{R})^{0 \cdot 25} \dfrac{l\bar{u}^2}{2gd}\right)$ and draw conclusions about the range of validity of each. Compare Strickler's formula ($\bar{u} = A \, k^{-1/6}m^{2/3}i^{1/2}$) with the general equation and show that it is an approximation valid in a small range only.

2. A channel 60 m wide sloping $1 : 1000$ conveys 280 cumec and Chézy's coefficient is $C = 47 \; \text{m}^{1/2}/\text{s}$. What is the normal depth?

Ans. 2·14 m.

3. Field data from a concrete lined irrigation ditch flowing at normal depth are :
Bottom width 1 m : side slopes 45°   width of water surface 3 m : discharge 3 cumec.

Level of bed at an upstream point A   256·42 m O.D.
Level of bed at a downstream point B   261·17 m O.D.
A and B are 4750 m apart.

What are the values of the coefficients in Manning's and Chézy's formulae ? What are the practical difficulties in carrying out these measurements accurately ?

Ans. $M = 73 \text{ m}^{1/3}/\text{s}: \quad C = 65\cdot5 \text{ m}^{1/2}/\text{s}.$

4. A sluice discharges 72 m³/s into a frictionless channel when the head upstream of the sluice is 6 m. Find the depth in the channel which is 6 m wide. An obstacle exerts a resistance to flow of 10 kN: find the depth beyond the obstacle.

Ans. 1·24 m : 1·51 m.

5. Find the downstream height of a hydraulic jump occurring on a level bed when the upstream depth is 1 m and the velocity is 10 m/s. What is the depth of water upstream of the sluice producing the 1 m depth of flow ?

Ans. 4·04 m : 5·97 m.

6. A jet, 1·3 m deep, with total head 10 m, issues from a sluice gate 6 m wide and then flows along a horizontal frictionless channel to a narrow culvert. Determine a safe width for the culvert so that the sluice is not ' drowned '.

Ans. 1·9 m.

7. A horizontal channel is 3 m wide and 2 m deep. A little farther downstream the width is 2·4 m, and the bed is 30 cm *higher*, but the water surface is 12 cm *lower*. What is the flow ? What must be the difference of bed levels at the two sections if the surface is to remain level ?

Ans. 7·5 m³/s : 0·5 m.

8. A rectangular channel 3·2 m wide has a horizontal bed. It is desired to measure the flow through it by a contraction in width which is to produce critical flow at the narrowest section (a Venturi flume). If the upstream depth is not to exceed 1·8 m when the flow is 8 cumecs, what should be the width at the throat ? What effect would be caused if the throat were narrower ? If it was desired to ensure critical flow by a low, streamlined weir 40 cm high at the throat, what now must be the width ?

Ans. 1·8 m : 2·56 m.

9. A frictionless channel of constant width sloping downward at 1 in 20 is fed by a sluice as broad as the channel and 1·6 m open (discharge coefficient 0·6). Find the depth 15 and 50 m from the sluice when the upstream stagnation level is 6·5 m. Find also the greatest length of channel sloping 1 in 10 upwards which will just not drown the sluice. How will friction affect the results ?

Ans. 0·90 m : 0·79 m : 64 m.

10. Using the generalized energy diagram for flow in open channels, sketch the changes of water-level when an oncoming fast flow meets a narrow part of the channel.

Ans. Rise in level.

11. Using only the momentum theorem of **6.1**, determine equation *14.12* directly, with no appeal to specific energy considerations.

Hint. Use fig 14.1, adding the shear stress τ_0 along the bed, but neglecting the energy line.

12. (*a*) A structure is required in an open channel to control the depth at a certain point. With sketches explain where the structure must be placed if the flow at that point is (i) fast, and (ii) slow.

(*b*) For the conditions of the figure, find the discharge if $z = 1$ m.

(*c*) If the sill in the figure is raised until $z = 2$ m, find the new value of y_1 if the discharge of (*b*) remains constant.

Ans. 1·165 m³/s/m width ; 4·51 m.

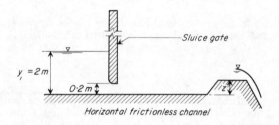

Horizontal frictionless channel

13. Define and contrast the normal and critical depths in a river. A long wide channel of bed slope 1 : 2000 has a Chézy C of 45 m$^{1/2}$/s. A flow of 5 m³/s per metre width is to be maintained at normal depth by a sluice-gate at the downstream end of the channel. Calculate the opening of the gate.

Ans. 0·73 m.

14. A flow of 12 m³/s per metre width enters a long open channel with a poor concrete surface equivalent to gravel of 0·5 cm diameter. Determine the eventual depth of flow in the channel if the bed-slope is (i) 1 in 1600 and (ii) 1 in 49.

If the channel were narrowed at one place, sketch the water surface profile for both cases (i) and (ii).

(*Hint.* In a turbulent boundary layer the velocity, u, varies according to

$$u = 5\cdot75 \, (\tau_0/\rho)^{1/2} \log_{10} 30y/k$$

where τ_0 is the boundary shear stress, y is distance from the bed and k is the equivalent roughness.)

Ans. $d = 3\cdot6$ m, 1·22 m ; $d_c = 2\cdot45$ m, so one is fast, other slow.

15. Discuss the significance of the Froude and Reynolds numbers as force-ratios in hydraulic models. What are the chief differences between two flows in open channels with Froude numbers of 0·5 and 1·5? The width of 10 m and discharge of 120 m³/s of an open channel are both to be accurately scaled for a model-study of surface waves. There is available in the laboratory a 1 m wide channel supplied by a pump with a maximum discharge of 0·25 m³/s. What is the linear scale ratio of the largest model which can be built, and what modifications of the apparatus will be necessary?

Ans. Scale 1 : 11·8.

15

HYDRAULIC MACHINERY—PUMPS AND TURBINES

15.1 The engineer is often called upon to design equipment to convert fluid potential or pressure energy into mechanical energy, making use of the potential energy of water provided by the rain that falls on the high places of the earth, or the pressure energy which is produced by the burning of a suitable fuel in air. The converse job is also frequently experienced, to convert mechanical energy into fluid energy. The equipment for the former job is termed a *turbine* or *motor*, and for the latter a *pump*. The machines to do either are basically the same, and indeed one machine can do both jobs though usually at a low efficiency.

A reciprocating piston and cylinder machine can be used as a pump or as a motor. There are many designs for this sort of energy converter, using either gas or liquid as a working fluid, but in general they present few problems of fluid mechanics although there are often difficult problems of mechanical engineering design in them. These piston pumps (or motors) become unwieldy if they are designed to pass large quantities of fluid. They must also have a delicate speed control coupled to any valves on the pipeline from their outlets, for they cannot continue working with impunity against a shut valve. Piston and cylinder machines will not be further examined here.

The other family of hydraulic machines is the so-called *rotodynamic machine* group. These comprise centrifugal and propeller pumps and turbines for liquids, and propellers and fans for air and other gases. All this family present problems of fluid mechanics. The common feature of all these machines is that they have a rotating element, and that the working fluid has at some stage a tangential velocity component around the axis of the shaft. This is called the *whirl* component of motion w. In the case of pumps or compressors, the rotating part of the machine imparts whirl to the fluid. Later the whirl is removed by a stationary part of the machine, the resultant deceleration increasing the pressure of the fluid. In the case of turbines, a stationary part of the machine converts the pressure energy of the oncoming fluid partly into whirl velocity energy: the rotor then removes the whirl and in doing so has exerted on itself a torque, thus supplying mechanical energy to the shaft.

15.2 Pelton wheels

The simplest sort of turbine is a Pelton wheel. This consists of a number of nozzles at the end of a pipe from which jets of fluid play on to a series of projections on the periphery of a wheel. Fluid at pressure in the supply pipe is converted to a high velocity in the nozzles, which are arranged to make their jets arrive tangentially at the wheel (fig 15.1 shows a single jet Pelton wheel for simplicity).

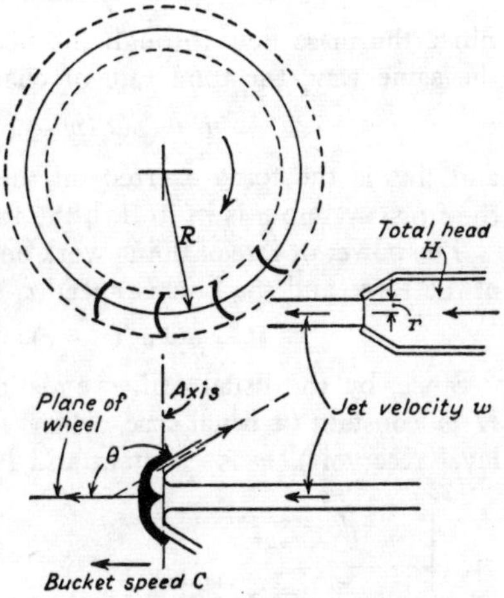

Fig 15.1 Diagram of a single jet Pelton wheel, showing the jet striking the wheel tangentially at a mean radius R. (*Below*) In plan view the jet is divided by the buckets and all the fluid is deflected through an angle θ.

The projections (or *buckets*) are so designed that if stationary they deflect the jets through the maximum possible angle (about 165°) consistent with the departing jet neither interfering with the oncoming jet nor striking the back of another bucket. In this way the maximum rate of change of momentum is imparted to the fluid which by its reaction exerts a force on the bucket and drives the wheel round.

Consider the single-jet Pelton wheel of fig 15.1. Fluid at a total head H (above atmospheric pressure) is applied to the nozzle which produces a jet of cross-sectional area a and of velocity w. Using the ordinary orifice equation of Chapter 8,

$$w = C_d\sqrt{(2gH)},$$

and since for a well-designed nozzle $C_d = 1 \cdot 0$ nearly,

$$w = \sqrt{(2gH)}.$$

The jet is applied tangentially to the wheel, and the velocity w is therefore a whirl velocity. On striking a bucket the jet is divided and turned through an angle θ : the fluid velocity relative to the bucket is $(w - c)$, where c is the circumferential speed of the bucket ; and this relative velocity is unchanged as the fluid passes over the bucket. Indeed, the buckets are usually highly polished to reduce to a minimum the retardation of the fluid. The momentum arriving at the bucket per unit mass of fluid is then $(w - c)$ in the direction of the jet, and that leaving the bucket in the same direction is

$$(w - c) \cos \theta.$$

The change of momentum per unit mass is therefore

$$(w - c) - (w - c) \cos \theta = (w - c) (1 - \cos \theta).$$

Since the mass flow through the nozzle is ρQ, and all is diverted in the same way, the total rate of change of momentum is

$$F = \rho Q (w - c) (1 - \cos \theta)$$

and this is the force exerted on the buckets. (Notice that since in the f.p.s. system ρ is in lb ft^{-3}, the force will be in poundals.)

The power or rate of doing work on the buckets is simply the product of the force and the bucket speed c, so

$$P = \rho Q c (w - c) (1 - \cos \theta) \qquad . \qquad . \qquad . \quad (15.1)$$

Since, by the usual orifice equation $Q = a w = a\sqrt{(2g H)}$, then if H is constant (a usual case when water is supplied from a high-level reservoir), w is constant and $P \propto c (w - c)$. This relationship

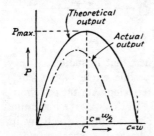

Fig 15.2   Theoretical and actual output power curves of a Pelton wheel at different bucket speeds c.

can be plotted, fig 15.2, and it is seen that there is a parabolic relationship between P and c. The maximum value of P occurs at a certain value c_m of bucket speed, found by differentiation.

Thus $dP/dc = d(cw - c^2)/dc$

or $w - 2 c_m = 0$ for P being a maximum

or $c_m = w/2 \quad . \qquad . \qquad . \qquad . \qquad . \quad (15.2)$

Thus for a given input head H and discharge Q, the theoretical maximum output power of a Pelton wheel is developed when the bucket speed is half the jet (whirl) speed and is

$$P_{max} = \rho \, Q \, w/2 \, (w - w/2)(1 - \cos \theta)$$

The input power to the nozzles given by H and Q is

$$P_{in} = g \, \rho \, Q \, H,$$

so that the efficiency of the machine at the maximum output power is

$$\eta_m = P_{max}/g \, \rho \, Q \, H$$
$$= w^2(1 - \cos \theta)/4 \, H \, g$$

or inserting $w = \sqrt{(2gH)}, \quad \eta_m = \tfrac{1}{2}(1 - \cos \theta).$

It is not possible to make $\theta = 180°$, and therefore $\eta_m = 100$ per cent, as the jet leaving such a bucket would strike other buckets, giving a retarding force on the wheel and a poor efficiency. With $\theta = 165°$, a typical value, $\eta_m = 98\cdot3$ per cent. This is the efficiency of the wheel itself in converting fluid to mechanical energy. Not all this mechanical energy appears at the shaft of the machine as useful work because some is degraded into heat partly by the friction of the bearings, and partly by the drag on the wheel caused by fluid friction as it spins in a mist of water droplets. The combined effect is to reduce the maximum overall efficiency of the whole machine to about 90 per cent and to reduce the bucket speed for this maximum to about $c_m = 0\cdot46 \, w$. For any particular design of machine this ratio must be obtained by experiment. The theoretical and experimental output curves of a typical machine are shown in fig 15.2.

15.3 The design of a Pelton wheel

Suppose it is desired to design a Pelton wheel with n jets to develop a power P at N rev/min when the input head is H ft of the fluid.

Then $P = \eta g \, \rho \, Q \, H \, n$

where Q is the flow per jet and η is the efficiency.
But $Q = a\sqrt{(2gH)}$, and if, as usual, the nozzles give circular jets of radius r, $a = \pi r^2$.

So that $P = \eta \, g \, \rho \, \pi \, r^2 \, \sqrt{(2g \, H)} \, H \, n$

and $r = \{ P/(\pi \, \eta \, \rho \, g \, \sqrt{(2g)} \, H^{3/2} \, n)\}^{1/2}$.   . (15.3)

The size of the jets is therefore fixed mainly by the power required and the head available.

Next consider the speed of the machine. It is clearly advantageous to work the wheel at its maximum efficiency, that is when $c = 0.46\,w$. If R is the radius of the wheel,

then
$$c = 2\pi R N/60$$

But
$$w = \sqrt{(2g H)}$$

so that
$$N\,2\pi R/60 = 0.46\sqrt{(2g H)}$$

or
$$R = 0.46\,\frac{30}{\pi}\sqrt{(2g)}\ \ H^{1/2}/N \qquad . \qquad . \quad (15.4)$$

The wheel size is therefore fixed by the available head and the required speed.

Now the design of a Pelton wheel can be well summarized by the ratio of the jet to wheel radius, and by the number of jets. That is, whatever the absolute size of the machine the hydraulic design will always be the same for given values of r/R and n (providing of course that θ is always about $165°$ for the reasons already stated, and that the machines are always to be used at maximum efficiencies). Using equations 15.3 and 15.4 for r and R, the ratio r/R is found as

$$r/R = 0.0765\,\frac{N\sqrt{P}}{n^{1/2}\,H^{5/4}}\,\eta^{-1/2}\,\rho^{-1/2}\,g^{-5/4}.$$

Now it is found that the overall efficiency η is rarely out of the range 85–90 per cent; so that for a water-operated wheel under the earth's gravitational field, the term $\eta^{-1/2}\rho^{-1/2}g^{-5/4}$ is a constant of value 0.00195 in the metric system of units (in which P is measured in watts).

Thus
$$r/R = 0.000149\ N\sqrt{P}\ \ H^{-5/4}\ \ n^{-1/2}$$

or
$$N\sqrt{P}\ H^{-5/4} = 6720 n^{1/2}\ \ r/R \qquad . \qquad . \quad (15.5)$$

For most engineering purposes, it is more convenient to measure P in kilowatts, which therefore gives

$$N\sqrt{P}\ H^{-5/4} = 212 n^{1/2} r/R$$

The group $N\sqrt{P}\ H^{-5/4}$ is called the *specific speed*, N_s, and it shows how N, P and H are grouped together to predict the design r/R of machine to be used for the given conditions.

It is also useful in other ways. It may be desirable to use for a certain job the smallest and most compact machine to develop a given power P. Since the wheel is the largest part of the machine, a large r/R ratio gives a compact machine. It is found in practice that the largest r/R ratio that can be used is about $1/9$, larger ratios leading to the difficulties that either the whole jet is not intercepted by the buckets or that the flow to one bucket is interrupted by the next, giving a low efficiency.

Putting $\dfrac{r}{R} = \dfrac{1}{9}$ in the specific speed equation 15.5,

$$N\sqrt{P}\ H^{-5/4} = 23.6\,n^{1/2}.$$

The speed N for a given P, H and n may therefore be predicted for the smallest possible machine. Since the sizes of the piping and power-house and other expensive construction depend on the size of the machine, there are always good reasons for using the most compact machine.

Lastly, the specific speed may be used to predict the performance of a large machine from experiments made on a small-scale model of precisely the same design. If the fluid used for the model test is the same as that used for the full-size prototype test then

$$N_m \ \sqrt{P_m} \ H_m^{-5/4} \ \eta_m^{-1/2} = N_p \ \sqrt{P_p} \ H_p^{-5/4} \ \eta_p^{-1/2}$$

where the suffixes m and p refer to the model and prototype respectively. It is found in practice that the efficiency is not greatly affected by the 'scaling down' from prototype to model size, so that

$$\eta_m/\eta_p = 1\cdot0 \text{ approximately}$$

and therefore $N\sqrt{P} \ H^{-5/4}$ is the same for both machines, if they are compared always at their maximum efficiency points. The prototype power P_p may therefore be predicted for given N_p and H_p, if H_m, N_m and P_m are found by experiment. If a different fluid is used in the model test than is used in the prototype, then from the original specific speed equation,

$$N_m \ \sqrt{P_m} \ H_m^{-5/4} \ \rho_m^{-1/2} = N_p \ \sqrt{P_p} \ H_p^{-5/4} \ \rho_p^{-1/2}.$$

Models are frequently used to predict the effect of modifications to machines of all sorts, and if the specific speed of the model is the same as that of its prototype, then the same fluid conditions will occur in both.*

15.4 Limitations of the Pelton wheel

It is instructive to use the equations derived for r and R to find the dimensions of Pelton wheels to give a certain power at different total heads, as the following example shows.

Find the jet and wheel diameters, and speeds, for single jet Pelton wheels of the most compact design, to work respectively under total heads of 625, 256, 81, 16 and 5 m, and each to develop 10,000 kW.

---

* The title *specific speed*, though hallowed by usage, is not a good one for $N \ \sqrt{P} \ H^{-5/4}$. The dimensions of the expression are not those of speed, rotational or translational. Nevertheless, the numerical value of $N \ \sqrt{P} \ H^{-5/4}$ of a particular design is the speed N at which a machine of that design would rotate if $P = 1$ and $H = 1$, if the same fluid is used for all sizes of machines of that design, and if all are running at the same efficiency.

Water is the working fluid, and the efficiency 90 per cent is the same for all machines.

The most compact single jet machine has

$$N_s = N\sqrt{P}\ \ H^{-5/4} = 23\cdot6 \text{ and } R = 9r$$

so from *15.3*, $r = \left(\dfrac{P}{\pi\,\eta\,g\,\rho\ \sqrt{2g}\ \ H^{3/2}}\right)^{1/2} = 9\cdot17\ \ H^{-3/4}$ for $\sqrt{P} = 100$.

Thus tabulate as follows :

H	$N = 0\cdot236\ H^{5/4}$	$r = 9\cdot17\ H^{-34}$	$R = 9r$
m	rev/min	cm	m
625	735	7·3	0·66
256	242	14·4	1·3
81	47	34·0	3·0
16	7·5	115	10·4
5	1·8	274	25

It will be seen that Pelton wheels to work under low heads are large, slowly rotating affairs if they are to develop large powers. Such wheels will be unwieldy, costly, and difficult to govern to a constant speed if the load should change. Further, the common requirement of a turbine is to generate electric power, and this demands speeds at least of the order of 50 rev/min if the generator is to be of an economical size. For all these reasons Pelton wheels are not normally used for heads much less than about 150 m if the power to be developed is fairly large. It should however be noticed that there are no reasons of principle in this decision, only those of size, economy, ease of construction, and of simplicity in governing.

15.5 More suitable turbines for low heads

It will be seen from the foregoing example that to have smaller, faster machines for a given power, it is necessary to arrange the design of a turbine so that N_s is greater than that applicable to a single-jet Pelton wheel. One way of doing this is to increase the number n of jets playing on the wheel, so that

$$N_s = 23\cdot6\ n^{1/2} \text{ for the } r/R = \tfrac{1}{9} \text{ design.}$$

But the maximum number of jets that it is possible to arrange is about $n = 6$ so that N_s cannot exceed about 58: if more jets are used, it is found that they interfere with each other and give a lower efficiency.

To obtain still greater values of N_s it is necessary to make a large change in the design, making the whole periphery around the wheel into one large 'slot' jet from which fluid plays on to the rotating wheel. The wheel design must be so adapted that the fluid is taken away in an axial direction from the centre of the wheel. While the fluid is in the wheel it has a radial component of velocity, so that the machines are often called *radial flow* turbine (see fig 15.3). The fluid has a radial component of velocity as well as a whirl component when it enters the wheel or *rotor*, thus contrasting with the Pelton wheel in which there is only whirl velocity at entry. The whirl is applied to the fluid in an asymmetrical entry chamber called a *scroll case* by means of stationary *guide vanes* which impose a tangential (whirl) component of velocity on the fluid as it emerges from the slot jet. A series of curved blades or *vanes* are arranged in the rotating wheel to remove all this whirl component of the incoming velocity.

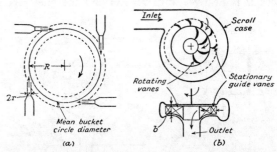

Fig 15.3   Methods of increasing the power from a given size machine, working at the same water pressure. (*Left*) A 4-jet Pelton wheel, the power of which is 4 times greater than that from a single-jet wheel of the same size and speed. (*Right*) The jets supplying water to the rotor now exist all round the circumference as a slot, the water leaving the rotor axially. A *reaction* or *radial flow* turbine.

On leaving the wheel, the fluid now has no whirl and is turned through a right angle and led away axially. This sort of turbine is also called a *reaction* or *Francis* turbine (no connection with the present author).

In order to obtain still greater values of $N_s (= N \sqrt{P}\ H^{-5/4})$, thus getting still more power from the same size wheel, it is necessary to increase the jet area through which the fluid flows on to the wheel. This involves increasing the entry width of the wheel, b in fig 15.3. If, however, b is made as large as is shown in fig 15.4 (a) it is found difficult to ensure that the whirl is all removed before the fluid is turned axially into the outlet pipe. Accordingly, the curved rotating vanes are extended towards the axis as shown in fig 15.4 (b), where they not only have curvature when viewed axially but also have curvature when viewed in elevation from the side. These turbines are some-times called *mixed-flow* turbines, for the fluid within the rotating portion has a mixture of axial and radial components of flow added to the whirl.

If the highest values of N_s are wanted, to give the greatest possible power with the least head and still have a fairly high rotational speed, the jet of fluid must be made still larger ; in fact, as large as the wheel itself.   In fig 15.4 (*c*) it is shown how the whirl is put into the fluid by a suitable scroll case, as before, but that it is then turned axially *before* it strikes the rotating vanes.   The rotor now has a centre boss or shaft with several blades attached to it, the whole resembling a ship's propeller.   Such turbines are called *axial-flow*, *propeller*, or *Kaplan* turbines, though the last name is strictly applicable only if the blade angle can be adjusted to allow for changing load conditions.

Fig 15.4 has been made assuming that the turbines are all for water, when the axis is nearly always vertical and the inlet pipe is nearly

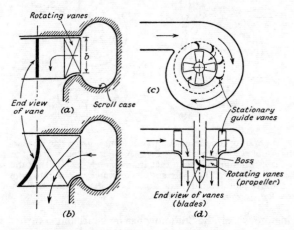

Fig 15.4 Methods of getting still greater values of the specific speed $N\,P^{1/2}H^{-5/4}$. (*a*) A wide inlet radial flow turbine (*b* large).   Notice that the water flows radially over all the blade before turning 90° to the outlet. (*b*) For the same width inlet, the water is turned less abruptly if the flow is partly axial over the blades—a *mixed-flow* turbine. (*c*) and (*d*) The greatest $N\,P^{1/2}\,H^{-5/4}$ is obtained if the 'jet' is the same diameter as the rotor, and there is no radial flow at all—an *axial-flow* turbine.

horizontal.   This is not necessarily so for gas turbines and occasionally for water turbines, where the inlet pipe may be axial to the rotor.   In this case the whirl is applied to the oncoming fluid by a stationary set of vanes again rather like a propeller and usually of a short radial length set on a large diameter boss.

Since an axial flow machine is the most compact way of converting fluid power into mechanical power it might be asked why any other design (Pelton wheels or radial flow) should ever be used.   The point will be more fully discussed later and it suffices to say now that the higher fluid velocities in machines of high N_s tend to produce cavitation

(Chapter 1) in water turbines, and compression shock-waves in gas turbines. These undesirable effects form a limit to the performance of axial flow machines, so that the less compact machines must be used. Axial flow water turbines having N_s as high as about 750 min^{-1}kW$^{1/2}m^{-5/4}$ have been successfully made, although sometimes they suffer operational restrictions due to cavitation (see **15.13**). Radial flow machines, with N_s in the range 75 and 300, provide useful compromises for the range of duties where Pelton wheels would still prove unwieldy but where restrictions are not tolerable.

15.6 Power developed by turbines

The power developed by axial and radial flow turbines may be found by consideration of the fluid velocities involved. It will be assumed that in either of these designs the rotating blades are large and numerous enough to ensure that all the fluid is intercepted and deflected to run parallel to them, and that no fluid escapes their effect. The upper half of fig **15.5** shows how in both designs the inlet fluid

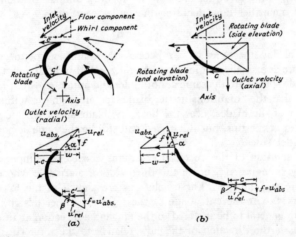

Fig 15.5 The fluid and rotor velocities for the rotating blades of (a) radial-flow and (b) axial-flow machines. The top two sketches show the velocities relative to the stationary casing of the turbine, the views shown being in the axial direction for the radial-flow machine, and at right angles to the axis on the axial-flow machine (see fig 15.4 for a complete sketch of each machine). The bottom two sketches are views of one rotating blade only with the velocity triangles superimposed to show the velocities relative to the blade as well as the absolute velocities. Note that the absolute velocities are in each case divided into two components, the 'flow' component f and 'whirl' component w : the latter is always in a tangential direction to the rotor.

approaches the rotor with a whirl component w already imposed by the scroll case, and with a 'flow' component f at right angles to w. For an axial-flow machine f is in the axial direction, and in a radial-flow machine it is in the inward radial direction. At outlet from the rotor, the fluid no longer has any whirl and it travels only radially (in the radial-flow machine) or axially, with a flow component f'. Usually the machine is designed so that $f' = f$ but this is not necessary for satisfactory operation.

These flow and whirl components may be combined to form the absolute velocity u_{abs} of the fluid at entry (u'_{abs} at outlet), and then used in velocity triangles to find the relationship between the fluid and the blade speeds. The tangential blade speed at the inlet is c, again absolute (i.e. relative to a fixed object). Thus the velocity of the fluid relative to the moving blade at the inlet u_{rel} is given by the vectorial difference of u_{abs} and c, or

$$c + u_{rel} = u_{abs}.$$

(The bold type for symbols implies that the quantities involved are vectors.) On the outlet side of the blade a similar relation holds, dashed quantities now denoting the outlet conditions.

$$c' + u'_{rel} = u'_{abs}$$

In radial flow machines $c' < c$ because the outlet end of the rotating vanes are at a smaller radius than the inlet. But in axial flow turbines the blade speeds are the same at both inlet and outlet, $c' = c$, providing always that the conditions at the blade tips are being examined. At the root of the blades, near the boss, the blade speed will be smaller than that at the tips, but this speed will still be the same at both inlet and outlet sides.

The solution of the vectorial equations above is a simple case of velocity triangles, u_{rel} being the third side of a triangle whose other sides are u_{abs} and c. These solutions are shown in the lower part of fig 15.5. At the entry side of the rotor (of either design), u_{rel} is found in general to be inclined to the tangential direction at an angle α and this is the direction of the flow relative to the rotor (u_{abs} is the flow relative to the stationary part of the turbine). The direction of the blades on the rotor should therefore also be inclined at α to the tangent, so that the fluid strikes the vanes end-on. If the blade direction and relative fluid direction were not the same then the flow will break away from the sharp end of the blade, and there will be a large eddy set up behind the blade; there will be a large energy degradation and consequent drop of efficiency (see fig 15.6).

At the outlet side of the rotor a velocity triangle may be made for

c', $\mathbf{u}'_{abs}$ and $\mathbf{u}'_{rel}$ which is right angled, because it is desired to arrange that $\mathbf{u}_{abs}$ has no whirl component remaining in it. Consequently $u'_{abs} = f'$ and $w' = 0$. The outlet angle β of the blade can be simply determined from this triangle (fig 15.5). If the blade did not have this angle, then u'_{abs} would be inclined at an angle other than $90°$ to c', and it would have a component w'. Some of the whirl which had been given to the fluid in the scroll case would then be discarded unused by the machine.

The shape of the velocity triangles and so the *directions* of the velocities is fixed by α and β, the designed blade directions, and also

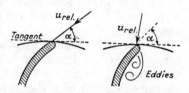

Fig 15.6 View of the inlet edge of a turbine rotor blade. If the relative velocity u_{rel} is in the same direction α as the tangent to the blade at inlet, then there is neither breakaway nor eddy formation and consequently no degeneration of energy into heat. The dotted line is the tangent to the circumference of the rotor.

by the direction of the oncoming flow (which is fixed by the shape of the scroll case and the stationary guide vanes). The *magnitudes* of the velocities are fixed either by a specified rotational speed N(rev/min) and radius R, for $c = 2\pi R N/60$: or by the head H which is forcing the fluid through the turbine and producing useful work. Thus if Q is the total volume of fluid per second passing, the energy given up per second by the fluid in passing through the turbine is $\rho Q H g$. Now only a change of the momentum due to the *tangential* component of velocity can produce a tangential force and therefore a torque on the rotor. All the tangential (i.e. angular) momentum at inlet, w per unit mass, is changed to zero at the outlet of the rotor (if $w' = 0$) so that the rate of change of tangential momentum is $\rho Q w$, and this is the tangential force on the rotor. Since the rotor speed is c, then the energy passed to the rotor per second is $\rho Q w c$.

All this energy is obtained from the fluid so that equating the fluid's loss of energy to the rotor's gain

$$\rho Q w c = \rho Q H g$$

or
$$H = cw/g \qquad . \qquad . \qquad . \qquad (15.6)$$

In this expression, H is the total energy per unit weight of fluid which has been converted to mechanical energy by the rotor. But as well as this energy, a certain extra amount is required to overcome the frictional forces of the fluid passing over the solid surfaces of scroll case, guide vanes, and rotor blades. This is usually expressed as a proportion of cw/g so that the energy per unit weight used by the whole turbine is

$$H' = \frac{1}{\eta}\frac{cw}{g} \qquad . \qquad . \qquad . \qquad . \quad (15.7)$$

where η is the efficiency, which may be of the order of 90 per cent for a large machine. Thus although a head H' is applied to the machine, only a head H, which is smaller than H', is converted to mechanical energy. If pressure intensity differences are given they must be converted into the corresponding heads H or H'. Since H is so connected to c ($= 2\pi RN/60$) and to w, which is fixed by the angles of the guide vanes and rotor blades, the design of a turbine can be made if H, N and D are specified, the power P, blade angles and w being computed.

The discharge Q through the turbine is found from the flow component f, which is determined in the velocity triangles from w, c and the angles of the blades. The area of flow perpendicular to the flow component velocity must also be found and this is differently assessed in radial and axial flow turbines. In the former case it is the cylindrical surface at the entry to the vanes, $2\pi Rb$ as in fig 15.7 (a): in

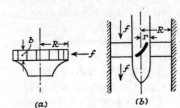

Fig 15.7　The 'flow area' of a turbine is differently defined for a radial flow turbine (*left*), when it is $2\pi Rb$, or an axial flow turbine (*right*), when it is $\pi(R^2 - r^2)$. The flow Q is the product of the flow component f and the flow area.

(a)　　　　(b)

the latter it is the annular space at right angles to the axis and between the boss and the wall, $\pi(R^2 - r^2)$, fig 15.7 (b).

Thus　$Q = f\ 2\pi Rb$　for a radial flow turbine
or　　$Q = f\ \pi(R^2 - r^2)$　for an axial flow turbine
$\left.\right\}$. (15.8)

Finally, the power P generated by the turbine is given by the usual power equation.

$$P = \rho g Q H = \eta H' \rho g Q = cw\rho\ Q$$

or in the obsolescent ft-slug-s system $P = \pi\rho g Q\ H'/550$ horse-power. (But remember ρ will be measured in slugs ft^{-3}.) Both H and Q are dependent upon the blade angles and rotational speed of the machine, or in short, upon the design adopted. The following example will show how these equations are applied.

Example

An axial flow water turbine has a rotor 7·5 m overall diameter, with a boss of 2·25 m diameter. The blade tips at the upper, inlet, side are inclined at $\tan^{-1} 2/5$ to the tangential direction and at the lower, outlet, side $\tan^{-1} 1/3$. If the turbine is to work under a pressure difference of 8 m, at an efficiency of 90 per cent, what will be its power output, speed and specific speed ?

For velocity triangles first see fig 15.5 (b). Consider conditions at the blade tips, where the circumferential velocity is c at both inlet and outlet sides of the rotor. The flow velocity will be f at both inlet and outlet, for the flow area is a constant annular ring.

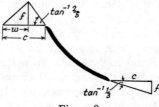

Fig 15.8

From outlet triangle (no whirl at outlet) $c = 3f$, since $\beta = \tan^{-1} 1/3$.

From inlet triangle $\quad c - w = \dfrac{5}{2} f$ since $\alpha = \tan^{-1} 2/5$.

So $\qquad\qquad 3f - w = \dfrac{5}{2}f \quad \text{or} \quad w = f/2$

Using the head equation $\quad H' = \dfrac{1}{\eta} \dfrac{cw}{g}$. $\qquad$. $\qquad$. $\qquad$. $\quad (15.7)$

$$0·9 \times 8 = \frac{3f}{g} . \frac{f}{2}$$

or $\qquad\qquad\qquad = 6·86 \text{ m/s}$

But $Q = f \dfrac{\pi}{4}(D^2 - d^2)$. $\quad$. $\qquad$. $\qquad$. $\qquad$. $\qquad$. $\quad (15.8)$

$$= 6·86 \frac{\pi}{4}(7·5^2 - 2·25^2) = 276 \text{ m}^3/\text{s}$$

and $P = \eta g \rho Q H = 0·9 \times 9·81 \times 10^3 \times 276 \times 8 \times 10^{-3} \text{ kW} =$
$$19,500 \text{ kW}$$

$\qquad c = 3f = 20·58 \text{ m/s} = \pi ND/60$

so $\quad N = \dfrac{20·58 \times 60}{\pi \times 7·5} = 52·4 \text{ rev/min}$

$N_s = N\sqrt{P} \quad H^{-5/4} = \dfrac{52·4\sqrt{19500}}{8^{5/4}} = 544 \text{ min}^{-1} \text{ kW}^{1/2} \text{ m}^{-5/4}$.

The high specific speed results in a comparatively compact machine for the power developed (compare, for example, a 6-jet Pelton wheel with $r/R = 1/9$ for the same power). An electric generator for 50 cycle A.C. would have 60 pairs of poles and would be a large but quite possible machine. Many larger turbines have been built though lower speeds are not usual. Herein lies the reason for a never-ceasing quest for machines of higher N_s.

15.7 Limitations of the simplified turbine design

The whole of the above analysis depends on there being a large number of blades so as to deflect all the fluid to the same extent. If there are fewer blades, then the fluid is not deflected uniformly and a much more elaborate theory of design must be invoked. This theory, which will not be given here, treats the blades as moving aerofoils, giving lift and drag forces to the fluid. In practice it is rare to find turbines with enough blades to deflect all the fluid to the angles of the blades, because the passages between the blades are then small, the frictional forces large, and the efficiency low. The above simple theory is, however, used in design of the machines, adding an empirical correction to the computed outlet and inlet angles of the fluid to obtain the necessary blade angles. The difference of direction of the mean flow of the fluid and the blade angle is often about 5°–10°.

15.8 Pumps

Rotodynamic pumps, like turbines, are also applications of the forced vortex principle, the rotor impressing whirl on fluid which has entered without whirl. If the incoming fluid to a pump is stopped, the machine still rotating and remaining full of fluid, then the conditions in the rotor are precisely those of a forced vortex (Section **11.5**). This is equivalent to shutting a valve on the delivery pipe of the pump. A pressure head is imparted to the fluid depending on the square of the velocity of rotation. If a flow now commences into the pump (i.e. the valve being opened), the vortex is continually diluted at the centre by fluid which has no whirl, and which must be accelerated to produce some whirl at the outlet from the rotor. The *average* angular speed in the vortex is therefore reduced by the dilution, the vortex is less marked, and the pressure head at the outlet falls. It is a well-known property of rotodynamic pumps that the head developed by them falls as the discharge increases, though this is sometimes masked by efficient design of the stationary part of the machine, where a somewhat opposing effect can be produced.

The fluid leaving the rotor, then having both a flow component f and a whirl component w, has a high absolute velocity which is reduced by removing w: by Bernoulli's equation such a deceleration should result in a rise of pressure. In fact, the rise of pressure is not as great as expected, because a deceleration of fluid inevitably gives rise to eddy formation and consequent energy degradation to heat (see Chapter 12). The stationary system which removes w is usually less complicated than that used in a turbine for imparting whirl, and is sometimes omitted altogether, because the saving of power by the elaborate guide

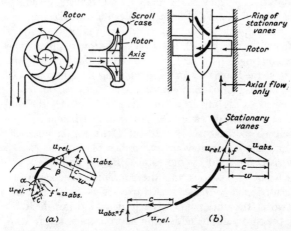

Fig 15.9 The fluid and rotor velocities in radial flow pumps (a) and axial flow pumps (b). The top sketches show the directions of flow relative to the stationary casing of the pump, and the bottom sketches show views of one blade only, with the velocity triangles giving the relative velocities. As with turbines, the absolute velocities are divided into f and w components.

vane system is only warranted in pumps of great power, which must work over a large range of quantity, head and speed. These are rare. The efficiency of a pump is inevitably lower than that of a turbine, again because the fluid in the former machine is always being forced from low pressure to high pressure, i.e. against the pressure gradient. Breakaway is thereby encouraged (see Chapter 12) and the resultant eddies degrade much energy to heat.

The velocities involved in a pump can be shown on a velocity triangle diagram just as was done for a turbine (see fig 15.9). In the figure the diagrams for both a radial and an axial flow pump are shown, and it will be seen that there is a family likeness to the triangles for a turbine. At inlet to a radial flow pump (sometimes called a centrifugal pump), the flow is entirely axial; the fluid is then turned through a right angle into the plane of rotation of the rotor, and approaches the rotating vanes entirely radially. At the outlet of the rotor the absolute velocity of the fluid has a whirl component w so that the direction of flow is inclined to the tangential direction. Stationary guide vanes can be fitted at this angle to form a series of diffusers wherein the fluid may decelerate without undue production of eddies. Outside the guide vanes is a spiral pipe which collects the fluid and conducts it to the outlet pipe. The guide vanes are often omitted, for if the pump is operated under other conditions than the designed speed, head and discharge, they can actually be a disadvantage and produce a low efficiency. It is usually not practicable to make the angle of the guide vanes adjustable for the varying conditions. An axial flow pump, shown in fig 15.9 (b), has a set of stationary guide vanes on the downstream (high pressure) side of the rotating propeller. The guides are shaped so as to turn the whirling fluid into the axial direction. In small pumps the guides are sometimes omitted, and the whirl allowed to die out in a considerable length of the outlet pipe. The eddies so caused result in a low pump efficiency.

Precisely as in the case of a turbine, the combination of a blade speed c and the resultant whirl w implies that a head $H = cw/g$ has been given to the fluid by the rotor. Both c and w are determined from the velocity triangles and the rotational speed. However, not all of the total energy H eventually appears as an increase of pressure of the fluid at the outlet, for some is degraded into heat by friction eddies in the rotor, and by eddies in the diffusers or spiral casing. The output energy (head) is therefore $H' = \eta_1 \dfrac{cw}{g}$, where η_1 is the efficiency of the pump. The power represented by this head is, by the usual power equation

$P = \rho g\, QH'$ (or, in obsolescent f.s.s. units, $P = \rho g\, QH'/550$ hp)

and this is called the *water power* of the pump. The power required by the rotor is greater than the water power, due to the energy degraded by the eddies, and

this is
$$P' = \rho g Q H = \frac{1}{\eta_1}\rho g Q H'.$$

Even more power must be supplied to the shaft of the pump for there are additional resistances to motion due to the small fluid filled clearances between the rotor and the stationary part of the pump, and due to the mechanical friction of bearings and glands.

Thus the total power supplied to the pump shaft is

$$P'' = \frac{1}{\eta_1}\frac{1}{\eta_2} g \rho\, Q\, H',$$

where η_2 is the mechanical efficiency, and $\dfrac{1}{\eta_1\eta_2}$ is called the *overall*

efficiency. An overall efficiency of 80–85 per cent is usually obtained by centrifugal pumps with guide vanes, and about 75–80 per cent for those without. The efficiency of a pump depends to some extent on its size, large pumps having better efficiencies than small ones of the same design. Large axial flow pumps used for irrigation and drainage work may have rather higher efficiencies, up to 90 per cent, if they are being used under their design conditions.

15.9 Performance curves for a pump or turbine

The whole of the preceding part of this chapter has been concerned with the performance of a machine under its designed, or highest efficiency, condition. Although it is always desirable to use a machine in this way, it is sometimes necessary to work at other speeds, powers or heads. For example, a pump may be throttled by a partly shut valve on the outlet so that the discharge is reduced : what then is the effect on the generated head ?

The case of a radial flow (centrifugal) pump is shown in fig 15.10,

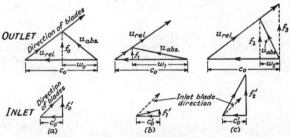

Fig 15.10 The velocity triangles for a pump working at constant speed, but varying discharge. (*a*) The triangles for the designed discharge, (*b*) for a much smaller discharge, (*c*) for a larger discharge. Note the changes of the whirl component, and of the angle between the inlet relative velocity and the blade direction, although the speed N and so circumferential velocity c_0 remains constant.

where the suffix o has been given to H, N and Q to denote the designed conditions. The resultant velocity triangles are shown in fig 15.10 (*a*) and it will be seen, as already described, that the direction of $\mathbf{u}_{rel}$ must be along the designed direction, i.e. along the rotating blades if there are a large number of them. Suppose now the discharge Q is reduced because a valve has been partly shut in the outlet pipe, while the speed N and so c remains constant. The flow component velocity f is then decreased proportionately, to a value f_1. The effect on the velocity triangles is shown in fig 15.10 (b). In the outlet triangle, c remains at the same value, and u_{rel} remains in the same direction along the blades. To close the triangle the intersection of u_{rel} and u_{abs} must move to give the reduced value of f, thus also increasing w. Vice versa, if the discharge and therefore f were increased then w must decrease (fig 15.10 (c)). It will be seen that the triangles bounded in each case by u_{rel}, f and $(c - w)$ are all similar so that $f \propto (c - w)$.

Since c is constant and $Q \propto f$

Then $Q \propto (\text{Constant} - w)$
or $w \propto \text{Constant} - Q.$

But the head generated by the pump is

$$H = cw/g = \text{Constant} \times w,$$

and substituting for w from above

$$H \propto \text{Constant} - Q.$$

A change in Q is therefore theoretically accompanied by a change in H, the *performance curve* of H against Q being a straight line as shown in fig 15.11. The maximum value of H is theoretically $H = c^2/g$, when $Q = 0$. Every value of H (and Q with it) is associated with a

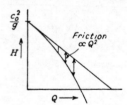

Fig 15.11   Theoretical performance curve for a radial flow pump (the straight line), and the modification to it caused by fluid friction of the fluid over the blades (the curved line).

particular shape of velocity triangle, and only the designed H and Q is associated with the designed velocity triangle.

In practice the head actually generated is less than H above for two reasons. Firstly, the frictional forces due to the passage of the fluid over the rotating blades causes a degradation of energy proportional to Q^2. The output energy or head is therefore decreased by this amount as shown also in fig 15.11 : the performance curve is modified to the lower line. Secondly, there is an additional energy degradation at the inlet end of the blades. Reference to fig 15.10 shows that if c'_0 remains constant, and f' changes with Q, so the relative velocity at the inlet, u'_{rel}, is only aligned along the blade under the designed conditions : at all other discharges u'_{rel} is inclined to the blade. If the angle between u'_{rel} and the blade is large enough (dependent on the shape of the end of the blade), then breakaway will occur and eddies will form on one side of the blade. If $f' > f'_0$ then the eddies are on the trailing side of the blade, and vice versa. There is a considerable degradation of energy in the eddies, which is approximately proportional to the square of the difference between Q and Q_0. This degradation must be deducted from the lower curve of fig 15.11, and the final performance curve is shown in fig 15.12. The final curve

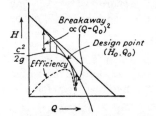

Fig 15.12 Actual performance curve of a radial flow pump showing the breakaway losses as well as the friction losses.

touches the lower curve of fig 15.11 at the design point only. At $Q = 0$, a forced vortex motion is impressed upon the fluid and there is no through flow; from Chapter 11 it will be found that the head rise between inlet and outlet is then $H = c^2/2g$. It is usually found that the final curve shows a maximum value of H at a small discharge. The efficiency of the pump is also affected by the degradation of energy due to these two causes, and the graph is usually of the shape shown.

A precisely similar analysis can be made for an axial flow pump, so far as the theoretical line and the first correction for frictional forces on the blades. The aerofoil shape of the blades, together with their usually small inclination to the tangential direction makes breakaway less likely to occur at the inlet edge, so that the second correction is far less marked. The resultant curve, fig 15.13, usually has the maximum value of H at $Q = 0$, that is, when the outlet valve is closed.

Fig 15.13 Performance curve for an axial flow pump.

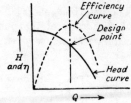

15.10 The effect of changing the speed

It has just been shown that every *shape* of an inlet and outlet triangle of a pump fixes one point on the performance curve. Now the *size* of any of these triangles is set by the length of the side c—the circumferential speed of the rotor—and this in turn is proportional to RN where N is the speed in revs/min and R the radius. Thus in a given shaped velocity triangle both w and f are proportional to NR, the constant of proportionality being fixed by the blade angles. That is

$$c = K_1\,NR: \quad w = K_2\,NR; \quad f = K_3\,NR.$$

Consider now a certain design of pump which is produced in a number of sizes. For each one of these pumps working at the design point on its performance curve $(H_0,\,Q_0)$, the head generated is

$$H_0 = \eta\,\frac{cw}{g}.$$

But c and w vary with R and N, in a way that depends only on the design, so that for all the pumps of this design,

$$H_0 = \eta\,K_1\,K_2\,N^2\,R^2.$$

Since η does not change much with the size of a pump

$$H_0/N^2R^2 = \text{Constant, approximately.}$$

Now consider the discharge Q_0 at the design point: from *15.8* the flow area through which all the discharge passes at right angles is $2\pi\,Rb$ for a radial flow design.

Thus $\qquad\qquad\qquad Q_0 = f_0\,2\,\pi\,Rb$

But since the pumps are of the same design, $b \propto R$

so that $\qquad\qquad\qquad Q_0 \propto f_0\,K_4 R^2.$

Substituting for f_0, $\qquad\quad Q_0 = K_3\,NR\,K_4\,R^2$

or $\qquad\qquad\qquad\qquad Q_0/NR^3 = \text{Constant.}$

The two constants $H_0/N^2\,R^2$ and Q_0/NR^3 therefore express the effect of the *design* of the pump upon the design performance, $H_0,\,Q_0,$ *whatever the size or speed.* In a similar manner the constants $H/N^2\,R^2$

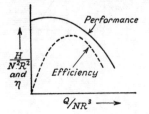

Fig 15.14 The ' unit ' method of plotting the performance curve of a certain design of pump, giving one curve for all sizes of pump as defined by the radius R, and for all speeds N.

and Q/NR^3 can be derived for the head and quantity found from any other velocity triangle, which is *not* the design velocity triangle. These constants can then be plotted as in fig 15.14 to give the so-called *unit performance curve*. This curve is of the head generated and discharge passed by a pump of the design quoted, of unit size and rotating at unit speed. If such a curve is available to the engineer he can multiply all the unit heads by $R^2 N^2$ and unit discharges by NR^3 to obtain the head and discharge for the desired size R and speed N.

15.11 Specific speed of a pump

With a method available of plotting all information for a given design on to one curve, as in fig 15.14, it is possible, in principle, to put on one diagram the curves for all designs of pumps. This is done in simplified form on fig 15.15. Axial flow machines give curves

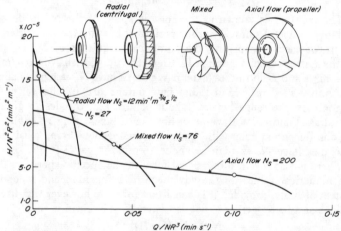

Fig 15.15 Combined performance curves, on a 'unit' basis, for four quite different designs of pumps. Circles show the maximum efficiency points for which the specific speeds N_8 have been calculated. If still lower N_8 are required, multi-stage pumps are used.

which are more nearly parallel to the Q/NR^3 axis than radial flow machines. In practice, of course, if every possible design was plotted on this diagram, there would be some confusion, for many designs comply with requirements other than that of good hydraulic performance; for example, pumps for mixtures of solids and liquids often have large passages in them to avoid choking. These designs then have too few blades in their rotors to give the correct flow directions to the fluid, and the head generated at a given R and N is lower than that for a conventional pump.

A diagram of the sort shown in fig 15.15 has on it all the information required for choosing a pump to do a particular duty. However there is an even more summarized way of expressing the most important feature, which is the performance at the best efficiency, i.e. at the design point. Each design has a pair of co-ordinates x, y on fig 15.15 giving this point, where x and y are numbers. So

$$x = QN^{-1} R^{-3}; \quad y = HN^{-2} R^{-2} \text{ at best efficiency.}$$

These are simultaneous equations, and one variable from the four, Q,H,N,R, can be eliminated from them. It is international practice to eliminate R so

$$R = x^{-1/3} Q^{1/3} N^{-1/3} = H^{1/2} N^{-1} y^{-1/2}$$

or $N^{2/3} Q^{1/3} H^{-1/2} = y^{-1/2} x^{1/3} = \text{a constant for the design}$

Converting the index of N to unity,

$$NQ^{1/2} H^{-3/4} = \text{Constant} = N_s$$

The constant is known as the specific speed of the pump design, and gives a useful summary of the performance at maximum efficiency. As in the case of a turbine, the numerical magnitude of N_s depends on the system of units employed. In metric units, with N in rev/min, Q in m³/s and H in metres, axial flow pumps have N_s as high as about 200 min^{-1} s$^{-1/2}$ m$^{3/4}$, and radial flow pumps are in the range 10 to 100. In the range between about 60 and 140, the design gives a mixed axial and radial flow rather like the turbines of fig 15.4 (b). In an obsolescent system with Q in Imperial gallons/min, axial flow machines have N_s as high as about 10⁴min$^{-3/4}$ gal$^{1/2}$ ft$^{-3/4}$.

There is also a non-dimensional form of the specific speed, so that the numerical value has the advantage of being independent of the system of units, provided it is consistent (observe however that use of gallons and feet together is not consistent). The form is then

$$N_s = N\sqrt{Q}(gH)^{-3/4}$$

where g is the gravitational acceleration and is in the same consistent system of Q and H. The speed N is proposed in radians per unit time of the system (usually seconds). On this convention, N_s is 1/53 of the value found in units of min^{-1} s$^{-\frac{1}{2}}$m$^{\frac{3}{4}}$. It is to be hoped that the non-dimensional form will supplant all others, although it involves somewhat unusual units, as judged by present-day industrial practice.

There is no design of pump with a low N_s which is comparable to a Pelton wheel. Such a design, if made, would be used to generate high pressures H with small discharges Q and might be suitable for boiler feed pumps and the like. The design involves considerable difficulties, not the least being that the kinetic energy of the emergent high-speed jet would be converted to pressure energy in a diffuser in which a large energy degradation would be inevitable. If high pressures and low discharges are required they are generated by *multi-stage pumps* which are a series of pumps each of higher N_s than that demanded by a single pump to do the job. The outlet of one pump feeds the inlet of the next and all are driven by the same shaft. The same discharge goes through each stage.

15.12 Performance curves for a turbine

The performance curves for a turbine can be derived in the same way as for a pump, though it is usual to treat the speed N as the principal variable when plotting the unit curve so that unit power $P/R^2H^{3/2}$, unit flow $Q/R^2 H^{1/2}$ and efficiency are plotted against unit speed $N R/H^{1/2}$. Typical unit performance curves are plotted

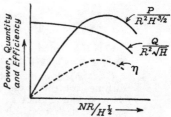

Fig 15.16 The 'unit' method of plotting the performance curve of a design of turbine with fixed vanes on both rotor and scroll case.

in fig 15.16 for a turbine, with fixed blades (radial or axial). The axes of the diagram are for the power generated, flow used and efficiency achieved by a turbine of the given design but of unit size working under unit head.

However, most turbines run at a constant speed, generating a variable power, as for example when they are coupled to electric alternators. Such changes of power could be obtained by changing H. Thus to reduce P below the maximum possible power would imply

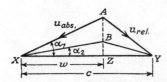

Fig 15.17 The velocity triangles at the inlet of a turbine working at a constant speed and head, but with the flow changed in order to vary the output power. Notice how the angle α of the stationary guide vanes must be changed from α_1 to α_2 to reduce f and so Q and P while keeping c and w constant.

degrading some of the energy available so that less energy is supplied to the machine. This could be done by partly shutting a valve in the supply pipe, causing great eddy formation. This method is wasteful of energy so another method is adopted. The stationary guide vanes, which impart whirl to the incoming fluid, are pivoted so that the angle α can be changed. Thus the direction of $\mathbf{u}_{abs}$ can be varied. In fig 15.17 the velocity triangles are shown for the

PLATE 9   Two hydraulic turbines.

(*Top*) A radial flow (Francis) turbine. The controlling mechanism for the guide vanes may be seen.

(*Bottom*) A scale model of the axial flow Kaplan turbines for the Owen Falls power station, Uganda, showing rotor, guide vanes and a section of the scroll case and draft tube. Notice how large these last two items are compared with the rotor ; a small reduction of the rotor size may make a large reduction in the civil engineering work in building scroll case and draft tube.

Photos by Boving & Co. Ltd.

PLATE 9

PLATE 10 Two pump rotors

(*Left*) For a radial flow pump with a 1·14 m diameter inlet pipe from a power station circulating water system. Specific speed
$N_s = 81 \ min^{-1} \ s^{-1/2} m^{3/4}$.
(*Right*) For an axial flow pump 60 cm diameter $N_s = 190$.

Photos by Gwynnes Pumps Ltd.

PLATE 11

(*Left*) A low specific speed (radial flow) centrifugal pump. The upper part of the casing is lifted to show the rotor, which is narrow compared with its diameter.

(*Right*) A large mixed-flow pump for circulating water through a steam turbine condenser. It discharges 9·1 m³/s against 23·2 m head at 265 rev/min, and has two suction pipes, one to each side of the rotor. $N_s = 75 \ \text{min}^{-1} \text{s}^{1/2} \text{m}^{-3/4}$

Photos by Allen Gwynnes Pumps Ltd.

PLATE 12

PLATE 12

(*Top*) A Pelton wheel rotor. The buckets are cast integrally with the wheel, and are made as large as possible so that a jet of large cross-sectional area may be used, developing the maximum power from a given size wheel.

(*Bottom*) An axial flow rotor for the turbines of the Owen Falls scheme. The circumferential speed *c* is lower at the boss than at the blade tips, so that the blades are twisted, having a coarser angle at the boss than at the tip.

design point of an axial flow turbine and also for the condition when α has been reduced. Since H is the same in both cases, for there is now no deliberate degradation of energy, then c and w must be the same in each triangle. The triangle AXY therefore changes to BXY. In doing so, the relative velocity u_{rel} changes its direction as well, so that to ensure that the fluid still meets the blade without breakaway, the blade angle must also change. It will also be seen that the flow component f decreases from AZ to BZ, so that the discharge Q and Power $P(= \eta\rho gQH)$ also decreases. In this way complete control of the output power may be arranged without waste of input energy.

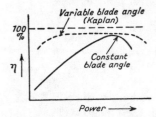

Fig 15.18 The efficiency power curves for a fixed blade (propeller) axial flow turbine, and a variable angle blade (Kaplan) turbine. The former is a much cheaper machine but must be run at the design point if the efficiency is to be kept at an economic level.

The changes of angle of rotor and guide vanes are in effect changes of the turbine design so that performance curves such as those in fig 15.14 are not now applicable for they are for fixed machines.

It is common to find axial flow water turbines designed so that the blade angles may be changed as well as the guide vane angles. They are then called *Kaplan turbines* and the rotors are large variable-pitch propellers. Since the blade angle is always arranged to be along the direction of u_{rel}, breakaway does not occur and there is little degradation of energy in the turbine. The efficiency is therefore always high and the water used economically. These turbines contrast with those having fixed blades. On the latter, breakaway occurs if the power is larger or smaller than the design power and there is a consequent decrease in efficiency. Sometimes to accommodate a large variation of power the design of Kaplan turbines makes it necessary to have a slightly lower peak efficiency than a propeller or fixed blade machine, but the efficiency at other powers is invariably better. Fixed blade machines are cheaper to build and are suitable for constant power (base load) operation, whereas the more expensive Kaplan turbines are used for peak load operation.

15.13 Draft tubes and diffusers

The fluid leaving a turbine has a fairly high axial velocity and, ideally, no whirl velocity, so that a considerable amount of kinetic energy is rejected. It would be wasteful to allow this jet of high-speed fluid to be dissipated purely by eddies in a manner similar to that described for an abrupt pipe outlet in Chapter 13. It is therefore usual to fit a gradually expanding pipe (diffuser) to the turbine outlet so that the eventual speed of rejection is low and the waste of kinetic energy is negligible. By Bernoulli's equation it will be seen that the effect of the deceleration is to cause a pressure rise in the diffuser. As the diffuser outlet pressure is atmospheric, the pressure at the turbine outlet is therefore below atmospheric. If there were no diffuser the turbine outlet pressure would have been atmospheric. Consequently, if the upstream, inlet, pressure to the turbine is constant, then the head H across the machine is slightly greater if there is a diffuser than if there is none. The output power $= \eta g \rho Q H$ is thereby slightly increased. It is usually an economic necessity to produce the maximum power from a given flow so that considerable care is taken to build satisfactory and efficient diffusers. The importance of a good diffuser is most marked in installations where H is small, the kinetic energy saved, $f^2/2g$, then being sometimes as much as 50 per cent of H.

The pressure in a water turbine with a diffuser can be found by Bernoulli's equation. Thus in fig 15·19, the total energy at the turbine outlet is $H_a = \dfrac{f^2}{2g} + h_s + p_a/\rho g$. The pressure p_a is reckoned as a gauge pressure (above atmospheric) and the datum level for potential

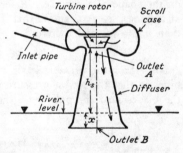

Fig 15.19 A mixed-flow turbine with a diffuser on the outlet so as to reduce the kinetic energy finally discarded to the river.

energy is the river level to which the turbine is exhausting. Now the total energy at the diffuser outlet is

$$H_b = \frac{u_b{}^2}{2g} - x + p_b/g\rho,$$

where p_b is the pressure at the outlet. But u_b is deliberately arranged to be small, and in the river the pressure increases hydrostatically so $p_b = \rho g x$. Thus H_b is sensibly zero. No diffuser is, however, perfect and there is a certain amount of eddying in it with a consequent degradation of energy. Putting $Kf^2/2g$ as this decrease of energy in the diffuser,

$$H_a - H_b = K\frac{f^2}{2g}$$

or

$$\frac{f^2}{2g} + h_s + p_a/\rho g = K\frac{f^2}{2g}$$

or

$$p_a/g\rho = \frac{f^2}{2g}(K - 1) - h_s .$$

Since K is always less than 1·0 (sometimes as low as 0·12 for a well-designed diffuser) $p_a/\rho g$ is always negative, that is p_a is below atmospheric pressure. The upper end of a diffuser must therefore be completely airtight.

It is also of great importance to know the lowest pressure within the turbine. This occurs somewhere on the leading side of each blade, in the direction of motion, and it is due to the relative motion of the water over the aerofoil shaped blades (see Chapter 8). The lowest pressure of the fluid in contact with the blade is found, by experiment and by aerofoil theory, to be related to the relative velocity u_{rel} by the expression

$$p_{min}/g\rho = K_1 u^2_{rel}/2g$$

where p_{min} is the amount by which this minimum pressure is below the mean pressure of the surrounding fluid. K_1 is a constant depending on the shape of the blade. Reference to the outlet velocity triangles of turbines, fig 15·5, shows that if the outlet blade angle is $\sin^{-1} 1/n$, then $u_{rel} = nf$, and therefore

$$p_{min}/\rho g = K_1 n^2 f^2/2g.$$

Now the mean pressure is already low at the outlet side of the turbine, so that the lowest pressure is found against the leading side of the blades near the outlet end (fig 15.20). Since the mean pressure

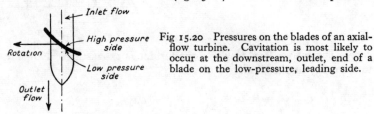

Fig 15.20 Pressures on the blades of an axial-flow turbine. Cavitation is most likely to occur at the downstream, outlet, end of a blade on the low-pressure, leading side.

there is $p_a/\rho g = f^2(K - 1)/2g$ $- h_s$ below atmospheric pressure, then the lowest pressure in the turbine is $K_1\dfrac{n^2 f^2}{2g}$ below $p_a/\rho g$ or,

$$p_{min}/\rho g = f^2(K - 1)/2g \quad - h_s - K_1 n^2 f^2/2g,$$

where p_{min} is the pressure below atmospheric pressure. Converting to absolute pressures by adding the atmospheric pressure p_{atm},

$$p_{min}/\rho g = p_{atm}/\rho g \quad - h_s + \quad f^2(K - 1 - n^2 K_1)/2g$$

above a vacuum, where $p_{atm}/\rho g$ is the height of a water barometer at the turbine site.

The danger of low pressures in water turbines is that if they fall as low as the vapour pressure of the water at the temperature concerned, then the water will boil and tiny bubbles of steam will form. This is called *cavitation*. The bubbles are carried downstream until they reach an area of slightly higher pressure where they collapse suddenly. If they collapse against the surface of the blades very local but high impact forces are produced against the metal, which eventually fails by fatigue. Severe damage soon occurs, usually by pitting of the blades. As well as this damage, the disturbance to the flow around the blades by the areas of steam is an additional source of eddies so that the turbine efficiency drops. If there is much air in solution in the water then bubbles of air may appear at a pressure rather above the vapour pressure. These bubbles produce *air cavitation*, which reduces the efficiency in the same way as vapour cavitation. It is always advantageous to avoid cavitation.

By putting p_{min} equal to the vapour pressure p_v into the previous equation, a value of h_s will be obtained which will be the greatest possible height at which the turbine can be placed above river level, if cavitation is to be avoided.

Thus $\dfrac{p_v}{g\rho} = \dfrac{p_{atm}}{g\rho} - h_s + f^2(k - 1 - n^2 k_1)/2g$. For the turbine designed in the example in section **15.6**, $n = 3$ and $f = 6.86$ m/s. If it is assumed that the turbine is at sea level, then $p_{atm}/\rho g = 10.3$ m It is also usual to adopt a conservatively high value for $p_v/\rho g = 2$ m approximately to allow for the possibility of air cavitation (the true vapour pressure at 20 °C is only about 30 cm of water). Also, usual values of K and K_1 are 0.12 and 0.1 respectively. Inserting these values into the last equation

$$2 = 10.3 - h_s + \frac{6.86^2}{2 \times 9.81}(0.12 - 1 - 9 \times 0.1)$$

or $\qquad h_s = 4.0$ m.

It will be seen that turbines working at high axial flow velocities f (implying a large Q for the size of machine); or working at higher altitudes than sea level; or with blades giving a high K_1; or with water at higher temperatures (in the tropics) must all be set nearer to river level than the one discussed above, if cavitation is not to set in.

The high-speed machines are those which are working under a high head, which forces a greater discharge through a given size machine. Thus an axial flow turbine used at a relatively high head must be set much lower than if it were working under a low head : sometimes such turbines are set at a negative h_s, that is below river level. Excavation costs are increased and maintenance is hindered by such an arrangement so that to avoid cavitation and to have small excavation and maintenance costs the other designs of turbines are used (see fig 15.4). The avoidance of both a low-level machine and also cavitation is the *only* reason why the compact axial flow design is not preferred

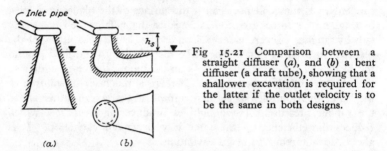

Fig 15.21 Comparison between a straight diffuser (*a*), and (*b*) a bent diffuser (a draft tube), showing that a shallower excavation is required for the latter if the outlet velocity is to be the same in both designs.

for all heads. Radial flow machines have a lower K_1 and f, and so can tolerate a greater h_s. It will also be observed that an inefficient diffuser (K large) would be a partial solution, allowing an axial flow machine to be used for high heads with a positive h_s. This solution could not be tolerated in practice for it would mean that there would be a waste of energy degraded to heat in the diffuser.

With the maximum height above river (or *tail water*) level fixed the outlet of an efficient conical diffuser for a large turbine would be a long way below water level (fig 15.21 (*a*)) and a vast excavation would be needed for the concrete structure generally used. It is therefore common to make the diffuser with a 90° bend in it (fig 15.21 (*b*)) and to discharge the water finally in a horizontal direction. This is called a *draft tube*. Draft tubes have slightly lower efficiencies than straight diffusers because even in the best designs the bend tends to produce eddies and secondary currents (Chapter 11).

15.14 Cavitation in pumps

A cavitation analysis can be made for the pressure in a roto-dynamic pump situated above the sump from which it is pumping. The minimum pressure on the blades is again dependent upon u_{rel}

and the suction height h_s, and also upon the frictional drop in pressure in the suction pipe. The last takes the place of the diffuser efficiency in the case of a turbine. It will be found that for a given pump and h_s, cavitation will commence at a given flow. It is essential to prevent cavitation in pumps and this can be done by making the suction pipe short, and setting the pump at or below sump water level.

15.15 Shock-waves in gas turbines and compressors

The last part of this chapter has dealt exclusively with the limitations imposed by cavitation on pumps or turbines working with water. Cavitation does not, of course, occur with gases so that there are on this account no limitations on the performance of gas turbines and compressors. However, another limitation exists in the form of shock-waves which occur if the relative speed of the fluid over the blades exceeds the speed of sound. There is no damage done to the blades by shock-waves, but the flow directions are so changed by them that the blade angles are incorrect for the desired whirl and flow velocities. The efficiency therefore falls and serious vibration may occur. Further, the shock-waves may extend over the whole flow area of the machine and cause it to be choked similarly to a Laval nozzle when the speed of sound is reached in the throat. The discharge and power is then fixed, and no further increases of speed or downstream pressure will affect them.

Axial flow machines are most sensitive to shock-wave phenomena on account of their inherently higher u_{rel} for a given pressure drop H across them. Radial flow machines with a lower u_{rel} are therefore sometimes used even if compactness is desired. Another way of developing large powers from axial flow gas turbines is to use a multistage machine, which has several rotors on the same shaft so that the pressure drop across each rotor is reduced, and shock-waves avoided. The compactness of the axial flow design is therefore preserved, though there are often difficult problems of design and manufacture of the turbine blades of the requisite strength. The performance of gas turbines and compressors is greatly modified by compressibility effects, and a great deal of advanced research work has been done to study them.

15.16 Conclusion

Mechanical energy and fluid energy can be mutually converted by suitable machines. Piston and cylinder reciprocating machines can be

PLATE 13

(*Above*) Flow over Sasumua Dam, Kenya, This is an old structure for a water-supply reservoir, recently raised to provide more storage. The layout is complicated, giving two fast streams combining at the foot of the spillway. A completely new structure would probably be laid out quite differently.

(*Below*) A 1:40 scale model in the laboratory, showing the complicated wave pattern downstream of the spillway. A model of this sort is the only way of determining this pattern and to find the heights of the water surface at all points with the complex geometry of the weir crests.

Photograph by Wimpey Laboratories Ltd.

PLATE 13

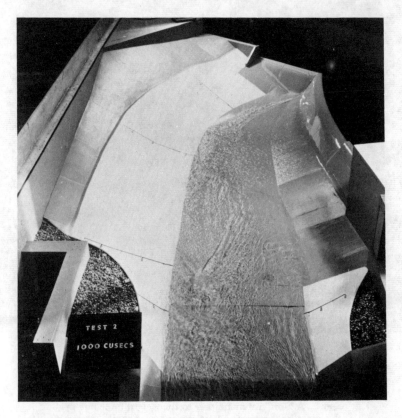

PLATE 14

A 26,000-' ton ' ship, 180 m long, travelling at its
designed speed. The wave pattern at the bow and
stern caused by its passage through the water can be
seen. A ' ton ' refers neither to the weight force nor to
the mass of the ship. It is the internationally agreed
name for an enclosed volume of 100 ft³ = 2·83 m³.

PLATE 15

A 5 m model of the ship of Plate 14 travelling at the
corresponding speed. Notice how the wave pattern
caused by the model is similar to that of the full-size
ship, though at a reduced scale.

Photo by Messrs. J. Brown & Co., Clydebank.

PLATE 16

PLATE 16 Photographs of the waves entering Napier Harbour, New Zealand.

(*Upper*) Aerial photograph of the Pacific swell being curved around the breakwater into the ship jetties. Notice the smaller wavelength waves set off inside the harbour parallel to the breakwater.

(*Below*) A distorted scale model, horizontal scale 1:240, vertical 1:120 used to study the wave pattern due to ' beats ' of the surf (fig. 16.10) in Napier. The close correspondence of the wave pattern with the aerial photograph is obvious.

Photos from Hydraulics Research Station, Wallingford.

so used but they are usually cumbersome for a given performance and are used only if high pressures are required. More frequently, machines are used which convert the motion of a rotor into rotary motion of the fluid, when a pressure increase results. These machines may take many forms but in all of them there are changes of the circumferential component of the fluid velocity. A combination of the power, head and speed, namely $N \sqrt{P} H^{-5/4}$ is an indication of the design of a machine and although any design could be used for any desired performance, it is found that limitations of size on one hand, and very low pressures on the other, usually prescribe the design to be used. The latter limitation, called cavitation, may be destructive of machines if they are placed too high relative to sump level (if a pump) or tail water-level (if a turbine). The performance of a machine at speeds, powers, heads or discharges other than the design conditions can be explained by analysis of the vectors of the fluid velocities.

PROBLEMS

1. A hydraulic turbine develops 9000 kW under a head of 10 m at a speed of 90 rev/min and gives an efficiency of 92·7 per cent. Calculate the water consumption and the specific speed. If a model 1/10 full size is constructed to operate under a head of 8 m, what must be its speed, power and water consumption to run under the similar conditions to the prototype ? How would the model efficiency compare with the prototype ?
   Ans. 99·1 cumecs : $N_s = 479$ min^{-1} kW$^{1/2}$ m$^{-5/4}$:
   805 rev/min : 64·5 kW : 0·885 m^3/s.

2. A turbine situated at an altitude of 1300 m above sea-level has a draft tube converting only 60 per cent of the turbine outlet velocity energy into pressure energy. The water temperature is 20 °C, vapour pressure 2 m of water and the velocity at the entrance to the draft tube is 7·5 m/s. If the lowest local pressure in the turbine is $1·2f^2/2g$ lower than the draft tube entrance pressure, calculate the maximum permissible height of the turbine above tail water-level, and the suction at draft tube entrance. The sea-level water barometer is 10·3 m high.
   Ans. 1·52 m : 3·23 m.

3. Sea water, sp. gr. 1·03, is to be circulated through condensers by a propeller pump 120 cm diameter. It is found that a scale model of the pump 25 cm diameter gives its best efficiency when pumping 97 litres/s of fresh water against a head of 4·20 metres when running at 2060 rev/min. What should be the speed of the full size pump to deliver 1550 litres/s and what pressure difference will it generate?
   Ans. 295 rev/min : 0·21 kg/cm².

4. Find the wheel and nozzle diameters for a 2-jet Pelton wheel, $N_s = 30$ min^{-1} kW$^{1/2}$ m$^{-5/4}$ to give 6000 kW at 500 m head.
   Ans. 95 cm ; 9·5 cm : 915 rev/min : 0·70 cumec/jet.

5. It is proposed to use a propeller turbine 3·2 m outer diameter 1·3 m boss diameter, to generate 20,000 kW under a head of 76 m at an efficiency of 88·2 per cent. The required speed is 120 rev/min. What is the specific speed, and what must be the angles which the flow makes with the plane of the propeller at the blade tips on the entry and outlet sides ?

If the draft tube recovers 70 per cent of the K.E rejected by the rotor, what must be the maximum height of the rotor above tail-race level if cavitation is not to take place ? (Assume data given in Chapter 15.) Compare the size of the machine with a Pelton wheel for the same job.

Ans. $N_s = 76 : 14°, 17°$.

6. A model propeller turbine rotor 30 cm in diameter develops 26 kW at 7·5 m head and 1200 rev/min. The prototype is to develop 7500 kW with 6 m head. Find the diameter and speed of the prototype.

Ans. 5·4 m : 59·5 rev/min.

7. It is desired to pump 2700 l/min of water per minute against a head, including friction, of 15 m. The only available pump, when tested at 600 rev/min, gave the following results—

Pressure produced	15	16·2	16·2	14·4	12·6	10·2	7·5	4·5	m
Water flow	0	450	900	1350	1580	1800	2030	2250	l/min
Efficiency	—	30	61	81	85	80	67	47	%

At what speed should it be driven to do the job, and what input power will be required ?

Ans. 823 rev/min : 70 per cent efficiency : 9·48 kW.

8. In a centrifugal pump test the discharge pressure gauge reads 700 kN/m² and the suction gauge 35 kN/m². Both gauges read above atmospheric pressure, and their centres are at the same level. The diameters of the suction and delivery pipes are 8 cm and 5 cm respectively. If oil, sp. gr. 0·85, is being pumped at 500 l/min, what is the power supplied to the pump, assuming an efficiency of 75 per cent ?

Ans. 8·15 kW.

9. A centrifugal pump with a 20 cm suction pipe was tested at sea-level with its axis 1·2 m *below* water-level in the suction sump. It just commenced to cavitate at 2440 rev/min when working at peak efficiency, and it then was giving 0·12 m³/s with a *total* head of 10·2 m.

The pump is eventually to be used on a plateau at 4000 m above sea-level, pumping from a reservoir with the water-level 3·5 m below its axis. At what speed would cavitation set in, and what will be the total head and discharge if it is to be used at maximum efficiency ? Ignore suction pipe friction.

Density of air at 2000 m is 0·93 kg/m³

Water-vapour pressure is 14 kN/m²

At sea-level atmospheric pressure is 101 kN/m²

Ans. 985 rev/min : 1·67 m : 0·049 m³/s.

10. Explain the significance of Q6, Chapter 5 in the design of pumps or turbines.

11. On a contractor's remote site there are several similar pumps available, all diesel driven and with the following characteristics at 1200 rev/min.

Head	(m)	30	33	34	34	32	28	19	7
Discharge	(m³/sec)	0	0·1	0·15	0·2	0·25	0·3	0·35	0·4
Efficiency	(%)	0	26	38	48	57	60	59	32

The diesels cannot be effectively run at speeds more than 20% different from 1200 rev/min. How could these machines be used to deliver 0·5 m³/s against a head, including pipe friction, of 50 m? If diesels use 0·25 kg/kW h, what is the likely fuel consumption?

Comment on the advantages and disadvantages of separate delivery pipes against one large, common delivery pipe.

12. A fan has the characteristic H–Q curve of the figure. It supplies air to a long length of ducting for which the friction law is

$$H(\text{cm of water gauge}) = 0\cdot01\ Q^2((\text{m}^3/\text{s})^2).$$

What will be the air discharge at a fan speed, N, of 900 rev/min? If the air discharge must be increased by 50% summarize all the advantages and disadvantages of

    (a) introducing a second fan in parallel with the first;

    (b) driving the existing fan with a different motor.

Ans. 38·3 m³/s.

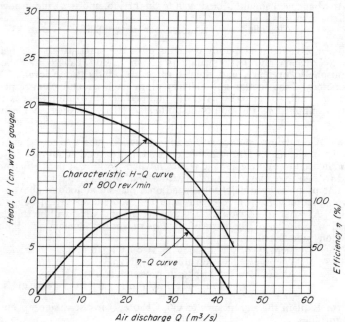

CHAPTER 16

NON-STEADY FLOW

16.1 The whole of the foregoing part of this book is concerned with steady flow, when the conditions do not change with time. Most engineering problems are concerned with this sort of flow, but occasionally the properties of a non-steady flow become of importance. Three cases of non-steady flow will now be reviewed but there are many other cases which sometimes arise.

16.2 The filling of a reservoir

The filling of a reservoir by the flow of a river is a case of non-steady flow of a simple sort. Reservoirs are frequently made in valleys by building a dam across a river and extending the embankment to both sides. If the reservoir is full, and water continues to be added, an overflow device such as a spillway must be provided so that the surplus is safely passed over the dam. If the water-level rises to a height h above the spillway crest, then there is a discharge, Q_{out}, which in

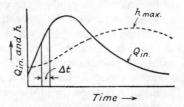

Fig 16.1 A *hydrograph*, which is a graph of inflow to a reservoir against time. Most rainstorms give hydrographs of this shape. The dotted line shows the height of water in the reservoir, which has a maximum much later than the maximum of the inflow.

general depends on h and so is not constant. The inflow to the reservoir Q_{in} is also not usually constant. Rainstorms on the catchment area of the river cause a fluctuation of Q_{in}, and a common shape of the inflow curve (a *hydrograph*) is shown in fig 16.1 as a graph of Q_i against time. The difference, $Q_{in} - Q_{out}$, is retained in the reservoir, increasing the volume of water there, and raising the water-level. The relation between the small change of level dh in a small time dt is therefore

$$Q_{in}\, dt = Q_{out}\, dt + A\, dh,$$

where A is the plan area of the water surface at a height h.

333

It is not usually possible to solve this differential equation by direct algebraical integration to find h at every t. Every term of the equation changes in a complicated way : Q_{in} changes with t so that it cannot be expressed as an easy algebraic function : Q_{out} can change with h in several different ways (though $Q_{out} \propto h^{3/2}$ for simple weirs, more complicated ways of spilling water are often used) : and A commonly increases somewhat with h again in no simple fashion. Thus approximate (that is, arithmetical) methods must be used to produce a curve of h against t.

One way of carrying out such an integration is to divide the inlet hydrograph into arbitrary and finite time intervals Δt, as in fig 16·1, and so to obtain $Q_{in} \Delta t$, which is the area under the hydrograph in this time interval, and is also the volume of water entering the reservoir. A tentative value of h is then guessed for the water-level at the end of the time interval, so that the *mean* water-level and thus the mean Q_{out} in this interval can also be guessed. From Q_{out}, a tentative value of $Q_{out} \Delta t$ is calculated, the volume allowed to escape from the reservoir. The difference, $Q_{in} \Delta t - Q_{out} \Delta t$ is then the tentative volume of water retained in the reservoir, $A \Delta h$. The area of the reservoir can then be estimated, if it changes with h, by using the guessed *mean* value of h. Using this, the calculated change in height Δh is

$$\Delta h = (Q_{in} \Delta t - Q_{out} \Delta t)/A,$$

which may be added to the height of the water surface at the beginning of the interval to produce the calculated height at the end. This is now compared with the guessed height used at the beginning of the calculation : if the guess was a good one, then the calculated value of h will be the same as the guessed one. Usually, of course, there will be a discrepancy so that the calculation must be repeated with a new guessed h, based on the result of the previous calculation. Eventually, fair agreement will be reached, so the computation proceeds to the next time interval using the calculated h from the preceding calculation as the starting-point. This time it is easier to make a good guess of h because the order of magnitude of Δh is known. In this way the computation is built up in layers and a graph of h against t is produced. The maximum value of h is always later than the maximum of Q_{in}, and it is this property of a reservoir in delaying the peaks of floods that is so useful if a catchment area of a river is subject to sudden storms. The following example shows the method.

Example

A reservoir has the following water surface areas : at 1000 ft O.D, 25×10^6 ft²; at 1003 O.D, 27×10^6 ft²; 1005 O.D, 30×10^6 ft²; at 1010 O.D, 39×10^6 ft². The worst rainstorm on the catchment gives the following inflow to the reservoir—Flow increasing from zero to 3×10^4 cusecs linearly in 2 hours, followed by a linear decrease to zero again in a further 8 hours. The only outlet from the reservoir is over a weir 400 ft long, crest at 1000 O.D, coefficient $4 \cdot 0$ ft$^{\frac{1}{2}}$/s. What will be the highest water-level in the reservoir, and when will it occur if the inflow commences when the water-level is at 1000 O.D ?

Weir discharge is $Q_{\text{out}} = 4 \cdot 0 \times 400h^{3/2} = 1600\ h^{3/2}$ cusecs where h is the height of the water surface above 1000 O.D. For change of h in the *first hour*—assume no water escapes over weir.

$Q_{\text{in}} = 0 \cdot 75 \times 10^4$ cusec on the average :

thus $\quad \Delta h = \dfrac{0 \cdot 75 \times 10^4 \times 3600}{25 \times 10^6} = \frac{27}{25}$ ft $= 1 \cdot 08$ ft for first hour.

Since there is actually some outflow, and the mean area of reservoir is rather greater than 25×10^6 ft², the Δh for the first hour will be a little less than $1 \cdot 08$, so try $1 \cdot 00$ ft as on pp. 336–337.

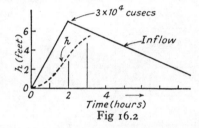

Fig 16.2

16.3 Non-steady flow in a pipe

Some important engineering problems arise when a fluid flow in a pipe is accelerated or decelerated. The pressure within the pipe may change temporarily so much that the pipe may burst or collapse if it is not strong enough. It is rarely economic to design a large pipe strong enough to take these pressures, and safety devices are usually essential.

Consider a long pipe from a reservoir to a consumer's valve. If the latter is fully open the mean speed in the pipe is u, and the pressure falls along the pipe in accordance with the hydraulic friction gradient (Chapter 13). Suppose now that the valve is shut instantaneously, thus completely stopping the fluid near it. Farther away upstream, the fluid is still moving so that the near fluid is compressed, increasing its pressure and density. In the piece of pipe shown in fig 16.3, the fluid near the valve is stopped, its pressure being p above the pressure in the moving fluid, so that to a first approximation its density is raised from ρ to $\rho(1 + p/K)$. K is the coefficient of compressibility of the fluid (Chapter 1). In a short time t, the length of the stationary

h (guessed value) ft	Time t from start hour	Δt hour	Mean Q_{in} (from inflow graph) cusecs	Vol. in during period concerned ft³	Mean head on weir (guessed) ft	Mean Q_{out} based on guessed mean head cusecs	Guessed vol. out during period ft³
0	0						
		1	0.75×10^4	2.7×10^7	0.500	565	0.20×10^7
1.00	.1						

For period 1–2 hours start with water-level at 1000·99

h (guessed value) ft	Time t from start hour	Δt hour	Mean Q_{in} (from inflow graph) cusecs	Vol. in during period concerned ft³	Mean head on weir (guessed) ft	Mean Q_{out} based on guessed mean head cusecs	Guessed vol. out during period ft³
0.99	1						
		1	2.25×10^4	8.1×10^7	1.45	2800	1.01×10^7
1.9	2						
		1	2.25×10^4	8.1×10^7	2.20	5230	1.88×10^7
3.4	2						

For period 2–3 hours start with water-level at

h (guessed value) ft	Time t from start hour	Δt hour	Mean Q_{in} (from inflow graph) cusecs	Vol. in during period concerned ft³	Mean head on weir (guessed) ft	Mean Q_{out} based on guessed mean head cusecs	Guessed vol. out during period ft³
3.34	2						
		1	2.81×10^4	10.1×10^7	4.67	16,100	5.8×10^7
6.0	3						
		1	2.81×10^4	10.1×10^7	4.37	14,600	5.27×10^7
5.4	3						
		1	2.81×10^4	10.1×10^7	4.27	14,100	5.08×10^7
5.2	3						
		1	2.81×10^4	10.1×10^7	4.22	13,850	4.98×10^7
5.1	3						

Volume stored in reservoir = Vol. in − Vol. out ft³	Mean area A of reservoir based on guessed mean head ft²	Δh computed = vol. stored/A based on mean (guessed) h during period	Computed water-level above O.D. ft	
			1000·0	
2·50 × 10⁷	25·3 × 10⁶	0·989		
			1000·989	Agreement with guessed value good enough

nd guess $h = 1\cdot9$ at end of period

			1000·99	
7·09 × 10⁷	26 × 10⁶	2·73		
			1003·72	Guessed h far too small. Try 1003·4
6·22 × 10⁷	26·5 × 10⁶	2·35		
			1003·34	Fair agreement

:003·34 and guess $h = 1006$ at end of period

			1003·34	
4·3 × 10⁷	29·5 × 10⁶	1·46		
			1004·80	Bad over-estimate. Try 1005·4
4·83 × 10⁷	29 × 10⁶	1·66		
			1005·00	Nearer : not good enough yet. Try 1005·2
5·02 × 10⁷	29 × 10⁶	1·73		
			1005·07	Nearer. Try 1005·1
5·12 × 10⁷	29 × 10⁶	1·77		
			1005·11	Very good agreement. Carry on integration

fluid increases, the junction between it and the moving fluid changing from XX to YY, a distance x. Due to the increase of density $\rho p/K$, the mass of fluid in the fixed volume XXYY has also increased,

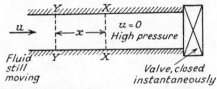

Fig 16.3 Portion of a pipe upstream of a valve which has just been shut instantaneously. XX and YY are two positions of the junction between compressed, stationary fluid, and moving, low-pressure fluid. The two positions are separated by a time t.

and this can only be achieved by a transport of mass of fluid through the section YY. During the whole of the time t, the fluid speed across YY is u, so that the transport of mass is $\rho\,u\,t\,a$, and so

$$a\,x\,\rho\,p/K = \rho\,u\,t\,a$$

where a is the cross-sectional area of the pipe.

That is $x/t = uK/p = c$.   .   .   . (16.1)

where c is the velocity of the junction of the moving and stationary fluid.

In order to obtain another expression for p and c, it is necessary to use the momentum theorem of Chapter 6. In fig 16.4 (a) the junction between stopped and moving fluid in the pipe is shown moving at velocity c towards the fluid which still has a velocity u. If the whole system is given a velocity c in the opposite direction to this, as in fig 16.4 (b), then the junction is stopped and the problem becomes one of steady flow into and out of the control volume shown. Now because K is large for most liquids, to a first order of approximation the density downstream of the now stationary junction is not greatly changed from the original value, so that the simplified momentum equation (6.3) may be used. That is, an incoming flow of $a(u+c)$ has its velocity changed by u so that the difference of the rate of flow of momentum into and out of the control volume is

$$\rho\,a\,(u+c)\,u$$

which is equal to the force imposed on the fluid, pa.

So substituting for c from 16.1

$$p\,a = \rho\,a(u + uK/p)\,u.$$

Again because K is very large compared with pressures usually experienced ($K = 2 \times 10^6\ \mathrm{kN/m^2}$ for water), so u may be ignored compared with $u\,K/p$.

That is $$p = \rho\, u^2\, K/p$$

or $$p = u\sqrt{(K\rho)} \qquad . \qquad . \qquad . \qquad . \quad (16.2)$$

Thus the pressure set up by the deceleration is independent of the size or length of the pipe. If water is the fluid concerned then by substituting numerical values for K and ρ it is seen that although p is small compared with K, it is large (4200 kN/m², or 40 atmospheres at $u = 3$ m/s) compared with the pressures usually imposed in steady flow. The pipes must therefore be thick walled for safety. Instantaneous closure of valves is clearly to be avoided if costs are to be kept low.

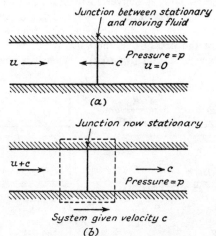

Fig 16.4   A junction between moving and stationary fluid moves with velocity c, as in (a), thus giving non-steady motion. By giving the whole system an equal and opposite velocity, the motion becomes steady as in (b), and the momentum theorem may be applied to the control volume shown by the dotted lines.

Substitution for p from 16.2 into 16.1 gives $c = \sqrt{(K/\rho)}$, from which it will be seen that c is always high though by no means infinite ($c = 1430$ m/s for water). Thus the assumption of ignoring u compared with c is justified. It will be recalled from elementary physics that $c = \sqrt{(K/\rho)}$ is also the speed of sound in a substance, so that in the pipe the high pressure fluid grows outward from the valve at sonic speed. The junction is a shock-wave which can be heard in the pipe as a knocking noise, sometimes called *water hammer*. Notice, however, that the expression for p involves the assumption that K is large ; if it is small (as with a gas for example), then the much more precise and elaborate analysis of Chapter 9 is required.

In the compressed fluid, energy is stored in the form of strain energy according to the usual law,

Strain energy per unit volume $= \frac{1}{2}$ Stress $\times$ Strain
$$= \frac{1}{2}p^2/K.$$

Substituting for $p = u\sqrt{(K\rho)}$,

Strain energy per unit volume $= \frac{1}{2}\frac{u^2}{K}(K\rho) = \frac{1}{2}\rho u^2.$

But $\frac{1}{2}\rho\, u^2$ is the kinetic energy per unit volume due to the velocity u (observe $u^2/2g$ is the kinetic energy per unit *weight* of fluid). Thus all the original kinetic energy of the fluid is transformed to strain energy at the junction, and none is converted to heat or otherwise degraded by the water-hammer phenomenon though such a degradation will of course occur in the pipe due to the usual pipe friction.

The history of the pressure at the valve (or at any other point in the pipe) can now be found (fig 16.5). When the valve is shut the

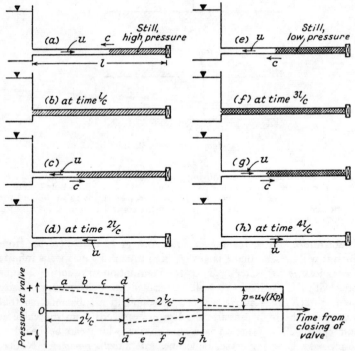

Fig 16.5   The history of pressure changes in a pipeline after the valve at the end has been shut instantaneously. The pressure-time graph at the valve is shown below the eight sketches (a) to (h). The dotted line shows the pressure if friction gradually degrades kinetic energy to heat.

junction of the moving and stationary fluid moves away from the valve until at a time l/c afterwards the whole pipe is filled with stationary high-pressure fluid (fig 16.5 (*a*) and (*b*)). This situation is unstable, for the high pressure is now not balanced by any deceleration of the fluid. The high pressure therefore commences to accelerate the fluid in the opposite direction, starting from the open, reservoir end. The junction moves back again towards the valve, the pressure remaining high there, fig 16.5 (*c*). When the junction reaches the valve, all the fluid is now moving away from the valve at the same speed as it originally moved in the opposite direction. To decelerate this reverse flow the pressure must therefore be reduced at the valve to give an inward force on the outward moving fluid. The conditions are exactly the same as occurred when the valve was shut, but reversed in sign. The pressure therefore falls to $p = -u\sqrt{(K\rho)}$ below the pressure at the reservoir and the junction moves away from the valve again, at the same speed c (fig 16.5 (*e*)). When the junction arrives at the reservoir end, fig 16.5 (*f*), the pipe is all filled with low pressure fluid, which is again in an unstable state : the higher pressure in the reservoir accelerates the fluid in the original direction and the junction moves back again towards the valve. The fluid now has its original velocity so as the junction gets to the valve the hydraulic conditions are exactly the same as occurred when the valve was first shut. The complete cycle of events is therefore repeated and goes on repeating if there is no degradation of the kinetic energy into other forms of non-available energy.

The cyclic nature of these pressure pulses is shown in fig 16.5 by a graph of the pressure at the valve, plotted against the time after the valve is closed. The full line shows the theoretical pulses as predicted in the preceding paragraph. The dotted lines show approximately how frictional forces on the moving fluid in the pipe steadily degrade the kinetic energy so that the strain energy in the stationary fluid is also steadily reduced. The magnitude of the pressure pulses is therefore reduced with time until they are imperceptible. If the negative pressure pulse is greater than the absolute hydrostatic pressure that the fluid possessed when it was originally moving, a further modification is made to the theoretical pulses. The pressure cannot fall below zero absolute (a perfect vacuum) so that if larger pulses are generated the fluid cavitates (boils), and temporarily fills part of the pipe with vapour. The low-pressure part of the pulses may thus be cut off short.

If the valve is not shut quite instantaneously but takes a short time, *less* than $2l/c$, then the pressure is gradually built up at the valve in this time. The maximum pressure remains the same, however, because eventually all the kinetic energy is converted to strain energy before the junction arrives back at the valve. But if the valve is shut in a time rather greater than $2l/c$, only part of the kinetic energy has been converted into strain energy by the time that the junction between stopped and moving fluid has returned to the valve as in fig 16.5 (*d*). Only a part of the increased pressure $p = \sqrt{(K\rho)}$ is therefore experienced by the valve : the situation of fig 16.5 (*e*) does not fully arise because some of the flow of fluid away from the valve is provided by fluid coming through the partly open valve. The flow is restricted to some extent by the valve so that a reduced negative pressure is experienced, compared with the case when the valve was fully shut.

16.4 Slow closing of a valve

If the valve is shut in a relatively long time compared to the time required for a shock-wave to travel twice along the pipe, say $10 \times 2l/c$, the pressure pulse will be hardly measurable. But a pressure rise of a different nature may quite well occur, and although this rise is usually much less than that caused by the compressibility effect above, it may still be too great for the safety of the pipe. The pressure rise is now determined by considering the fluid to be incompressible and originally travelling at a speed u. If a deceleration α is caused by the slowly shutting valve, then a deceleration force must be applied to the whole mass of fluid. This force is the increase of pressure at the valve, above the pressure at the supply end of the pipe. If h' is the head of static fluid corresponding to this pressure increase, then the deceleration force is $\rho g h' a$ (newtons in metric system ; poundals in f.p.s. system) on the whole cross-sectional area a of the pipe. Since the mass of fluid being decelerated is $\rho a l$, where l is the length of the pipe, then by Newton's Second Law

$$\rho g h' a = \rho a l \alpha$$

or $$h' = l\alpha/g.$$

If the valve is made to move in such a way that the deceleration is uniform in time t, then $\alpha = u/t$ and $h' = l u/g\, t$. This does not imply that the rate of closing the valve is uniform, as will be later explained. The increase of pressure due to the deceleration is therefore dependent on both the length of the pipe and on the time of closing the valve : a result which should be contrasted with that for the case of the valve shutting suddenly, when the pressure is independent of both these variables.

The effect of the deceleration pressure on the hydraulic gradient of a pipeline is shown in fig 16.6. The valve, X, is at the far end of a long pipeline from a reservoir O. The hydraulic gradient for a steady flow might be the line OA (the pressure at X being fixed by the downstream pressure, another reservoir, for example). In this diagram the usually small energy degradations at the inlet, and the kinetic energy $u^2/2g$ have been neglected. If X is now shut slowly to give a decelerating pressure h', the gradient line initially moves upward to OB, where $AB = h'$, before neither the velocity u nor the friction head $h = 4f\dfrac{l}{d}\dfrac{u^2}{2g}$ (see Chapter 13) has changed significantly.

As the deceleration takes effect, u decreases and so does h, while h'

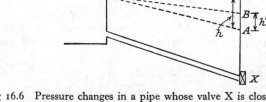

Fig 16.6 Pressure changes in a pipe whose valve X is closed slowly. OA is the steady flow pressure line, and as soon as the fluid is decelerated a head h must have been applied opposing the motion. OC is the pressure line just before the motion ceases.

stays constant if the deceleration is uniform. The gradient line therefore steadily rises, decreasing the hydraulic gradient. At the instant of complete closure of the valve, both u and h are zero, but h' still remains. The gradient line is therefore now sloping upwards to OC, and the pressure at the valve is greater than that due to the hydrostatic pressure. It is this additional pressure which may damage pipe or valve. An instant after complete closure, the pressure falls to hydrostatic.

It will now be seen how the pressures generated by a deceleration change radically according to whether the time of closure of the valve is greater or smaller than $2l/c$. Both types of action can occur successively in one operation of the valve in the following way. A valve decelerates a flow by introducing a degradation of energy additional to that caused by friction in the pipe. In the case of a sluice valve (*gate* valve) the pipe is partly blocked so that the flow area is reduced to a_2 from the full bore of the pipe a_1. Downstream of the valve the flow expands again to a_1, and so there is a degradation which is approximately given by $E = (u_2 - u_1)^2/2g$. (For a proof, see problem 5 on p. 97.)

The total degradation in the whole system is the sum of the pipe friction degradation and this valve degradation, and the sum equals the total change in pressure h between the ends of the pipe.

Thus
$$h = E + 4f \frac{l}{d_1} \frac{u_1^2}{2g}$$

where $a_1 = \pi d_1^2/4$ and u_1 is the velocity in the pipe.

Substituting, $h - (u_2 - u_1)^2/2g - 4f \dfrac{l}{\sqrt{a_1}} \sqrt{(4/\pi)} \dfrac{u_1^2}{2g} = 0$

or
$$h - \frac{u_1^2 a_1^2}{2g} \left(\frac{1}{a_2} - \frac{1}{a_1} \right)^2 - 4f \frac{l}{\sqrt{a}} \sqrt{(4/\pi)} \frac{u_1^2}{2g} = 0$$

or
$$K_1 - K_2 u_1 \left(1 - \left(\frac{a_2}{a_1} \right) \right)^2 - K_3 u_1^2 = 0$$

where K_1 , K_2 , K_3 are constants for the particular system.

The equation may be solved for u_1 in terms of a_2/a_1 and a curve plotted. The shape is as shown in fig 16.7 (a), the curvature depending

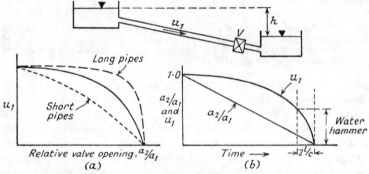

Fig 16.7 (a) Typical curves showing the decrease of fluid speed in a long pipeline as the valve is shut. (b) The high rate of deceleration of the fluid when the valve is approaching its seating at a constant speed may give water hammer unless the valve movement is deliberately decelerated in the later stages of shutting.

on the relative values of the constants K_1 , K_2 , K_3 . It will be seen that the initial part of the closing of the valve causes only a small change in u_1 , but that later the same change of a_1 causes a much larger change of u_1 . If the valve is shut so that a_2 decreases uniformly with time, as in fig 16.7 (b), then the deceleration in the pipe increases as the valve shuts. In the final period of time $2l/c$ before closing, the pressure at the valve is according to the water hammer equation

$p = u \sqrt{(K\rho)}$, and if the velocity curve is sufficiently steep, p may be large and may cause serious damage. Consequently valves on long pipelines are frequently arranged so that they begin to shut quickly, but later the closing motion is slowed down to avoid water hammer.

16.5 Surge tanks

In hydro-electric installations the turbines are often supplied with water through a long pipeline or tunnel. As has been explained, high and perhaps destructive pressures can be developed if there is a change in the discharge, which occurs quite suddenly if the electrical load is taken off the generators : the turbines start to race, and the governors react, closing the guide vane openings (of a radial or axial flow turbine) or the jets of a Pelton wheel. The consequent deceleration of the water in a tunnel or pipeline several km long might prove disastrous if there was not a *surge tank*, a vertical shaft of steel or tunnelled in rock, placed near the turbines (fig 16.8). The water rises in the shaft

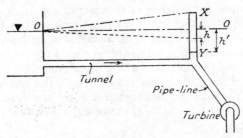

Fig 16.8 A *surge tank* on a hydro-electric scheme. If the flow to the turbine is suddenly stopped the water can only rise in the surge tank to X before it spills over, thus limiting the pressure on the tunnel. When the turbine starts the level falls to Y, to give an accelerating force on the water in the tunnel due to the pressure head h'.

to provide the hydrostatic pressure which decelerates the fluid in the tunnel. When the water comes finally to rest the water level in the tank is, of course, the same as that in the reservoir. If an abnormally high deceleration occurs, the water pours from the top of the surge tank, which therefore limits the maximum pressure in the tunnel. The short length of pipe from surge tank to the turbine is not protected from high pressures, and must therefore be strongly built.

The surge tank also holds a supply of water to operate the turbine when starting, when an accelerating pressure must be applied to the water in the tunnel. The water surface in the surge tank falls below the no-flow level by an amount h' in order to provide this accelerating force on the upstream water. As the speed in the tunnel approaches the steady flow value, the surge tank water-level rises until it is below reservoir level by only the friction head h in the tunnel. The diameter of the surge tank, and the level of the intersection with the tunnel must be chosen so that there is sufficient water in the tank to drive the turbine during the time when the water in the tunnel is accelerating. Surge tanks are often large structures, sometimes 15 m or more in diameter, but it is economical to build them rather than to make the tunnel stronger.

Although after a change in turbine load the water level in the surge tank eventually comes to a new equilibrium level, it does so only after a number of oscillations about this mean. The reservoir, tunnel and surge tank act like a U-tube in which the water level has been disturbed. If the electrical load also has an oscillation which has the same period as that of the hydraulic system, resonance will occur and the amplitude of the oscillations grow until damage is caused. For this reason, and also to determine if a surge tank is large enough, it is necessary to estimate the oscillations by calculation at the design stage, and to determine the damping of the system.

At one instant of time when the surge tank level is z below the reservoir, and the water speed in the tunnel is u, the head h degraded to heat by friction may be estimated by the Darcy law, and written $h = ku^2$. At equilibrium, then $z = h = ku^2$, and there would be no acceleration of the water in the tunnel. But if the system is not in equilibrium, the difference between z and ku^2 is a head tending to accelerate or decelerate the flow, according to the slow closure rule of 16.4 so that

$$ku^2 \pm z = \frac{l}{g}\frac{\mathrm{d}u}{\mathrm{d}t}$$

In this equation the positive sign applies when the friction head and the rise of the level in the tank are acting together to decelerate the flow; the negative sign applies when the level in the tank is below equilibrium level.

As well as this dynamical relation, the ‘continuity’ condition must be satisfied; that is, the flow through the tunnel must equal the flow to the turbines plus the flow into or out of the tank. Thus,

$$uA_t = A_s\frac{\mathrm{d}z}{\mathrm{d}t} + Q$$

where A_t and A_s are respectively the cross-sectional areas of tunnel and surge tank, and Q is the flow still going to the turbine.

The two differential equations must be solved simultaneously to find how z varies with t. An approximate ‘step by step’ method is usually necessary and one of the many possible computations is shown in the following example.

Example

In a small hydro-electric scheme the proposed tunnel is 1·2 m dia and has $f = 0·01$. At 150 m along the tunnel from the reservoir there is a simple, open surge tank 3·6 m dia. The steady full load flow to the turbines is 2·3 cumecs.

Show how to estimate the maximum rise of water level in the surge tank after the full flow has been suddenly rejected by the turbines.

Full load tunnel speed $= v_0 = 2·3/\frac{1}{4}\pi \times 1·2^2 = 2·04$ m/s

Full load friction head in tunnel $= kv_0^2 = \dfrac{4 \times 0·01 \times 150 \times 2·04^2}{1·2 \times 2 \times 9·81}$

$= 1·06$ m below still water level

After full load rejection $Q = 0$, so for a small but finite change Δz, the continuity condition gives

$$z = \frac{A_t}{A_s}v\,\Delta t = \frac{v}{9}\Delta t$$

where Δt is the small but finite time during which Δz takes place, and v is a mean tunnel velocity during this time.

The dynamic conditions are rearranged to give

$$\Delta v = -\frac{g}{l}(z \pm kv^2)\Delta t$$

where Δv is the small but finite change of tunnel speed in Δt, and z is the mean height of water in the surge tank during this interval.

These equations must be solved for successive intervals each of Δt. The choice of a numerical value for Δt is a matter of experience and of trial; a value of $\Delta t = 5$ seconds is suitable in this case, though for larger installations a longer time is appropriate.

Thus $\qquad \Delta z = \dfrac{5}{9}v \quad$ and $\quad \Delta v = -0·328(z \pm 0·254v^2)$

(a) Period 0 to 5 seconds after load rejection: *first approximation*: put v as the velocity at the beginning of the interval but z as the water level at the end of the interval.

then $\qquad \Delta z_1 = 5 \times 2·04/9 = 1·13$ m

so $\qquad\quad z = -1·06 + 1·13 = +0·07$ m at end of interval

and $\qquad \Delta v_1 = -0·328(0·07 + 0·254 \times 2·04^2) = -0·37$ m/s

or $\qquad\quad v = 2·04 - 0·37 = 1·67$ m/s at end of period.

second approximation : mean $v = \frac{1}{2}(1·67 + 2·04) = 1·85$ m/s

then $\qquad \Delta z_2 = \frac{5}{9} \times 1·85 = 1·03$ m

so $\qquad\quad z = -1·06 + 1·03 = -0·03$ m

and mean $\quad z = -1·06 + \dfrac{1·03}{2} = -0·55$ m

and $\qquad \Delta v_2 = -0·328(-0·55 + 0·254 \times 1·85^2) = -0·11$ m/s

or $\qquad\quad v = 2·04 - 0·11 = 1·93$ m/s

third approximation : same method as second approximation
  using mean $v = \frac{1}{2}(2 \cdot 04 + 1 \cdot 93) = 1 \cdot 99$ m/s
  gives $z = + 0 \cdot 04$ m and $v = 1 \cdot 88$ m/s.

fourth approximation : same method as second and third,
  gives $z = + 0 \cdot 03$ m and $v = 1 \cdot 89$ m/s.

(*b*) Period 5 to 10 seconds after load rejection : *first approximation :*
same as first approximation for the first time interval
  gives $z = + 1 \cdot 08$ m and $v = 1 \cdot 24$ m/s at end of period.

Second and third approximations as before, using mean values of z and v
finally give
$$z = + 0 \cdot 98 \text{ m and } v = 1 \cdot 48 \text{ m/s}$$

(*c*) Successive 5 second periods are similarly computed and a curve
drawn of z against time. The maximum height is about $1 \cdot 85$ m above
still water level at about 22 seconds after load rejection.

If only the first approximation method is applied to the same Δt
periods, without the refinements of the later approximations, a maximum
is found of $1 \cdot 7$ m at about 21 seconds after rejection. The close agreement of this result with that of the more exact approximations has been
observed in many cases of this sort. The later history of water level
in the surge tank is sketched (not to scale) in the figure below. With
$f = 0 \cdot 01$, the system is unusually heavily damped.

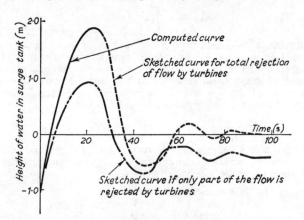

16.6 Wave motions

The motions in a fluid caused by waves on a liquid surface present
another class of non-steady flow. These motions are essentially
periodic and so do not eventually settle down to steady flow.

A discussion has already been given in the Appendix to Chapter 14
of the properties of single, or *solitary* waves in shallow water. In

these waves, which travel at a speed depending on the depth, the water is, firstly, accelerated and moved in the direction of progress of the wave, then decelerated to a standstill after the wave has passed overhead. The surface water must also rise and fall in this period, so that the paths of particles near the surface are lines which have a hump in them, while particles near the bottom, where there is less rise and fall, follow nearly straight line paths (fig 16.9 (c)). All particles are displaced during the passage of a solitary wave so that fluid is moved forward by the wave. When the wave reaches the end of the channel it may either break on a sloping beach, or be reflected by a wall to return in the opposite direction. In the latter case the particles of water will be replaced to their original position as the wave passes over on its return passage. But in the former case the water moved forward by the wave is piled up on the beach as the wave breaks so that the water-level at the beach is rather higher than elsewhere. This condition is unstable and a slow return motion commences to return this water uniformly all along the channel. The particles already considered have therefore a slow backward movement following the fast forward movement as the wave passes over. The waves of the sea as they approach the land become a series of solitary waves, each one of which is completely independent of its neighbours and travelling at a speed determined only by the depth. There is a steady outward current (undertow) to replace the water brought forward by the waves.

When waves are travelling in deep water their properties are quite different from those of solitary waves. In general, the waves of the deep sea can be regarded as a succession or *train* of waves, one wave following another at more or less regular intervals. The interval of distance from one wave crest to the next is the wave-length L: the interval of time between succeeding wave crests passing a fixed point is the wave-period T. The motions of the water under each wave interact with the motions of the neighbouring wave so that the particle movements become less and less like those of the solitary wave as the depth of water becomes greater. A full analysis of the motions involved is too advanced for this volume, and a much less rigorous and complete explanation is given here.

In general there is always on the sea surface a number of wave trains each of different wave-length, period and height, each superimposed on the others. The combination forms a *spectrum* of wavelengths. On a windless day the smooth-sided 'swell' waves are composed of a spectrum which is restricted to a narrow range of wavelengths. When a strong wind blows the spectrum is widened, and there are waves present which vary in wave-length from a few cm to hundreds of metres. Each wave travels at its own speed c, which may depend upon its wave-length L, height h, the depth of water d, and since a rise or fall of the surface involves a gravitational force, the acceleration g. Thus c may depend on L, h, d, and g. So by the method of Dimensions (Chapter 10) one possible way in which the variables may be grouped is

$$c = (gL)^{1/2} \, \phi(d/L) \, (h/L).$$

Some advanced theoretical work (see Lamb's *Hydrodynamics*) shows that if the waves are low compared with the height, that is h/L is small, then the value of h/L does not affect the velocity c. Furthermore, it can be shown that

$$c^2 = (gL/2\pi) \tanh (2\pi d/L).$$

If d/L is large, as in the deep ocean, then

$$c^2 = gL/2\pi,$$

and if d/L is small, that is, in shallow water, then $c^2 = gd$, as has already been proved.

It will be seen that if the spectrum of the waves on the sea consists of one wave-length only (as occurs when a 'swell' on a windless day approaches the coast) then all waves travel at the same speed. If there are a selection of wave-lengths present, then the longer, faster ones are continually overtaking the smaller ones. As two wave crests coincide, an instantaneous wave is produced the height of which is the sum of their amplitudes. It is this ever-changing appearance of the sea due to the overtaking that is so evident when the wind is creating waves. Despite some approximations made in the theoretical analysis, experiments show that the speed of waves is in excellent agreement with the above equations. If T is the period of the waves, defined as the time taken for a crest or trough to travel a distance equal to L at a speed c,

then $\qquad T = L/c = L\sqrt{(2\pi/gL)} = \sqrt{(2\pi L/g)}.$

Thus reliable estimates of wave-lengths can be made by timing the wave crests past a fixed object. The wave-lengths so found can be used for model studies so that the model waves are truly to scale.

The motions in the water if d is great compared with L, prove to be such that all particles describe circular paths or orbits in deep water, making one complete circle in each wave period T (fig 16.9 (a)). The diameters of the orbits decrease downward by an exponential law, being equal to the trough-to-crest height h for surface particles, and being only $h/535$ at a depth equal to the wave-length. If the water is not deep, but there is a solid bottom at a finite depth, then the orbits are distorted into ellipses as they approach the bottom. Adjacent

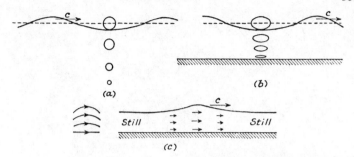

Fig 16.9 A comparison of water movements below different sorts of waves.
(a) Deep-water waves have motions which are circles whose radii decrease
exponentially downwards. (b) Deep-water waves approaching the shore
have motions which are ellipses more distorted near the bottom than at the
top, where they are nearly circles.   (c) Solitary waves create fluid motions
only under themselves and there is stationary fluid before and after them.
Thus the paths of particles are lines in one direction and are ' humped '
as shown on the left.   There is a slower return motion only if the wave
breaks subsequently on a beach.

to the bottom the particles can only move linearly, of course, as was
the case of the solitary wave. It is the rapid decrease of the water
motions downwards that allows small particles of sand and silt to
remain unmoved on the sea bed, despite the raging of storms overhead
(see fig 16.9 (a) and (b), and Plate 5, p. 148).

In all the foregoing paragraphs, it will be seen that the wave height
from trough to crest h does not appear in any of the equations derived
for T or c. A small, second order, correction can be calculated to
account for an increase of c with h, but it is by no means certain if
this correction is justified by experiment. Ocean waves are usually
low compared with their length : it is only waves with a large ratio
h/L whose speed would be affected by the correction. The wave
height is, however, a major variable when the energy of waves is considered. A wave possesses both potential and kinetic energy, the
former because the water has been raised or lowered from its equilibrium (still water) level, the latter because of the velocity of the orbital
motions under the wave. In all, the total energy of a travelling wave
train is

$$E = \tfrac{1}{8}\,\rho\,g\,h^2\,L \text{ per wave,}$$

for a unit width of wave across the direction of motion.

Though the waves themselves travel at a speed c relative to the
water in which they are produced, it is by no means certain that the
energy which they possess is carried forward at the same speed. The
question can be resolved by considering the combination of two wave

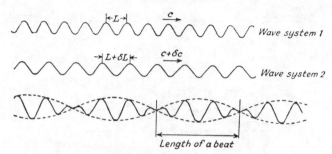

Fig 16.10   Two wave systems of unequal wave-lengths and speeds 'beat' together to form a more elaborate combined system.

systems of slightly different wave-lengths.   If there are just two wave-lengths in a particular spectrum, the two trains of waves combine together to 'beat' in the same way as electromagnetic or acoustic wave systems will do.   Over a length of time of several wave periods, the combined wave height (amplitude) observed at one stationary point builds up to a maximum, then decreases to zero and then increases again (fig 16.10).   It is this phenomenon that has led to the old seaside belief that every seventh (or fifth, or third ?) wave is a large one.

A 'beating' system can be considered as composed of two wave systems each of constant amplitude, one of wave-length L, the other $L + \delta L$.   Each wave of the shorter wave-length travels at velocity c, the longer at $c + \delta c$.   Now to make one 'beat' the number n of waves in the first system just occupies the same space as $n - 1$ waves of the second system.   In this space the combined system's amplitude goes through a complete cycle.

That is $n L = (n - 1) (L + \delta L)$

or ignoring δL compared with L, then $L = n \delta L$.

Thus the distance from one end of the beat to the other is

$$n L = L^2/\delta L.$$

A beat of waves will possess a certain amount of energy, being the sum of the energies of all the waves in the beat.   No energy can pass the nodes (the points where there is no wave motion) so that if the waves are to transfer any energy from one place to another, the beat itself must move, though not necessarily at the speed of either train of waves.   The beat is formed in the time that one longer wave completely overtakes one smaller wave, taking the whole length of the beat to do so.   Since the relative velocity between the two sizes of wave is δc, and the distance which the faster wave has to travel relative to the slower one is L in order to overtake, then the time of overtaking is $t = L/\delta c$. But the effect of the overtaking on the combined pattern at a point moving with the speed of the slower waves is to cause the amplitude to undergo a complete cycle of change from zero to maximum (sum of the two amplitudes) to zero again. Thus in this time of over-taking, a complete beat, from node to node, has passed the moving point. Since the beat is $L^2/\delta L$ long, and it passes the point in time $L/\delta c$, its speed, *relative to the moving point*, is

$$\frac{L^2}{\delta L} \bigg/ \frac{L}{\delta c} = L\delta c/\delta L.$$

Any part of the beat, a node for example, travels *backward* relative to the waves. (If a stationary, or standing, wave were to meet a wave system, the combined wave would show a sudden increase of height which would remain stationary relative to the ground, with the waves continually travelling into it, giving it a backward motion relative to the oncoming waves.)

The absolute velocity of the beat (and of any part of it, such as a node) is then

$$c' = c - L\,\delta c/\delta L,$$

or if the wave systems are nearly of the same size and speed

$$c' = c - L\,dc/dL.$$

So far no mention has been made of the law connecting c and L. In fact the preceding analysis for beat speed c' is perfectly general for any sort of wave motion, fluid, electromagnetic or acoustic. If the waves are deep water ones

$$c = \sqrt{(gL/2\pi)} = K L^{1/2}$$

so

$$dc/dL = \tfrac{1}{2} K L^{-1/2}$$

and thus

$$c' = K L^{1/2} - L^{1/2} K L^{-1/2}$$
$$= \tfrac{1}{2} K L^{1/2}$$
$$= \tfrac{1}{2} c.$$

So that in deep water, a beat travels at half the speed of the individual waves. Now if the two wave systems above are only infinitesimally different in wave-length and so in speed, then a small portion of the beat can be regarded as a *group* of waves all of the same length and height, such as might be caused by a laboratory wave-making machine which has worked for a few strokes and then stopped. This group will travel at the beat speed c' even though the waves themselves travel at $2c'$: they have a relative velocity forward through the group, so that if attention is given to one particular wave it will appear initially from the back of the group, run forward and then disappear at the front of the group as another appears at the back.

Since a group represents a constant amount of energy that has been given to the fluid by some means (for example, by the wind on the sea, or by an oscillating plate in a laboratory tank), the speed at which this energy is transferred is the speed c' of the group. Therefore the rate at which energy is passing a given point is the product of the wave energy per unit length, and the speed at which this energy is approaching the point.

So   Energy per unit length of water surface
and per unit width across wave direction $= \frac{1}{8}\rho g h^2 L/L$

and   Rate of arrival of energy or Power per
unit width across the waves $= \frac{1}{8} g \rho h^2 c'$

$$= \frac{1}{8} g \rho h^2 c/2$$

$$= \frac{1}{8}\rho g h^2 \left(\frac{g}{2\pi}\right)^{1/2} L^{1/2}/2$$

This power in a deep water wave system may be considerable. For example, waves of $h = 3$ m and $L = 64$ m would carry forward a power of 55 kW per metre width of wave across its direction of travel. Thus no less than 55 kW could be obtained per metre if the whole of the oncoming power could be extracted from the waves, leaving a plane surface. This power has come from the wind which has acted upon the sea surface to form the waves. Engineers have from time to time proposed methods of harnessing this wave energy to produce electrical power, but no economical method of doing so has yet been put forward. The power is normally degraded to thermal energy by turbulence in the sea when the waves finally break upon the beach.

No mention has yet been made about the way in which waves are modified as they approach the shore. As the water depths decrease, a train originally of deep water waves becomes more nearly a succession of solitary waves whose speed is governed by the depth and not by the wave-length. The orbital movements within the waves remain circular for particles near the water surface but are distorted in lower layers to ellipses until at the solid surface of the sea bed the motions are merely straight line oscillations. With decreasing depths of water both the wave speed and the speed at which the energy travels are reduced so that energy is travelling out of the water at the shallower end of a fixed length at a lower rate than it is arriving at the deeper end. The wave energy, $\frac{1}{8}g\rho h^2 L$ per wave, in such a length therefore increases, while because the waves are decelerating, the interval between waves, originally L, also decreases. The height h therefore increases and so does the *steepness ratio* h/L. When this ratio approaches a limiting value of about 1 : 10, when the depth is about 1·2 h, the wave is too high for its length and it crashes over as a breaker. The resulting turbulence degrades most of the wave energy into heat, leaving a little energy to supply the motion as the broken water runs up the beach.

PROBLEMS

1. In a Pelton wheel installation, a pressure tunnel 9·5 km long and cross-sectional area 7·5 m² conducts water from a reservoir to a surge tank, from which a steel pipeline 700 m long and 2 m diameter leads to the turbines. The nozzles are 300 m below, and the surge tank top 15 m above the reservoir level. If the machines are giving 10,000 kW at 80 per cent overall efficiency (includes pipe friction losses), what is the minimum time in which the valves may be closed so that water does not spill from the surge tank ? What is the maximum pressure in the pipeline ?

Ans. 36·5 s : 1·94 × 10³ kN/m².

2. Find the sequence and magnitude of the events following the sudden closure of a valve at the downstream end of a rigid pipe 1500 m long, conveying at 3 m/s water of elasticity 20 × 10⁵ kN/m².

3. The flow entering a lake on a certain day is

Time	Flow m³/s	
until noon	28	⎫
1 p.m.	170	⎬ With sinusoidal increase
2 p.m.	310	⎱ and decrease.
7 p.m.	170	⎭
midnight and after	28	

The lake discharges over a simple weir with 30 m of crest for which $Q = 1·65bh^{3/2}$. The surface area of the lake is 3·7 × 10⁶ m² at crest level, plus 3 × 10⁵ m² per metre of rise. Find the maximum level in the lake and the time at which it occurs.

Ans. 1·7 m at 8.40 p.m.

4. The discharge of a river model passes into a channel 15 m long and 1·4 m wide, and is measured by a broad crested weir 0·7 m wide at the end of the channel. The maximum weir head is 20 cm. How long will the system take to settle down when starting from zero flow ? Between readings the flow is changed by 20 per cent ; how many readings can be expected in an hour ? The error of the flow is not to exceed ½ per cent.

Hint. Search for an exact integral solution of the reservoir equation.

Ans. 131 s : about 35.

5. A long, wide canal has a water flow 1·8 m deep at 1·2 m/s in it. Accidentally, a control gate at the downstream end is shut suddenly. Calculate the height of the consequent surge, and the speed at which it travels upstream.

Hint. Use the technique of the pressure wave computation in **16.3**, reducing the problem to a steady flow hydraulic jump by imposing the wave velocity backwards on the whole system.

Ans. 0·55 m : 3·94 m/s.

PLATE 17 Photographs of the Bore in the River Severn.

(*Upper*) A view of the full size bore progressing upstream. The phenomenon is that of a weak hydraulic jump which travels upstream faster than the fresh water current is going downstream. Weak jumps appear as a series of smooth waves. Observe the canoeists surf-riding.

Photograph by E. J. Wynter, Esq.

(*Lower*) The same phenomenon in a 1:600 scale model of the river. The waves, now much smaller, have greater curvatures so that surface tension forces begin to be of importance. There is more hydrodynamic damping present than in the full size, so that waves die out more quickly, and fewer waves can be seen. The breaking of the waves at the sides of the river is reproduced in the model, but again due to surface tension, there is less breaking into droplets.

Photograph by Hydraulics Research Station, Wallingford.

PLATE 17

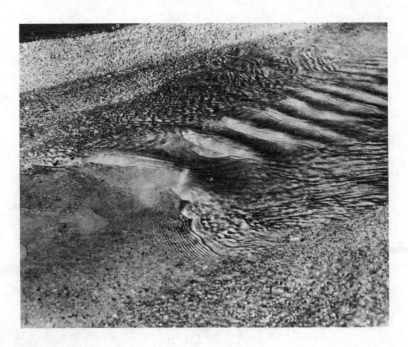

PLATE 18

Facing page 357

PLATE 18

(*Above*) The flip bucket dissipator at Legadadi Dam, Ethiopia in operation. Compare the air entrainment with that of the model, below, which has much larger (to scale) water droplets. Air-entrainment is much controlled by surface tension forces which cannot be easily scaled at the same time as the Froude effect is scaled. The model is thus misleading in this respect although it gives a good indication of the general shape of the water jet.

Photo by E. A. Jackson Esq.

(*Lower*) A 1:36 scale model of the ' flip-bucket ' energy dissipator at Legadadi Dam, Ethiopia. The high speed flow from the spillway is turned upwards to dissipate its energy by air-entrainment before it falls into a pool.

Photograph by Wimpey Laboratories Ltd.

357

APPENDIX

Additional Problems in the f.p.s. system of units.

1. A ' pressurized ' aeroplane flying at 30 000 ft has a cabin pressure equivalent to a height of 8000 ft. What load does each square foot of cabin wall have to withstand, if at sea level the barometer stands at 30 in of mercury, and the temperature is 15 °C ?
[Rate of decrease of temperature 1·5 °C per 1000 ft :
Gas constant for air 96 ft lbf lb^{-1} °C^{-1}.]
Ans. 927 lbf ft^{-2}.

2. A cubical tipping bucket designed to hold 1 cu yd of concrete weighs 4500 lbf. Its centre of gravity is 16 in above the floor and the axis of tipping is 4 in higher. Determine if it will be safe to fill the bucket to the rim with a thin mortar weighing 100 lbf ft^{-3}.
Ans. No : 2700 lbf in torque overturning, 1800 lbf in restoring.
Hint. The shape of the volume of mortar changes like PQCD in fig 3.2.

3. An aircraft jet engine takes in 200 lb of air per second at 15 °C, and burns enough fuel to raise the exhaust temperature to 300 °C. The outlet orifice is 3 ft diameter. What thrust force is generated if the aircraft is (a) stationary, (b) flying at 240 mile/h ?
Ans. (a) 4580 lbf : (b) 2380 lbf.

4. Water flows at a rate of 10 ft^3/s through a right-angle bend in a pipe of cross-sectional area $\frac{1}{4}$ ft^2 and discharges into the atmosphere through a nozzle of exit-area $\frac{1}{10}$ ft^2. Neglecting friction and gravity, find the force and moment at a flange in the supply-pipe 5 feet upstream of the bend.
Ans. Force components 1936 lbf : 2810 lbf : Moment 9·680 lbf ft.

5. A power house has a water turbine, 90 per cent efficient developing 10 000 H.P. The inlet channel is 30 ft wide and flows 15 ft deep at a speed of 7 ft/s. The outlet channel is 50 ft wide, and flows 5 ft deep. Find (a) the flow, (b) the energy lost by the water per second, (c) the energy lost per lbf of water, and (d) the difference of level between the beds of the entry and outlet channels.
Ans. 3150 cusecs ; 61 × 10^5 ft lbf : 31 ft lbf/lbf ; 22·71 ft.

6. A closed tank, 3 ft diameter and 6 ft high, empties through a 1 in diameter well-rounded orifice in the bottom. The air vent is a vertical pipe the lower end of which is 2 ft above the bottom of the tank. Plot the discharge as a function of the height of the water level, and determine approximately the time to empty the tank.
Ans. 15·2 min.

7. A Venturi meter 0·8 in diameter at the throat, and on a 2 in pipe, gives a pressure difference of 36·0 in on a mercury manometer when 0·170 cusecs of water are passing. What is the coefficient of discharge ? What will be the pressure difference on the same manometer if the meter now passes the same quantity of petrol (s.g 0·82).

Note Watch buoyancy effect on mercury.

Ans. 0·977 : 35·2 in.

8. An axial-flow fan in a 3 in diameter pipe is driven by compressed air flowing from a large container in which the gauge pressure is kept constant at 40 lbf/ft² and the density is constant at 0·0025 slug/ft³. The air is discharged from the 3 in pipe into the atmosphere with a speed of 100 ft/s. Calculate the pressure just upstream of the turbine, the turbine horsepower and the axial force in the turbine shaft. Calculate also the discharge velocity when the turbine is stopped. State carefully any assumptions.

Ans. 27·5 lbf/ft² : 0·24 H.P : 1·35 lbf : 179 ft/s.

9. Air is discharged from a tank through a Laval nozzle into a region where the absolute pressure is 0·7 m of mercury. The gauge pressure in the tank is 50 lbf/in² and the temperature is 100° F. The throat and exit diameters of the nozzle are 1·00 in and 1·05 in respectively. Will there be a compression shock in the nozzle ?

Ans. No.

10. A rocket motor with nozzle exit diameter of 2 ft produces 50 000 lbf of thrust at sea-level, where it runs at the design pressure ratio. What thrust would be developed at an altitude of 40 000 ft, where the atmospheric pressure is 381·7 lbf/ft² ?

Ans. 55 450 lbf.

11. A seaplane float with a very smooth surfaced skin plating (and therefore negligible skin friction) is fixed to a flying-boat with take-off speed of 85 m.p.h. A 1/10 scale model is to be tank tested. At what speed should corresponding conditions apply ? If 0·152 h.p is required to tow it at this speed, what h.p will be required by the full-size float if the tank is filled with fresh water and the flying-boat is to operate from the sea ?

Ans. 26·9 mile/h : 494 h.p.

12. A curved duct 5 ft square in section has a mean radius of 17·5 ft. Calculate the discharge when the difference of pressure-head between inner and outer walls is 6 in. Assume (*a*) free vortex, (*b*) constant velocity, (*c*) forced vortex.

Ans. (*a*) 184 : (*b*) 188 . (*c*) 188 cusecs.

13. An extensive water stream at 5 ft/sec passes over a surface roughened with sand 0·1 in effective diameter. The boundary layer is 1 ft thick. Calculate the reduction of momentum per second of the fluid passing through the layer if

(*a*) The velocity varies linearly with distance from plate
(*b*) The velocity varies parabolically
(*c*) The velocity varies as the 1/7 power of the distance

(*d*) The velocity varies logarithmically, assuming that the velocity is zero at 1/30 of the sand size from the plate.
Graphical methods may be used.

Ans. (*a*) 8·07 lbf per ft width (*b*) 6·46
      (*c*) 4·72   (*d*) 4·31.

14. A 2-ft diameter pipe 4000 ft long carries 27 cusecs of water from one reservoir (water-level 100 ft above Ordnance Datum) to another (w.l 45 ft O.D). The centre-line of the pipe passes through the following points :

Distance from inlet (ft)	0	1500	3000	4000
Elevation (ft O.D)	90	90	25	40

What is the water pressure at these points at centre-line level (*a*) when the water is flowing freely, and (*b*) after a valve at the downstream end has been shut ? (*c*) What would be the effect of putting a water turbine in the pipeline to develop some power ? (*d*) What is the horse-power lost in case (*a*) due to friction in the pipeline ?

Ans. Pressures in ft of water
      (*a*) + 8·85, − 11·35, + 33·45, + 5·00
      (*b*) 10, 10, 75, 60
      (*d*) 168·5 hp.

15. Two reservoirs whose surface levels differ by 100 ft are connected by a pipe 10 000 ft long. The pipe crosses a ridge whose summit is 30 ft above the water-level of, and 1000 ft distant from, the higher reservoir. Find the minimum excavation needed at the ridge so that the pressure in the pipe does not fall below 10 ft of water absolute.

Ans. Pipe centre 16·6 ft below ground.

16. A pipe already existing, 10 miles long and 30 in in diameter, now supplies 10 m.g.d. Ultimately 30 m.g.d will be needed, so a second pipe will be laid beside the first. However, the immediate need is for 13 m.g.d, so for the present the second pipe will be constructed for part of the way only.

Find the second pipe's diameter and length, assuming the total fall is unchanged.

Note. 1 m.g.d = 10^6 gallons/day.

Ans. 3·3 ft : 4·6 miles.

17. A pipe 10 000 ft long and 1 ft diameter, $f = 0·004$, connects two reservoirs whose water-levels differ by 20 ft. It is necessary to increase the flow by 50 per cent. Compare the running costs of an electric pump at 1p per kilowatt-hour with the alternative of paying 5 per cent interest on a second pipe 1 ft diameter costing £5 per yard laid, extending for an appropriate distance before joining the original pipe. The pump efficiency is 80 per cent. Discuss whether a more expensive pump giving greater efficiency would be profitable.

Ans. 11·9 hp, £784 p.a : *l* = 7420 ft, £619 p.a.

18. The water-levels in two reservoirs A and B are respectively 67 and 62 ft above datum. A pipe joins each to a common point D where the pressure is 103 kN/m² gauge and height is 45 m above datum.

Another pipe connects D to another tank C.   What will be the height of the water-level in C assuming the same value of f for all pipes ?

Pipe	Length m	Diameter cm
AD	2400	30
BD	2700	45
CD	3100	60

Ans. 51·5 m.

19. A 12-in pipe 1000 ft long supplies reservoir B from reservoir A which is 35 ft higher.   A third reservoir C, level with A, is to be supplied through another 12-in pipe 250 ft long by a pump drawing from E, the midpoint of AB.   There is a valve at B and the flow needed there is 3·14 cusecs.   Find the maximum delivery to C, and the hp of the pump.

Find also the delivery to C if no electric power were available and the pump had to be driven by a turbine supplied from the flow in EB. Assume 75 per cent efficiency, $f = 0.007$ and neglect loss in fittings. Plot the hydraulic gradients.

Ans. 6·13 cusecs : 27·6 hp : 4·92 cusecs.

20. A fire hydrant E supplying 1600 gallons/min lies within a quadrilateral network ABCD of eight pipes.

Pipe	Length ft	Diameter in	f
AB	800	6	0·008
BC	1100	8	0·006
CD	1400	8	0·006
DA	1500	8	0·006
AE	600	4	0·010
BE	500	4	0·010
CE	800	8	0·006
DE	1000	4	0·010

Determine the flows and the loss of head between A, where the system is supplied with water, and E.

Hint. For first approximation note large resistance of DE, so its flow can be ignored.

Ans. AB 1·55 : BC 1·03 : DC 1·67 : AD 2·10 : AE 0·74 : BE 0·52 : EC 2·7 : DE 0·43 cusec. Head loss 79 ft.

21. You are required to find the flow passing through a proposed unlined rock tunnel, flowing full, length 35 000 ft, diameter 11·5 ft, under a head difference of 32 ft.   Another tunnel driven in the same rock gave 4942 cusec under 13·5 ft head, with a diameter of 30 ft.   (Allowance had been made for entry and exit losses.)

Assuming that the roughness of the rock surface is the same in both tunnels, compare the two estimates of discharges from the new tunnel.

(a) using the exact logarithmic equation

$$1/\sqrt{f} = 4 \log_{10} r/k + 3.48$$

(b) using the Manning equation with the same value of M as that of the first tunnel.

What value of M must be used to obtain agreement between the two calculations ?

Ans. log. formula $Q = 300 \cdot 0$ cusecs ;

Manning $Q = 316 \cdot 5$ cusecs ; $M = 47 \cdot 1$ ft$^{1/3}$/s.

22. A water turbine to develop 50 000 H.P. under 80 ft head is to run at 75 revs/min and 90 per cent efficiency. It is desired to make a 1/20 scale model to run on compressed air at 5 atmospheres, the pressure difference across the model being 5 lbf in^{-2}. What will be the model speed ? If the model is estimated to have an efficiency of 85 per cent, what power will it generate, and what will be the air flow ? What are the advantages and disadvantages of using compressed air as a testing fluid ?

Hint. Do not ignore any terms in specific speed equation.

Ans. 7600 rev/min : 81 hp : 72 cusecs.

23. A three-stage centrifugal (radial flow) pump has impellers 15 in diameter and ¾ in wide at outlet. The outlet blade angle is 45°, and the blades occupy 8 per cent of the outlet area. The hydraulic efficiency is 84 per cent and the overall efficiency 75 per cent.

What head will the pump generate when running at 900 revs/min, discharging 780 gall/min ? What is the input hp?

Ans. 227 ft : 72 hp.

24. A 12-in diameter pipeline 10 000 ft long, $f \times 0 \cdot 004$, is laid at a slope of 1·2 ft per mile from a reservoir in which the water-level is 10 ft above the pipe centre line. The other end of the pipe has a short transition piece to bring the section to 10 in square, where there is a sluice valve. The square section then discharges to another reservoir in which the water-level is 3 ft above the centre line. Calculate the flow through the pipe when the valve is

(a) Fully open (b) Half shut (c) $\frac{9}{10}$ shut (d) 99 per cent shut.

Plot the flow against the valve opening. Ignore entry and outlet losses to the pipe and assume that there is a degradation of energy downstream of the valve according to that given by a sudden expansion from the vena contracta (0·62 of the valve opening) to the full pipe size.

Ans. (a) 1·52 (b) 1·50 (c) 0·905 (d) 0·105 cusecs.

25. In question 3, if the valve is shut so that the water velocity in the pipe is retarded uniformly in 10 seconds, find the pressure that the valve must withstand

(a) with the valve just beginning to shut,
(b) when the valve has just reached its seating,
(c) under static conditions.

Ans. (a) 63 ft : (b) 72·28 ft : (c) 12·28 ft.

26. Water discharges from a lock through a submerged orifice 10 ft² in area into a tidal harbour where the tide rises at 0·001 ft/s. There is a constant leakage into the lock through the upper gates of 2·5 cusecs and the lock has a plan area of 5000 ft². Find the time taken for the water-level in the lock to equal the level outside if the initial difference is 16 ft. The coefficient of discharge of the orifice is 0·625.

Ans. 12 minutes.

27. A trapezoidal channel is to be designed to convey 10^4 ft³/min of water per minute at normal depth. Determine the cross section from the following data—Slope 1 : 1600 ; sides inclined at 45° ; cross-sectional area to be a minimum ; Chézy's $C = 90$ ft$^{1/2}$ sec^{-1}.

Ans. Depth 5·04 ft ; bottom 4·17 ft wide.

28. Find the force on the gate of a sluice discharging 3000 cusecs at 30 ft/sec : the sluice and the channel are 20 ft wide throughout and the bed is horizontal.

Ans. 60 000 lbf.

29. A steep roughened spillway has Chézy's $C = 50$ ft$^{1/2}$ s^{-1} when the depth is 1 ft. The critical depth is 6 ft and the normal depth is 3 ft. Find the slope and plot the surface curve when $d = 6$ ft at $x = 0$ ft. *Hint.* C will change with depth.

Ans. 0·0605.

30. The stream flowing at 64 ft/sec from a spillway 20 ft wide is 8 ft deep. It is to be retarded by obstacles to safeguard the bed of the river into which it discharges. What is the maximum force that can be applied without affecting the flow on the spillway, and to what speed will it reduce the stream ?

Ans. 27 900 × 20 lbf : 25·4 ft/s.

31. A long rectangular channel 8 ft wide slopes at 1 in 500 and ends in a weir which keeps the stream 4 ft deep there. There is a sluice 1000 ft upstream of the weir, allowing a jet 6 in deep to emerge. Chézy's C is 90 ft$^{1/2}$ s^{-1} and the normal depth is 3 ft.

Calculate the surface profile between sluice and weir. If there is a hydraulic jump, where will it occur and what will be its height ?

Ans. 2·15 ft : approx 131 ft downstream of sluice.

32. A long, 50 ft wide, irrigation canal is to take 10 000 ft³ sec^{-1} on a slope of 1 : 1000. The rigid bed is of stones with an equivalent roughness k of 1 inch. Assuming only the logarithmic velocity distribution for turbulent flow, $u = 5·75 \ (\tau/\rho)^{1/2} \log_{10} 33y/k$, estimate the depth d. Comment on the likelihood of the occurrence of waves.

Ans. 16·0 ft ; Froude Number 0·55, well below critical so no waves likely.

BIBLIOGRAPHY

FURTHER READING LIST

General Fluid Mechanics

Modern Developments in Fluid Mechanics. Vols. I–IV. Oxford University Press.
> Vols. I and II deal with low-speed flow, Vols. III and IV with high-speed flow only. A unique work incorporating both theoretical and experimental data, and a constant source of reference in all branches of Fluid Mechanics.

Hydrodynamics. H. Lamb. Cambridge University Press.
> Deals with ideal fluid potential flow problems and is indispensable in this field, though mathematics often complicated.

Applied Hydrodynamics. H. R. Vallentine. Butterworth.
> Ideal, potential flow treated simply, with many engineering examples.

Hydraulic Measurements. H. Addison. Chapman & Hall.
> A compendium of methods of measurement of fluid phenomena in water.

Essentials of Fluid Dynamics. L. Prandtl. Blackie.
> Contains applications to meteorology, aeronautics and many other branches of engineering.

Shape and Flow. A. H. Shapiro. Heinemann.
> The book of the film, well illustrated, giving a good introduction to many ideas.

Civil Engineering Fluid Mechanics

Engineering Hydraulics. Edited by Hunter Rouse. John Wiley.
> Each chapter written by an expert. Represents American practice.

Engineering Fluid Mechanics. C. Jaeger. Blackie.
> Represents European practice.

Loose Boundary Hydraulics. A. J. Raudkivi. Pergamon.
> Review and explanation of sediment flows in rivers.

Coastal Hydraulics. A. M. Muir Wood. Macmillan.

Scale Models in Hydraulic Engineering. J. Allen. Longmans.
> Many river and coast models described. This book is now out of print, but it is in most engineering libraries.

Open Channel Flow. F. M. Henderson. Macmillan.

Mechanical Engineering Fluid Mechanics

Engineering Applications of Fluid Mechanics. J. C. Hunsaker and B. G. Rightmire. McGraw-Hill.
A general textbook, but with a definite mechanical engineering bias.

Centrifugal and Axial Flow Pumps. A. S. Stepanoff. John Wiley.
Complete design details of pumps.

The Dynamics and Thermodynamics of Compressible Flow. Vols. I and II. A. H. Shapiro. Ronald Press, New York.

Thermofluid Dynamics. A. J. Reynolds. Wiley.

Aeronautical Engineering Fluid Mechanics

Aerofoil and Airscrew Theory. H. Glauert. Cambridge University Press.
An old but classic book.

Elements of Gas-dynamics. H. W. Liepmann and A. Roshko. John Wiley.
The fundamental theory of compressible flow.

Incompressible Aerodynamics. Edited by B. Thwaites. Oxford University Press.
A comprehensive review of flow past aerofoils.

Foundations of Aerodynamics. A. M. Kuethe and J. D. Schetzer. John Wiley.
An up-to-date introductory text.

Princeton Aeronautical Paperbacks. Princeton University Press.
A group of highly specialized reprints of articles by different authors.

History

History of Hydraulics. Hunter Rouse and S. Ince. Dover Publications.
Excellent reading, showing the relations between fluid mechanics and other branches of study.

INDEX